A TREATISE ON
RADIATIVE TRANSFER

A TREATISE ON
RADIATIVE TRANSFER

by

V. V. SOBOLEV

TRANSLATED BY

S. I. Gaposchkin, Ph.D.
Astronomer, Harvard College Observatory

D. VAN NOSTRAND COMPANY, INC.
PRINCETON, NEW JERSEY

TORONTO   NEW YORK   LONDON

D. VAN NOSTRAND COMPANY, INC.
120 Alexander St., Princeton, New Jersey (*Principal office*)
24 West 40 Street, New York 18, New York

D. VAN NOSTRAND COMPANY, LTD.
358, Kensington High Street, London, W.14, England

D. VAN NOSTRAND COMPANY (Canada), LTD.
25 Hollinger Road, Toronto 16, Canada

Published simultaneously in Canada by
D. VAN NOSTRAND COMPANY (Canada), LTD.

PRINTED IN THE UNITED STATES OF AMERICA

PREFACE OF THE TRANSLATOR

There is no gainsaying that there always exists a scientific discipline which epitomizes power of human intellect or a region of exact thought where man's genius shines at its best.

For a long time such was the field of "Celestial Mechanics" woven by great theoreticians whose mathematical analyses still shine with un-diminishing brilliance comparable only to that of stars themselves.

At the present time it is "Radiative Transfer" linked with the Internal Constitution of Stars which fascinates and challenges astronomers all over the world.

Among the trailblazers and the coryphees in this field none are more profound, none more illustrious than two contemporary astronomers: an American, Chandrasekhar, and a Russian, Sobolev.

An attempt to translate their "chef d'oeuvres" produces in the trans-lator a tremulous humility and at the same time an ardent inspiration, for, on one hand he feels his knowledge of all intricacies of the two languages is not sufficient inasmuch as the translator, having perhaps only a peripheral connection with the subject, is called to be on "a par" with the author; and on the other hand the following of the broad path of exploration "zieht uns hinan" ("Inspires us," from *Faust* by Goethe).

In this state of mind I undertook the translation of Sobolev's book, *Transport of Radiant Energy in Stellar and Planetary Atmospheres*. This is the direct American translation of the title of the book in Russian. I call it simply *A Treatise on Radiative Transfer* in its full meaning. From this altered title, the American reader will be able to grasp more readily what the book is about ("radiative transfer" is a well-known expression, whereas "the transport of radiant energy" is quite unfamil-iar). Sobolev does not limit himself to atmospheres; he discusses all kinds of radiative transfer problems, among them gaseous nebulae and the sea. As a matter of fact it is here that it took my breath away to discover that from the study of "infinitely" hot and "infinitely" distant stars a superior mind can explain why the belly of the fish is almost universally white. According to Sobolev it is a protective coloration.

Every profound writer writes not only in his native tongue; he has his own, in addition. Sobolev employs not only terms, symbols, and ex-pressions in accordance with a general usage in the West but he has his own style.   This and the fact that there exists an inevitable chaos of notations and expressions in the field of "radiative transfer" made the translation more difficult.   My main reference was *Radiative Transfer* of Chandrasekhar.   I consulted also the American, English, German, and Russian (rarely French) literature on the subject.

In general, Russian march of thought is analogous to American. But sometimes it is different: a common Russian expression like

samo soboiu razumeietsia

has no equivalent in American.   (In German: "Es ist selbstverständlich"; in French: "Ça va de soi".)   The meaning is rather obvious: "It goes without saying."

An attempt was made to overcome advantageously such difficulties. At the same time I entertained the hope of lending to the presentation of the subject clarity and a dynamic touch reflecting the original.

This American translation of the Sobolev book is greatly enlarged by including his latest articles, which in a way epitomize the whole problem of the Radiative Transfer.   They were translated by me and adapted to the book by slight modification of their form without changing the content.

SERGEI I. GAPOSCHKIN

Lexington, Mass.
December, 1962

INTRODUCTION

The theory of radiative transfer is the most important part of theoretical astrophysics: first, because radiative transfer plays a great part in the physical phenomena occurring within the heavenly bodies; further, radiative transfer governs the light in the outer parts of the heavenly bodies and determines the character of their spectra, which are fundamental for astrophysical investigations.

We meet problems of radiative transfer also in geophysics, in investigating the Earth's atmosphere and bodies of water, and in some other branches of physics. Recently, the problem of neutron diffusion, which in its application is similar to that of radiative transfer, has become of great importance.

The importance of radiative transfer has caused many investigations in this field with considerable progress made especially in the years after World War II. Some of the results were given by S. Chandrasekhar, *Radiative Transfer,* Oxford University Press, 1950, and by V. Kourganoff, *Basic Methods in Transfer,* Oxford University Press, 1952. Their works, however, do not represent all the results obtained up to the present time in the theory of radiative transfer, and reflect essentially their own interests, which is quite understandable.

In the present book we propose several new methods in the theory of radiative transfer and also indicate their application to the solution of various astrophysical problems. Special attention is given to diffuse radiation with redistribution in frequency and to nonstationary processes of radiative transfer, inasmuch as these questions have not previously been considered in detail. The content of the book is as follows:

In the first chapter we deduce the basic equations of the theory of radiative transfer and by means of these equations we formulate problems of radiative transfer in atmospheres of stars and planets. The second chapter contains in abbreviated form the basic methods used for the solution of the above-mentioned equations in astrophysics.

In the third chapter we consider methods of V. A. Ambartsumian. They are based on the formation of functional equations for the determination of parameters which are most interesting in practice: intensities of the emergent radiation. Having found these intensities, one can find rather easily the march of light in the medium. In the fourth chapter we derive linear equations for determination of emergent radiation intensities. The solution of these equations is finite if the medium has an infinitely large optical depth. In the fifth chapter we treat the diffusion of polarized radiation by means of the former equations.

In the sixth chapter we introduce a new quantity: the probability of quantum exit from the medium. This quantity does not depend on the location of radiation sources but only on the optical properties of the medium. That is why, having found this probability, we easily solve, by means of an integration, all the problems of radiation of a given medium differing from each other by the locations of radiation sources. By this method we have solved several problems connected with the formation of stellar spectra. Later the method is applied also to other problems.

In chapter seven we consider the luminescence of a medium with a surface that reflects radiation. The most important example of such a medium is the atmosphere of a planet with its boundary.

In chapter eight we investigate diffuse radiation with redistribution in frequency. In the beginning we consider diffusion of resonance radiation in a very rarefied medium, for example, in a gaseous nebula. Then we determine contours of absorption lines in stellar spectra with so-called "completely noncoherent scattering."

The ninth chapter deals with nonstationary processes of diffuse radiation. In particular we consider here the change of ionization of atoms in the medium as a function of time. The results are then used in the interpretation of the radiation of novae.

In the last, the tenth chapter, we give an approximate solution of the problem of radiative transfer for a medium with sufficiently general assumptions in respect to its optical properties. The solution is applied to finding the optical properties in the atmosphere of the earth and those of the planets. We apply it also to problems of the optics of the sea.

In the chapters from four to ten we use essentially our own old material. In chapters six and seven some results are given, however, for the first time.

In this book we have not considered questions directly connected with the diffusion of neutrons; however, the methods given here may be applied in such a case.

CONTENTS

CHAPTER 1

FORMULATION OF THE PROBLEM

The subject of radiative transfer is the analysis of a radiation field in a medium able to absorb and emit radiating energy. If the absorbing and emitting properties of the medium are given, one can find the intensities of radiation very easily. The problem gets much more complicated when the amount of energy emitted by an elementary volume depends on the amount of energy absorbed by the same volume, that is, on the intensity falling on the volume and on the ability of the volume to absorb the radiation. In this case the problem is reduced to the solution of an integral equation. The theory of radiative transfer deals with the solution of such integral equations.

The process of radiative transfer is, generally speaking, very complicated. In stellar atmospheres, for example, it is connected with a transformation of radiant energy into heat energy and with the reverse process, with a change of spectral composition of radiation, and so on. In some cases radiative transfer may be, however, considered as multiple diffusion of light quanta in the medium. Even in stellar atmospheres, such a treatment is possible in individual cases by selecting special parameters which characterize diffusion of light in the elementary volume. Therefore, we shall often speak of **scattering** (**or diffusion**) of radiation instead of radiative transfer.

In this chapter we derive the basic equations of the theory. One of them is the *equation of radiative transfer*, which determines the change of intensity along the path. Another equation is called the *equation of radiative equilibrium* and expresses a relation between an amount of energy emitted and absorbed by the elementary volume. These equations are then written for the case of planetary and stellar atmospheres. The chapter ends with an example of the diffusion of light in a one-dimensional medium.

1. THE RADIATION FIELD

A fundamental quantity that governs the radiation field is the *intensity of radiation*. We define it with the following example. Let us take an elementary surface area normal to the direction of the radiation in question. If the area is $d\sigma$ and the radiation falls in a specific frequency interval $(\nu, \nu + d\nu)$ within a solid angle $d\omega$ and in time dt, then the amount of radiant energy dE_ν, incident on the area will be proportional to $d\sigma d\nu d\omega dt$; for example, it will be

$$dE_\nu = I_\nu \, d\sigma d\nu d\omega dt \tag{1}$$

The coefficient of proportionality I_ν, entering in this equation is then called intensity of radiation. In other words, the intensity of radiation is an amount of radiant energy falling per unit of frequency, of time, of solid angle, and of surface area normal to the direction of radiation. Generally speaking, the intensity of radiation depends on coordinates of a fixed point, on direction of radiation, and on its frequency.

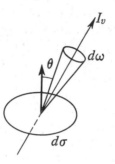

Fig. 1.1

With a known intensity of radiation one can easily compute other quantities which govern the radiation field. One of these quantities is *density of radiation*, for example, an amount of radiant energy per unit of volume.

We denote the amount of radiant energy in frequency interval $(\nu, \nu + d\nu)$ per unit of volume as $\rho_\nu d\nu$. The relation between ρ_ν and I_ν is found in the following way. Consider radiation falling on $d\sigma$ and normal to it in frequency interval $(\nu, \nu + d\nu)$, within a small solid angle $\Delta\omega$ and in time dt. According to Eq. (1) the amount of radiant energy on $d\sigma$ will be $I_\nu d\sigma d\nu d\omega dt$. Evidently this energy will occupy the volume $d\sigma \cdot cdt$, where c is the velocity of light. Therefore, the amount of radiant energy in the frequency interval $(\nu, \nu + d\nu)$ per unit of volume will be $I_\nu d\nu (\Delta\omega / c)$. Thus, in our case, we have

$$\rho_\nu = I_\nu \frac{\Delta\omega}{c} \tag{2}$$

In a general case, when radiation falls on a given volume from all sides, the density of radiation is expressed as

$$\rho_\nu = \frac{1}{c} \int I_\nu \, d\omega \tag{3}$$

where the integration is carried over all solid angles.

If radiation is isotropic, for example, intensity of radiation does not depend on direction, we write:

$$\rho_\nu = \frac{4\pi}{c} I_\nu \tag{4}$$

Further, an important quantity governing radiation field is *flux of radiation*. The flux is an amount of radiant energy transported per unit of area, of time, and of frequency. We shall denote the flux of radiation by H_ν. Then the amount of radiant energy flowing through an area $d\sigma$, in time dt, in frequency interval $(\nu, \nu + d\nu)$ is equal to $H_\nu d\sigma dt d\nu$. On the other hand, we can find the same quantity of energy in another way. Let us consider radiation traversing $d\sigma$ in the direction forming an angle θ with the normal to $d\sigma$ (see Fig. 1.1). In this case the surface of the elementary area normal to the direction of radiation is equal to $d\sigma \cos \theta$. Therefore the amount of radiant energy transmitted by area $d\sigma$ under an angle θ to the normal within the solid angle $d\omega$, in time dt, in frequency interval $(\nu, \nu + d\nu)$ will be equal to $I_\nu d\sigma \cos \theta d\omega dt d\nu$. If an integration of this formula is carried over all values of the direction, one obtains a quantity which we denoted earlier by $H_\nu d\sigma dt d\nu$. Consequently,

$$H_\nu = \int I_\nu \cos \theta \, d\omega \tag{5}$$

In the system of polar coordinates with the z axis as the normal to the area $d\sigma$, the elementary solid angle is equal to

$$d\omega = \sin \theta \, d\theta d\phi \tag{6}$$

where ϕ is azimuth of the chosen direction. Therefore the expression for the flux can be rewritten in the form:

$$H_\nu = \int_0^{2\pi} d\phi \int_0^\pi I_\nu \cos \theta \sin \theta \, d\theta \tag{7}$$

We see in Eq. (7) that the flux, H_ν, appears to be the difference between two quantities:

$$H_\nu = E_\nu - E'_\nu \tag{8}$$

where

$$E_\nu = \int_0^{2\pi} d\phi \int_0^{\pi/2} I_\nu \cos \theta \sin \theta \, d\theta \tag{9}$$

and

$$E'_\nu = - \int_0^{2\pi} d\phi \int_{\pi/2}^{\pi} I_\nu \cos\theta \sin\theta \, d\theta \tag{10}$$

The quantity E_ν represents the illumination of the area from one side, and $'E_\nu$ the illumination of the area from another side. Thus the flux of radiation traversed through any one area is a difference between these illuminations of the area.

It is clear that the flux of radiation depends on the direction of the normal to the area. To find this dependence we choose the system of Cartesian coordinates, with x, y, z as axes, and we denote the corresponding angles formed by them and by the direction of radiation as θ_1, θ_2, θ_3. Then the quantities:

$$H_{\nu x} = \int I_\nu \cos\theta_1 \, d\omega \qquad H_{\nu y} = \int I_\nu \cos\theta_2 \, d\omega$$

$$H_{\nu z} = \int I_\nu \cos\theta_3 \, d\omega \tag{11}$$

will represent flux of radiation along the coordinate axes. Further, we denote the angles between the normal to area and the coordinate axis by α_1, α_2, α_3. Then the cosine of the angle between the direction of the normal to the area and that of radiation will be equal to

$$\cos\theta = \cos\alpha_1 \cos\theta_1 + \cos\alpha_2 \cos\theta_2 + \cos\alpha_3 \cos\theta_3 \tag{12}$$

Inserting this expression in Eq. (5) and remembering Eq. (11), we obtain

$$H_\nu = H_{\nu x} \cos\alpha_1 + H_{\nu y} \cos\alpha_2 + H_{\nu z} \cos\alpha_3 \tag{13}$$

Thus the flux of radiation in a given direction may be represented as a projection vector, with the components defined by Eq. (11) and projected in the same direction.

In addition to these quantities I_ν, ρ_ν, and H_ν, one uses also the quantities I, ρ, and H in investigating radiation field. They are

$$I = \int_0^\infty I_\nu \, d\nu, \qquad \rho = \int_0^\infty \rho_\nu \, d\nu, \qquad H = \int_0^\infty H_\nu \, d\nu \tag{14}$$

They represent corresponding *integrated intensity*, *integrated density*, and *integrated flux*. It is easily seen that the quantities I, ρ, and H are connected with each other by relations analogous to Eqs. (3) and (5), namely:

$$\left. \begin{array}{c} \rho = \dfrac{1}{c} \int I \, d\omega \\[2mm] H = \int I \cos\theta \, d\omega \end{array} \right\} \tag{15}$$

For the application of these formulas we consider the radiation field around a star. In the interest of simplicity we assume that the radiation emitted by the star does not depend on direction.

First we find the quantities ρ_ν and H_ν on the surface of the star. According to Eq. (3), the density of radiation on surface of the star is

$$\rho_\nu = \frac{2\pi}{c}I_\nu \tag{16}$$

This quantity is twice as small as ρ_ν for the isotropic radiation because here the radiation falls only on one side and is not incident on the

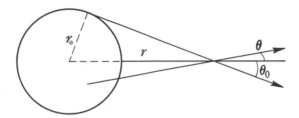

Fig. 1.2

other side. Meanwhile the flux is found with the help of Eq. (7) by setting $I = $ const in the interval $0 < \theta < \pi/2$. It is

$$H_\nu = \pi I_\nu \tag{17}$$

Incidentally, if the radius of a star is r_*, we have the total energy radiated by the star in frequency ν; for example, the luminosity of a star is

$$L_\nu = 4\pi r_*^2 \cdot \pi I_\nu \tag{18}$$

We find now the quantities ρ_ν and H_ν at a distance r from the center of the star, $r \geqslant r_*$. Using the system of polar coordinates with a given volume as center and with the z axis as radius-vector, we find, from Eq. (3),

$$\rho_\nu = \frac{1}{c}\int_0^{2\pi} d\phi \int_0^{\theta_0} I_\nu \sin\theta \, d\theta \tag{19}$$

where θ_0 denotes angle θ for the radiation coming out of the boundary of the star (Fig. 1.2). With the $I_\nu = $ const, Eq. (19) gives

$$\rho_\nu = \frac{2\pi}{c}I_\nu(1-\cos\theta_0) \tag{20}$$

or, taking into consideration the fact that $\sin\theta_0 = r_*/r$ (see Fig. 1.2), we find

$$\rho_\nu = \frac{2\pi}{c}I_\nu\left[1-\sqrt{1-\left(\frac{r_*}{r}\right)^2}\right] \tag{21}$$

We see that this quantity differs from the quantity ρ_ν for the isotropic radiation by the factor:

$$W = \frac{1}{2}\left[1 - \sqrt{1 - \left(\frac{r_*}{r}\right)^2}\right] \tag{22}$$

This coefficient is called *dilution coefficient* (weakening) of radiation. By the way, on the surface of the star $W = \frac{1}{2}$ and at the great distances from the surface of the star,

$$W = \frac{1}{4}\left(\frac{r_*}{r}\right)^2 \tag{23}$$

To find the flux of radiation at a distance we use, as before, Eq. (7). Assuming that the area is perpendicular to the radius of the star, we obtain

$$H_\nu = \int_0^{2\pi} d\phi \int_0^{\theta_0} I_\nu \cos\theta \sin\theta \, d\theta \tag{24}$$

With the $I_\nu = $ const we find that

$$H_\nu = \pi I_\nu \sin^2\theta_0 = \pi I_\nu \left(\frac{r_*}{r}\right)^2 \tag{25}$$

One can obtain the last formula in another way by remembering that in our case the flux is equal to the luminosity of the star divided through the surface of the star with a radius of r, that is,

$$H_\nu = \frac{L_\nu}{4\pi r^2} \tag{26}$$

Inserting the expression for the luminosity of the star given in Eq. (18) into Eq. (26), we find Eq. (25).

We should remark that in this example the flux coincides with the luminosity, because the radiation falling on the surface from the other side is absent.

2. The Equation of Radiative Transfer

We assume that the medium in which the radiation is transported has properties both to absorb and to emit radiation. In such a case the intensity of radiation will change along the ray. Later in this chapter we will derive an equation which determines the law of this change. However, first we will introduce some other quantities which characterize absorbing and emitting properties of the medium.

We assume that the radiation of intensity I_ν falls on area $d\sigma$ situated on the normal to the direction of radiation incident within a solid angle $d\omega$, in a frequency interval $(\nu, \nu + d\nu)$, and in time dt. The amount of energy falling on the area is $I_\nu\, d\sigma d\omega d\nu dt$. If the medium absorbs the radiation, then some fraction of this energy will be absorbed along the path ds, and it will be proportional to ds. We denote this fraction by $\alpha_\nu\, ds$. Thus the amount of the absorbed energy along the path ds will be

$$\alpha_\nu\, ds\, I_\nu\, d\sigma d\omega d\nu dt \qquad (27)$$

The quantity α_ν is called *absorption coefficient*. Because the fraction of the absorbed energy $\alpha_\nu\, ds$ is a dimensionless quantity, the absorption coefficient α_ν has a dimension opposite to the length. By the way, the absorption coefficient depends on frequency of radiation and on the coordinates of the given points, but it does not depend on the direction of radiation in an isotropic medium.

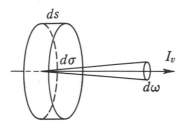

Fig. 1.3

If the medium also emits energy, the amount of energy radiated by the volume dV within a solid angle $d\omega$ in the frequency interval $(\nu, \nu + d\nu)$ in time dt will be proportional to $dVd\omega d\nu dt$. We denote this quantity by

$$\epsilon_\nu\, dVd\omega d\nu dt \qquad (28)$$

and we call the quantity ϵ_ν the *emission coefficient*. Consequently, the emission coefficient is the amount of energy emitted by the unit of volume per unit of solid angle, of frequency, and of time. The emission coefficient depends on frequency ν, on coordinates of the given point, and, generally speaking, on the direction of radiation.

With the given quantities of α_ν and ϵ_ν, we find now how the intensity of radiation changes along the path. We assume that the radiation field is stationary, that is, it does not change with time.

We take an elementary cylinder whose axis coincides with the direction of the ray (see Fig. 1.3). We assume the lower area of the cylinder is equal to $d\sigma$ and the height ds; therefore the height is relatively small in relation to dimension of the area. We consider the radiation entering the cylinder and leaving it within the solid angle $d\omega$ in the frequency interval $\nu, \nu + d\nu$ and in time dt. If the intensity of radiation entering the cylinder is I_ν, the amount of energy entering the cylinder will be equal to

$$I_\nu \, d\sigma d\omega d\nu dt$$

Letting $I_\nu + dI_\nu$ be the intensity leaving the cylinder, we find that the amount of energy leaving the cylinder will be

$$(I_\nu + dI_\nu) \, d\sigma d\omega d\nu dt$$

The difference between these amounts of energy is due to the fact that the energy is absorbed in, and is emitted by, the cylinder. The amount of absorbed energy is determined by Eq. (27) and the amount of emitted energy will be given by Eq. (28) if, in it, we substitute the quantity dV by the volume of the cylinder, that is, if we set $dV = d\sigma ds$. Thus we obtain

$$(I_\nu + dI_\nu) \, d\sigma d\omega d\nu dt = I_\nu \, d\sigma d\omega d\nu dt - \alpha_\nu \, ds \, I_\nu \, d\sigma d\omega d\nu dt + \epsilon_\nu \, d\sigma ds d\omega d\nu dt$$

and after some necessary abbreviations,

$$\frac{dI_\nu}{ds} = -\alpha_\nu I_\nu + \epsilon_\nu \tag{29}$$

This is the desired equation which determines the change of intensity of radiation transmitted through an absorbing and emitting medium. It is called *equation of radiative transfer.*

We consider now some special cases of this equation.

If $\alpha_\nu = 0$ and $\epsilon_\nu = 0$, then $I_\nu = $ const. Consequently, in a vacuum, that is, in the absence of absorption and emission, the intensity of radiation does not change along the path. We employed this obvious property of the radiation previously when we considered the radiation field around a star and assumed that the intensity of radiation on the surface of the star and at any distance from it is the same.

If the medium absorbs the radiant energy but does not emit it (that is, $\alpha_\nu \neq 0$ but $\epsilon_\nu = 0$), then, instead of Eq. (29), we have

$$\frac{dI_\nu}{ds} = -\alpha_\nu I_\nu \tag{30}$$

Integrating this equation, we have

$$I_\nu(s) = I_\nu(0) e^{-\int_0^s \alpha_\nu(s') ds'} \tag{31}$$

where $I_\nu(0)$ is an intensity of radiation for $s = 0$, for example, intensity of radiation entering the medium.

The dimensionless quantity

$$\int_0^s \alpha_\nu(s') \, ds'$$

is called *optical distance* between two points. The intensity of radiation passing through the elementary optical distance diminishes by e times.

Generally, that is, for $\alpha_\nu \neq 0$ and $\epsilon_\nu \neq 0$, we solve Eq. (29) in respect to I_ν as follows:

$$I_\nu(s) = I_\nu(0)e^{-\int_0^s \alpha\nu(s')ds'} + \int_0^s \epsilon_\nu(s')e^{-\int_{s'}^s \alpha\nu(s'')ds''}ds' \tag{32}$$

Equation (32) can be called the equation of radiative transfer in integral form.

We see that generally the intensity of radiation consists of two parts. The first part represents the intensity of the original radiation at the point $s = 0$ diminished by absorption on the path from 0 to s. The second part is an intensity of radiation due to the emission of the radiant energy on the path from 0 to s and diminished by the absorption on the way from the place of emission s' to the given place s.

We emphasize that the equation of radiative transfer refers always to definite frequency. Only in a case when absorption coefficient does not depend on frequency ($\alpha_\nu = \alpha$) can we obtain, having integrated Eq. (29), an analogous equation for computing of *integrated intensity*. This equation is

$$\frac{dI}{ds} = -\alpha I + \epsilon \tag{33}$$

The quantity entering in this equation,

$$\epsilon = \int_0^\infty \epsilon_\nu \, d\nu \tag{34}$$

represents the *integrated emission coefficient*.

In reality, the absorption coefficient α_ν depends usually on the frequency ν; nevertheless, one uses Eq. (33) also in this case for computing the integrated intensity of radiation I: here one understands under α an absorption coefficient somehow averaged over the frequency. However, the results of such use of Eq. (33) may be far from accurate.

With a few exceptions we shall consider in the future the radiation field with a definite frequency ν; however, for simplicity of writing we shall simply write I for I_ν and H for H_ν, etc. This notation should not be confused with the corresponding quantities which characterize the integrated radiation.

3. Scattering of Light in an Elementary Volume

If the absorption coefficient α and emission coefficient ϵ are given, one can easily find the intensity of radiation, as we have shown in

Eq. (32). It is much more difficult to compute the radiation field in a case where the radiant energy absorbed by the elementary volume is re-emitted, that is, when there is a diffusion of radiation in the medium. In this case the absorption coefficient is no longer known and depends on the intensity of radiation which falls on the elementary volume from all sides. At the same time the intensity of radiation depends on the emission coefficient ϵ along the path. Thus the problem is reduced to the determination of two unknown functions: emission coefficient ϵ and intensity of radiation I.

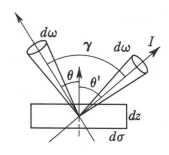

Fig. 1.4

To formulate the problem exactly one should know the law of diffusion of radiation by the elementary volume of the medium.

We take an elementary volume with a surface base $d\sigma$ and height dz (Fig. 1.4). We let the intensity of radiation fall on this volume within the solid angle $d\omega'$ and in the direction forming an angle θ' with a normal to the base. An amount of energy falling on the volume in unit frequency and in unit time will be $I d\omega' d\sigma \cos \theta'$. Because the path traversed by radiation in volume is equal to $dz \sec \theta'$, a fraction of energy will be absorbed which is equal to $\alpha dz \sec \theta'$. Consequently, the amount of absorbed energy will be

$$\alpha \, dz d\sigma I \, d\omega'$$

The factor $dz d\sigma$ is the absorbing volume. Thus the amount of radiant energy absorbed by unit volume is

$$\alpha I \, d\omega'$$

The quantity α is often called the *volume absorption coefficient*, that is, the absorption coefficient computed for unit volume. Sometimes instead of α one uses the absorption coefficient computed for unit mass or for unit frequency; the former is equal to α/ρ, where ρ is the density of the matter, and the latter is equal to α/n, where n is the number of particles in 1 cm³.

As stated previously, we shall assume that only a part of the radiant energy absorbed by the volume will be transformed into another form of energy, that is, will suffer a **real absorption**. The other part will be re-emitted by the volume, that is, will be **scattered**. The ratio of the scattered radiation to the total amount of energy absorbed by the volume we denote by λ; then the fraction of energy suffering real absorption will be $1 - \lambda$. The quantity $\lambda\alpha$ we shall call the *coefficient of scattering*, and the quantity $(1 - \lambda)\alpha$ the *coefficient of real absorption*. (The quantity λ does not have a generally accepted name. Sometimes it is called the probability of quantum lifetime; at other times, the albedo of a particle.)

In practice we are confronted often with a case where there is only a scattering of light and no true absorption in the medium. In this case $\lambda = 1$; we shall say that in such a medium *pure scattering* occurs.

Generally speaking, the probability of scattering of light by the elementary volume in different directions is dissimilar. The probability depends on the angle γ between the direction of the incident radiation and that of the scattered radiation (see Fig. 1.4). We denote the probability that the radiation is scattered within a solid angle under an angle γ by

$$x(\gamma)\frac{d\omega}{4\pi}$$

Let us call the function $x(\gamma)$ *indicatrix of scattering*. Evidently the following condition should be fulfilled:

$$\int x(\gamma)\frac{d\omega}{4\pi} = 1 \tag{35}$$

or because $d\omega = \sin \gamma \, d\gamma \, d\phi$,

$$\tfrac{1}{2}\int_0^\pi x(\gamma) \sin \gamma \, d\gamma = 1 \tag{35'}$$

We should select a case of *isotropic scattering*. Here the probability of scattering of light in different directions is similar, that is,

$$x(\gamma) = 1$$

Such an indicatrix is called *spherical*.

With known quantities of α, λ, and $x(\gamma)$ it is easy to write an expression for the amount of energy scattered by an elementary volume in a fixed direction. One has only to multiply the amount of energy absorbed by the volume, that is, the quantity $\alpha I d\omega'$, by the fraction of this energy scattered in the direction considered, that is, the quantity $\lambda x(\gamma) d\omega/4\pi$, and then integrate the expression so obtained over all directions of radiation incident on the volume. The result is the following expression,

$$\lambda \frac{d\omega}{4\pi} \alpha \int Ix(\gamma) \ d\omega'$$

which represents an amount of energy scattered, per unit of volume, of time, and of specific frequency, within a solid angle $d\omega$ and in a given direction. If the medium only scatters the radiation, this quantity becomes $\epsilon \ d\omega$. Consequently, the coefficient of radiation in this case is

$$\epsilon = \lambda \alpha \int Ix(\gamma) \frac{d\omega'}{4\pi} \tag{36}$$

In general, when the medium produces light scattering as well as true absorption, we have to write:

$$\epsilon = \lambda \alpha \int Ix(\gamma) \frac{d\omega'}{4\pi} + \epsilon_0 \tag{37}$$

instead of Eq. (36). The quantity ϵ_0 one may call the *coefficient of true radiation*.

Incidentally, having integrated Eq. (37) over all solid angles and having made use of Eq. (35), we obtain

$$\int \epsilon \ d\omega = \lambda \alpha \int I \ d\omega' + \int \epsilon_0 \ d\omega \tag{38}$$

Equation (38) represents the net balance of energy per unit of volume.

In the future we shall regard as given the afore-mentioned quantities α, λ, and $x(\gamma)$, defining the scattering property of an elementary volume. It is understood, of course, that the values vary for different mediums. Up to the present time there have been many investigations concerning the quantities α, λ, and $x(\gamma)$ and in reference to physical properties of medium. We shall discuss some of them when we apply the general theory to concrete examples. We limit ourselves here to a few remarks on possible values of these quantities.

We have no interest in the absorption coefficient α because we discuss optical distances instead of geometric ones; the former quantities may vary in a wide interval: from 0 to ∞.

The quantity λ representing the ratio of the scattering coefficient to the sum of coefficients of scattering and true absorption is usually found by means of two entirely different methods. Let us assume, for example, a case of scattering of light within a resonance line. If there are no other processes in the elementary volume we have pure scattering ($\lambda = 1$). In reality, however, in addition to this process there will be collisions of excited atoms with outside particles which produce true absorption of radiation. Because the number of collisions is proportional to the density of matter, the quantity λ may have all values from 0 to 1.

The indicatrix of scattering (γ) may be assumed spherical in several instances, for example, in the case of diffusion of radiation in a spectral line. In other instances the indicatrix of scattering appears to be more involved.

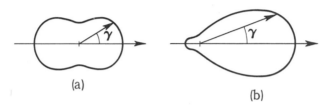

(a)

(b)

Fig. 1.5

Rayleigh[1] was the first to study the problem of light scattering by particles whose dimensions were small in comparison with the wavelength of light. He showed that in this case the indicatrix of scattering has the form

$$x(\gamma) = \tfrac{3}{4}(1 + \cos^2\gamma) \tag{39}$$

The Rayleigh scattering of light is produced partly by molecules and free electrons.

Mie[2] gave the foundations of the theory of scattering of light by particles whose dimensions are comparable with the wavelength. The indicatrix of scattering depends here on a ratio of the radius of a particle to the length of a light wave and on refractive index of the particle material. His theory has been developed by many authors. Among them one should mention Shuleikin[3] and Shifrin[4].

Figure 1.5 shows a comparison of Rayleigh's indicatrix of scattering, above, with that of Shuleikin, below; we see that the second indicatrix is greatly elongated forward.

Shifrin's thorough investigation of the problem of light scattering by separate particles is published in his book.[4]

[1] Rayleigh, On the Scattering of Light by Small Particles, *Phil. Mag.* **41**, 102, 447 (1871).

[2] G. Mie, Beitrage zur Optik truben Medien, Speciell killoidaler Metallosungen, *Ann. d. Phys.* **25** (1908).

[3] V. V. Shuleikin, Scattering of Light by Very Big Colloidal Particles, *Phil. Mag.* **48** (1924).

[4] K. S. Shifrin, Light Scattering in a Turbid Medium, *Gos. Tech. Publ.* (1951).

4. The Fundamental Problem in the Theory of Radiation Scattering

In previous sections we derived the basic quantities which characterize the radiation field as well as the medium in which the radiation is transported. This gives us the possibility of making an exact formulation of the problem which will occupy us presently.

We assume a medium of definite form and definite size upon which falls radiation whose distribution and strength are given. The medium absorbs and scatters radiation; the property of scattering of an elementary volume with characteristic quantities α, λ, and $x(\gamma)$ is known. We are required to analyze the radiation field within and outside the medium.

As we have stated, the problem consists of simultaneous computation of two quantities: intensity of radiation I and coefficient of radiation ϵ. Here the coefficient of radiation ϵ is determined as true radiation per unit of volume as well as radiation scattered by this same volume.

The two equations necessary for finding I and ϵ have been obtained. They are the equation of radiative transfer, Eq. (29) and Eq. (37), which expresses the condition of radiative equilibrium. In other words, the problem is reduced to a simultaneous solution of the two following equations:

$$\frac{dI}{ds} = -\alpha I + \epsilon \tag{40a}$$

$$\epsilon = \lambda \alpha \int Ix(\gamma)\frac{d\omega'}{4\pi} + \epsilon_0 \tag{40b}$$

By means of these equations one can solve the problem of luminescence of any medium with any sources of radiation affecting it. However, for astrophysical and geophysical applications, the greatest interest lies in two cases: (1) the medium consists of plane parallel layers; (2) the medium has spherical symmetry. Very often one can assume that the outside layers of the spherical symmetry are approximately plane-parallel. Therefore great importance is attached to the problem of scattering in a medium with plane-parallel layers. This is the very problem with which we deal presently.

We understand by a medium with plane-parallel layers a medium with optical properties such that the quantities α, λ, and $x(\gamma)$ are dependent only on one coordinate—depth z counted along the normal to the layers. At the same time we assume that the intensity of radiation produced by sources of radiation will also not be dependent on other coordinates except the depth z. In such a case the intensity of scattered radiation will be a function only of the coordinate z and of the direction of radiation (Fig. 1.6).

It is convenient to introduce *optical depth* τ instead of depth z:

$$\tau = \int_0^z \alpha(z)\, dz \qquad (41)$$

The optical depth τ and the geometrical depth z are counted from one of the boundary planes, and we call one an upper and the other a

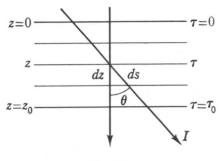

Fig. 1.6

lower boundary plane. At the same time, instead of a geometric thickness z_0 of the medium, we introduce an optical thickness τ_0 by means of the following relation:

$$\tau_0 = \int_0^{x_0} \alpha(z)\, dz \qquad (42)$$

For analysis of directions we choose a spherical system of coordinates with polar axis passing in the direction of increased depth in each place of medium. The polar distance we denote by θ and the azimuth by ϕ. Thus the required quantities I and ϵ will be functions of τ, I and ϕ.

It is obvious that in the present case the angles θ and ϕ do not change along the path if we neglect refraction. Consequently, only the co-ordinate z changes along the path and $dz = ds\cos\theta$. Therefore the equation of radiative transfer for plane-parallel layers has the following form [see Eq. (40a)].

$$\cos\theta \frac{dI}{dz} = -\alpha I + \epsilon \qquad (43)$$

As we have stated, we transform the depth z into the depth τ by the relation $d\tau = \alpha\, dz$; setting

$$\epsilon = \alpha B \qquad (44)$$

we get, instead of Eq. (43),

$$\cos\theta\frac{dI}{d\tau} = -I + B \qquad (45)$$

We make an analogous transformation of Eq. (40b). Taking into consideration Eq. (44) and also setting

$$\epsilon_0 = \alpha B_0 \qquad (46)$$

we obtain

$$B = \lambda \int Ix(\gamma)\frac{d\omega'}{4\pi} + B_0 \qquad (47)$$

In this way we change the system of Eqs. (40) into the system of Eqs. (45) and (47). Here the unknown functions are $I(\tau, \theta, \phi)$ and $B(\tau, \theta, \phi)$. The function $B(\tau, \theta, \phi)$ is often called "source function" or "recoil" (re-emission).

Generally speaking, the medium may shine under radiation, sources of which are located inside, as well as outside, the medium. The existence of radiation sources within a medium is taken into account by the term B_0 of the equation. The radiation falling on the medium from outside sources of light can, however, be analyzed by means of two methods.

1. By writing corresponding boundary conditions in which the intensity of radiation entering the medium should be given.

2. By separating the field of direct radiation—that is, radiation coming directly from outside sources—from the field of diffused radiation of the medium.

We denote the intensity of direct radiation by I_1 and we can rewrite Eq. (47) in the form:

$$B = \lambda \int Ix(\gamma)\frac{d\omega'}{4\pi} + B_0 + B_1 \qquad (48)$$

where

$$B_1 = \lambda \int I_1 x(\gamma)\frac{d\omega'}{4\pi} \qquad (49)$$

In Eqs. (45) and (48) I now expresses the intensity of scattered radiation. The boundary conditions should then express the fact that radiation entering the medium is absent.

From now on we shall use the system of Eqs. (45) and (48), that is, we shall select that part of the total radiation which comes directly from the outside sources of light.

We rewrite the system of Eqs. (45) and (48) in an explicit form. We now define the direction of radiation scattered by the volume by angles θ and ϕ and that of diffuse radiation incident on the volume by

θ' and ϕ'. Knowing that $d\omega' = \sin\theta'\, d\theta'\, d\phi'$, we change the aforementioned equations into

$$\cos\theta \frac{dI(\tau,\theta,\phi)}{d\tau} = -I(\tau,\theta,\phi) + B(\tau,\theta,\phi) \tag{50a}$$

$$B(\tau,\theta,\phi) = \frac{\lambda}{4\pi}\int_0^{2\pi} d\phi' \int_0^{\pi} I(\tau,\theta',\phi')x(\gamma)\sin\theta'\, d\theta'$$
$$+ B_0(\tau,\theta,\phi) + B_1(\tau,\theta,\phi) \tag{50b}$$

where the angle γ is defined by the following formula, known from spherical trigonometry

$$\cos\gamma = \cos\theta\cos\theta' + \sin\theta\sin\theta'\cos(\phi-\phi') \tag{51}$$

We should add to Eqs. (50) also boundary conditions. They, as stated previously, should express the absence of diffuse radiation incident on the upper boundary from above and on the lower one from below. In other words, the boundary conditions are of the form:

$$\left.\begin{aligned}
I(0,\theta,\phi) &= 0 \quad \text{for} \quad \theta < \frac{\pi}{2}\\[2ex]
I(\tau_0,\theta,\phi) &= 0 \quad \text{for} \quad \theta > \frac{\pi}{2}
\end{aligned}\right\} \tag{52}$$

The system of Eqs. (50) and the boundary conditions of Eqs. (52) are rigorous for finding the quantities $B(\tau,\theta,\phi)$ and $I(\tau,\theta,\phi)$.

The system of Eqs. (50) provides **one integral** equation for finding $B(\tau,\theta,\phi)$: one solves Eq. (50a) in respect to $I(\tau,\theta,\phi)$ and substitutes the expressions found for $I(\tau,\theta,\phi)$ into Eq. (50b).

Indeed, Eq. (50a) gives for boundary conditions of Eqs. (52):

$$I(\tau,\theta,\phi) = \int_0^{\tau} B(\tau',\theta,\phi)e^{-(\tau-\tau')\sec\theta}\sec\theta\, d\tau' \quad \left(\text{for} \quad \theta < \frac{\pi}{2}\right) \tag{53}$$

and

$$I(\tau,\theta,\phi) = -\int_{\tau}^{\tau_0} B(\tau',\theta,\phi)e^{-(\tau-\tau')\sec\theta}\sec\theta\, d\tau' \quad \left(\text{for} \quad \theta > \frac{\pi}{2}\right) \tag{54}$$

Inserting Eqs. (53) and (54) into Eq. (50b), we obtain

$$B(\tau,\theta,\phi) = \frac{\lambda}{4\pi}\int_0^{2\pi} d\phi' \left[\int_0^{\pi/2} x(\gamma)\sin\theta'\, d\theta'\right.$$
$$\times \int_0^{\tau} B(\tau',\theta',\phi')e^{-(\tau-\tau')\sec\theta'}\sec\theta'\, d\tau'$$
$$\left. -\int_{\pi/2}^{\pi} x(\gamma)\sin\theta'\, d\theta'\int_{\tau}^{\tau_0} B(\tau',\theta',\phi')e^{-(\tau-\tau')\sec\theta'}\sec\theta'\, d\tau'\right]$$
$$+ B_0(\tau,\theta,\phi) + B_1(\tau,\theta,\phi) \tag{55}$$

Equation (55) provides a solution for the function $B(\tau, \theta, \phi)$. Having found this function we can find the intensity of radiation $I(\tau, \theta, \phi)$ in accordance with Eqs. (53) and (54).

These equations are considerably simplified for the case of a spherical indicatrix of scattering. In this case the function B depends only on τ and the intensity of radiation I—only on τ and θ. Therefore, instead of the Eqs. (50), we have for $x(\gamma) = 1$:

$$\left.\begin{aligned}
\cos\theta\frac{dI(\tau, \theta)}{d\tau} &= -I(\tau, \theta) + B(\tau) \\
B(\tau) &= \frac{\lambda}{2}\int_0^\pi I(\tau, \theta')\sin\theta'\, d\theta' + g(\tau)
\end{aligned}\right\} \tag{56}$$

where

$$g(\tau) = B_0(\tau) + B_1(\tau) \tag{57}$$

Here we assume as usual that the function B_0 depends only on τ, although, generally speaking, it may also depend on θ and ϕ.

For the spherical indicatrix of scattering, the integral Eq. (55) changes into

$$B(\tau) = \frac{\lambda}{2}\int_0^{\pi/2}\sin\theta'\, d\theta'\int_0^\tau B(\tau')e^{-(\tau-\tau')\sec\theta'}\sec\theta'\, d\tau'$$
$$-\frac{\lambda}{2}\int_{\pi/2}^\pi\sin\theta'\, d\theta'\int_\tau^{\tau_0} B(\tau')e^{-(\tau-\tau')\sec\theta'}\sec\theta'\, d\tau' + g(\tau) \tag{58}$$

Replacing $y = \cos\theta'$ in the first and $y = -\sec\theta$ in the second integral and inverting the order of integration, we obtain

$$B(\tau) = \frac{\lambda}{2}\int_0^\tau B(\tau')\, d\tau'\int_1^\infty e^{-(\tau-\tau')y}\frac{dy}{y}$$
$$+\frac{\lambda}{2}\int_\tau^{\tau_0} B(\tau')\, d\tau'\int_1^\infty e^{-(\tau'-\tau)y}\frac{dy}{y} + g(\tau) \tag{59}$$

The kernel of the integral Eq. (59) represents the so-called *integrated indicative function* defined by the equation

$$\mathrm{Ei}\, x = \int_1^\infty e^{-xy}\frac{dy}{y} \tag{60}$$

That is why Eq. (59) can be rewritten:

$$B(\tau) = \frac{\lambda}{2}\int_0^{\tau_0} B(\tau')\mathrm{Ei}|\tau - \tau'|\, d\tau' + g(\tau) \tag{61}$$

The integral Eq. (61) plays a very important part in the theory of scattering of light; originally it was derived for a special form of the function $g(\tau)$ by a professor of Petersburg University, Hvolson,[5] who investigated light scattering in milk glass.

Table 1.1 contains the values of the function Ei x.

TABLE 1.1 VALUES OF THE FUNCTION Ei x

x	Ei x	x	Ei x	x	Ei x	x	Ei x
0	∞						
0.01	4.0379	0.20	1.2227	0.39	0.7194	0.90	0.2602
0.02	3.3547	0.21	1.1829	0.40	0.7024	0.95	0.2387
0.03	2.9591	0.22	1.1454	0.41	0.6859	1.00	0.2194
0.04	2.6813	0.23	1.1099	0.42	0.6700	1.10	0.1860
0.05	2.4679	0.24	1.0762	0.43	0.6546	1.20	0.1584
0.06	2.2953	0.25	1.0443	0.44	0.6397	1.30	0.1355
0.07	2.1508	0.26	1.0139	0.45	0.6253	1.40	0.1162
0.08	2.0269	0.27	0.9849	0.46	0.6114	1.50	0.1000
0.09	1.9187	0.28	0.9573	0.47	0.5979	1.60	0.08631
0.10	1.8229	0.29	0.9309	0.48	0.5848	1.70	0.07465
0.11	1.7371	0.30	0.9057	0.49	0.5721	1.80	0.06471
0.12	1.6595	0.31	0.8815	0.50	0.5598	1.90	0.05620
0.13	1.5889	0.32	0.8583	0.55	0.5034	2.00	0.04890
0.14	1.5241	0.33	0.8361	0.60	0.4544	2.10	0.04261
0.15	1.4645	0.34	0.8147	0.65	0.4115	2.20	0.03719
0.16	1.4092	0.35	0.7942	0.70	0.3738	2.30	0.03250
0.17	1.3578	0.36	0.7745	0.75	0.3403	2.40	0.02844
0.18	1.3098	0.37	0.7554	0.80	0.3106	2.50	0.02490
0.19	1.2649	0.38	0.7371	0.85	0.2840		

We emphasize some properties of Ei x. For $x = 0$ it is logarithmic. For small x the values of Ei x may be computed by means of the series:

$$\text{Ei } x = -\gamma - \ln x + x - \frac{x^2}{2 \cdot 2!} + \frac{x^3}{3 \cdot 3!} - \cdots \tag{62}$$

where $\gamma = 0.5772$ or Euler's constant. For large values of x the function Ei x is expanded into a series:

$$\text{Ei } x = \frac{e^{-x}}{x}\left(1 - \frac{1}{x} + \frac{2}{x^2} - \frac{6}{x^3} + \cdots\right) \tag{63}$$

5. THE CASE OF PURE SCATTERING

For cases of pure scattering we should make $\lambda = 1$ in the equations derived in the previous section. Because the case of pure scattering occurs very often in practice, we are particularly interested in a case

[5] O. D. Hvolson, Grundzüge einer mathematischen Theorie der inneren Diffusion des Lichtes, *Isv. Petersburg Akademie Nauk.* **33**, 221 (1890).

when, for $\lambda = 1$, the foregoing equations permit two first simple integrals. One of them we find by means of an integration of Eqs. (50) in respect to all solid angles with the result:

$$\frac{d}{d\tau} \int I \cos\theta \, d\omega = -\int I \, d\omega + \int B \, d\omega \tag{64}$$

$$\int B \, d\omega = \lambda \int I \, d\omega + g_1(\tau) \tag{65}$$

where

$$g_1(\tau) = \int (B_0 + B_1) \, d\omega \tag{66}$$

While deriving Eq. (65), we have used Eq. (35).

Equations (64) and (65) give, for $\lambda = 1$,

$$\frac{d}{d\tau} \int I \cos\theta \, d\omega = g_1(\tau) \tag{67}$$

Consequently,

$$H(\tau) = \int_0^\tau g_1(\tau) \, d\tau + C_1 \tag{68}$$

where

$$H(\tau) = \int I \cos\theta \, d\omega \tag{69}$$

and C_1 is an arbitrary constant.

The quantity $H(\tau)$ represents the flux of radiation normal to the plane-paralleled layers and Eq. (68) represents the *flux integral*.

Another integral of Eqs. (50) we find by means of an integration of these equations over all solid angles, after we have multiplied them by $\cos\theta$, namely:

$$\frac{d}{d\tau} \int I \cos^2\theta \, d\omega = -H(\tau) + \int B \cos\theta \, d\omega \tag{70}$$

$$\int B \cos\theta \, d\omega = \frac{\lambda}{4\pi} \int I \, d\omega' \int x(\gamma) \cos\theta \, d\omega + g_2(\tau) \tag{71}$$

where

$$g_2(\tau) = \int (B_0 + B_1) \cos\theta \, d\omega \tag{72}$$

Expanding the scattering indicatrix $x(\gamma)$ into a series of Legendre polynomials and applying the addition theorem of spherical harmonics, we have

$$\frac{1}{4\pi} \int x(\gamma) \cos \theta \, d\omega = \frac{1}{3} x_1 \cos \theta'$$ (73)

where x_1 is the first coefficient in the expansion of $x(\gamma)$ with Legendre polynomials (see Ch. 3, Sec. 2).

We can rewrite Eq. (71) with the aid of Eq. (73) as follows:

$$\int B \cos \theta \, d\omega = \frac{\lambda}{3} x_1 H(\tau) + g_2(\tau)$$ (74)

It follows from Eqs. (70) and (74) that

$$\frac{d}{d\tau} \int I \cos^2\theta \, d\omega = -\left(1 - \frac{\lambda}{3} x_1\right) H(\tau) + g_2(\tau)$$ (75)

For $\lambda = 1$ the quantity $H(\tau)$ is given by Eq. (68). Consequently, for this case and substituting

$$K(\tau) = \int I \cos^2\theta \, d\omega$$ (76)

we obtain

$$K(\tau) = -\left(1 - \frac{x_1}{3}\right)\left[\int_0^\tau d\tau' \int_0^{\tau'} g_1(\tau'') \, d\tau'' + C_1\tau\right] + \int_0^\tau g_2(\tau') \, d\tau' + C_2$$ (77)

where C_2 is a new arbitrary constant. Equation (77) is the so-called *K-integral*.

6. Scattering of Light in Planetary Atmospheres

The luminescence of planetary atmospheres is due to their scattering of solar light. The intensity of the radiation which is reflected by the planetary atmosphere determines the brightness and spectrum of the planet. A comparison of theoretical and observed intensities is the only source of our information about planetary atmospheres. Therefore great importance is attached to the problem of diffuse reflection of light by the atmosphere of a planet.

In the case of the Earth's atmosphere, we are much more interested in the intensity of radiation that is transmitted diffusely by the atmosphere. This radiation determines the brightness of the sky in different directions. The study of brightness distribution over the sky permits us to obtain valuable information about the optical properties of the Earth's atmosphere.

As a first approximation we can assume that atmospheric layers are plane-parallel. We make such an assumption because the thickness of the atmosphere, that is, the thickness of those layers in which noticeable absorption of light occurs, is small in comparison with the radius of the planet. Because of the great distance from a planet to the sun, the solar rays incident on the planet can be considered as parallel. Therefore, the study of planetary atmospheres is reduced to the problem of the scattering of light in a medium consisting of plane-parallel layers and illuminated by parallel rays.

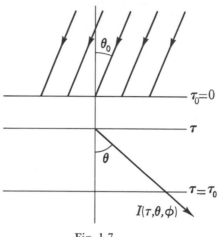

Fig. 1.7

Equations defining the intensity of radiation scattered by a planetary atmosphere are only a particular case of Eqs. (50). Because in planetary atmospheres there is no source of radiation, we can take $B_0 = 0$ in Eqs. (50). On the other hand, the quantity B_1 can be determined as follows.

Assuming that solar rays are falling on the atmosphere at an angle θ_0 to the normal with an azimuth ϕ_0 (Fig. 1.7) and denoting the illumination of an area on the upper boundary of the atmosphere perpendicular to rays by πS, for $\tau = 0$, it is obvious that illumination of the same area at the optical depth τ will be $\pi S e^{-\tau \sec \theta_0}$.

For computing the quantity B_1 defined by Eq. (49), we assume that radiation is incident on the atmosphere within a small solid angle $\Delta \omega$. Then the quantity B_1 is

$$B_1 = \frac{\lambda}{4\pi} x(\gamma_1) I_1 \Delta \omega \tag{78}$$

where γ_1 is the angle between the solar radiation and radiation scattered by the given volume of the atmosphere. In this case, we have

$$I_1 \Delta \omega = \pi S e^{-\tau \sec \theta_0} \tag{79}$$

Consequently, instead of Eq. (78), we have

$$B_1 = \frac{\lambda}{4} x(\gamma_1) S e^{-\tau \sec \theta_0} \tag{80}$$

The angle γ_1 entering in this equation is determined by a formula analogous to Eq. (51):

$$\cos \gamma_1 = \cos \theta \cos \theta_0 + \sin \theta \sin \theta_0 \cos (\phi - \phi_0) \tag{81}$$

Thus the fundamental problem of theory of scattering of light in planetary atmospheres is reduced to a solution of the following system of equations:

$$\left.\begin{array}{c} \cos \theta \dfrac{dI(\tau, \theta, \phi)}{d\tau} = -I(\tau, \theta, \phi) + B(\tau, \theta, \phi) \\[2ex] B(\tau, \theta, \phi) = \dfrac{\lambda}{4\pi} \displaystyle\int_0^{2\pi} d\phi' \int_0^{\pi} I(\tau, \theta', \phi') x(\gamma) \sin \theta' \, d\theta' \\[2ex] + \dfrac{\lambda}{4} x(\gamma_1) e^{-\tau \sec \theta_0} \end{array}\right\} \tag{82}$$

where the angles γ and γ_1 are found by means of the corresponding Eqs. (51) and (81).

We can obtain from Eq. (82) an integral equation for finding the function $B(\tau, \theta, \phi)$:

$$B(\tau, \theta, \phi) = \frac{\lambda}{4\pi} \int_0^{2\pi} d\phi' \left[\int_0^{\pi/2} x(\gamma) \sin \theta' \, d\theta' \right.$$

$$\times \int_0^{\tau} B(\tau', \theta', \phi') e^{-(\tau - \tau') \sec \theta'} \sec \theta' \, d\tau' - \int_{\pi/2}^{\pi} x(\gamma) \sin \theta' \, d\theta'$$

$$\left. \times \int_{\tau}^{\tau_0} B(\tau', \theta', \phi') e^{-(\tau - \tau') \sec \theta'} \sec \theta' \, d\tau' \right] + \frac{\lambda}{4} x(\gamma_1) S e^{-\tau \sec \theta_0} \tag{83}$$

which is a particular case of Eq. (55). The integral Eq. (83) was first analyzed by Ambartsumian[6].

For the spherical indicatrix of scattering we have, instead of Eq. (83),

$$B(\tau) = \frac{\lambda}{2} \int_0^{\tau_0} B(\tau') \mathrm{Ei} |\tau - \tau'| \, d\tau' + \frac{\lambda}{4} S e^{-\tau \sec \theta_0} \tag{84}$$

For obtaining the integral Eq. (83) from the system of Eqs. (82), we made boundary conditions of Eqs. (52). These conditions express the absence of diffuse radiation both incident on the upper boundary

[6] V. A. Ambartsumian, Scattering and Absorption of Light in Planetary Atmospheres, *Uch. Sapis. LGU*, No. 82 (1941).

of medium from above and on the lower boundary from below. The planetary atmosphere has, however, a boundary at the surface of the planet which can reflect the radiation. Therefore the second boundary condition for $\tau = \tau_0$ should correspondingly be changed; however, we shall not discuss this problem. The problem of the luminescence of a medium bounded by a reflecting surface will be discussed in detail at the end of Chapter 7. We should also note that in planetary atmospheres the indicatrix of scattering and the parameter λ change with the height. We shall, however, consider them as constant in the theory presented now. Therefore the result obtained by application of this theory to planetary atmospheres should be considered approximate. The problem of scattering of light in a medium with changing optical properties has not been investigated in detail. Some investigation of that problem will be mentioned in Chapter 10.

As stated previously, the greatest interest attaches to the intensity of radiation diffusely reflected and diffusely transmitted by an atmosphere, that is,

$$I(0, \theta, \phi) \quad \text{for } \theta > \frac{\pi}{2}, \quad \text{and} \quad I(\tau_0, \theta, \phi) \quad \text{for } \theta < \frac{\pi}{2}$$

These quantities are defined by the formula $B(\tau, \theta, \phi)$ and

$$I(0, \theta, \phi) = - \int_0^{\tau_0} B(\tau, \theta, \phi) e^{-\tau \sec\theta} \sec\theta \, d\tau \tag{85}$$

$$I(\tau_0, \theta, \phi) = \int_0^{\tau_0} B(\tau, \theta, \phi) e^{-(\tau_0 - \tau)\sec\theta} \sec\theta \, d\tau \tag{86}$$

which are derived from Eqs. (53) and (54).

In the following, instead of the intensities

$$I(0, \theta, \phi) \qquad \text{and} \qquad I(\tau_0, \theta, \phi),$$

we often use the so-called *coefficients of brightness* $\rho(\theta, \phi)$ and $\sigma(\theta, \phi)$ which are determined from the relations:

$$\left. \begin{aligned} I(0, \theta, \phi) &= S\rho(\theta, \phi) \cos\theta_0 \\ I(\tau_0, \theta, \phi) &= S\sigma(\theta, \phi) \cos\theta_0 \end{aligned} \right\} \tag{87}$$

The physical meaning of the coefficients of brightness can be seen if we consider the following.

Suppose an absolutely white orthotropic area of 1 cm² is situated on the upper boundary of the atmosphere. The orthotropic character of the area means that the intensity of its scattered radiation does not depend on direction. Denoting this intensity as I_*, we find that the amount of energy scattered by the area per 1 sec is equal to πI_*. On the other hand, the amount of energy incident on the area per 1 sec, that is, its illumination, is obviously equal to $\pi S \cos \theta_0$. Because of the assumption that the area is absolutely white, these two quantities should be equal. It follows then that the intensity of radiation scattered by an absolutely white orthotropic area is defined by

$$I_* = S \cos \theta_0 \tag{88}$$

By means of Eqs. (87) and (88), we have

$$\rho(\theta, \phi) = \frac{I(0, \theta, \phi)}{I_*}; \quad \sigma(\theta, \phi) = \frac{I(\tau_0, \theta, \phi)}{I_*} \tag{89}$$

Consequently, the coefficient of brightness represents the ratio of the intensity of radiation scattered by the atmosphere to the intensity of radiation scattered by the absolutely white orthotropic area situated at the upper boundary of the atmosphere.

Minnaert[7] has found, from physical considerations, that the coefficients of brightness ρ and σ are symmetrical functions of the angle of reflection (or transmission) and that of the incident light. Later (Ch. 6, Sec. 2) this conclusion will be derived from the equations of Radiative Transfer.

7. Radiative Transfer in a Stellar Atmosphere (the Continuum)

The brightness of a star is due to the energy originating in the interior regions of the star. The spectrum of a star is produced by a very complicated process of energy transport from the internal regions outward. By means of the spectrum we recognize the structure of a star's atmosphere and the processes occurring in it. That is why the analysis of stellar spectra is one of the fundamental problems in theoretical astrophysics.

In solving this problem one makes the following assumptions: (1) Energy transport in the atmosphere occurs in the form of radiation; (2) the atmosphere has neither sources nor reservoirs of energy; and (3) the atmosphere is stationary. In other words, we assume the presence of *radiative equilibrium* in the atmosphere: each volume element emits as much energy as it absorbs.

The amount of energy emitted per unit of volume and per 1 sec is

$$4\pi \int_0^\infty \epsilon_\nu \, d\nu$$

[7] M. Minnaert, The Reciprocity Principle in Lunar Photometry, *Astrophysical J.* **93**, 403 (1941).

and the amount of energy absorbed by the same unit is

$$\int d\omega \int_0^\infty \alpha_\nu I_\nu \, d\nu$$

We have, therefore, the condition for radiative equilibrium:

$$4\pi \int_0^\infty \epsilon_\nu \, d\nu = \int d\omega \int_0^\infty \alpha_\nu I_\nu \, d\nu \tag{90}$$

Another equation with the quantities I_ν and ϵ_ν is the well-known equation of radiative transfer. Atmospheric layers of stars as well as those of planets may be regarded as plane-parallel. Then the equation of radiative transfer has the form:

$$\cos \theta \frac{dI_\nu}{dr} = -\alpha_\nu I_\nu + \epsilon_\nu \tag{91}$$

where I_ν is the intensity of radiation at the distance r from the center of the star and passing at the angle θ to the radius-vector (Fig. 1.8).

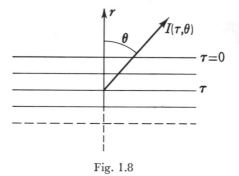

Fig. 1.8

If the absorption coefficient α_ν does not depend on frequency ($\alpha_\nu = \alpha$), we have instead of Eq. (90),

$$4\pi\epsilon = \alpha \int I \, d\omega \tag{92}$$

where ϵ is an integrated absorption coefficient, and I is an integrated intensity of radiation. Integrating Eq. (91) over all frequencies, we obtain another equation for determination of ϵ and I:

$$\cos \theta \frac{dI}{dr} = -\alpha I + \epsilon \tag{93}$$

Generally speaking, the absorption coefficient appears to be a rather complicated function of frequency. Nevertheless, one often uses Eqs.

(92) and (93) instead of (90) and (91), with the understanding that α represents a certain average absorption coefficient.

Corresponding to the average absorption coefficient α we introduce the optical depth τ in a stellar atmosphere:

$$\tau = \int_r^\infty \alpha \, dr \qquad (94)$$

Introducing a notation $\epsilon/\alpha = B$, we can now rewrite Eqs. (92) and (93) in the form:

$$\cos\theta \frac{dI(\tau, \theta)}{d\tau} = I(\tau, \theta) - B(\tau) \qquad (95a)$$

$$B(\tau) = \tfrac{1}{2}\int_0^\pi I(\tau, \theta) \sin\theta \, d\theta \qquad (95b)$$

To Eqs. (95) we should add the boundary condition

$$I(0, \theta) = 0 \qquad \text{for } \theta > \frac{\pi}{2} \qquad (96)$$

expressing the fact that there is no radiation from outside of the star. For a complete evaluation of the quantities I and B one should also give the total flux,

$$H = \frac{L}{4\pi r_*^2} \qquad (97)$$

where L is the luminosity and r_* is the radius of the star.

With the boundary condition of Eq. (96), we derive from Eqs. (95) the following integral equation for finding the function $B(\tau)$:

$$B(\tau) = \tfrac{1}{2}\int_0^\infty B(\tau') \mathrm{Ei}|\tau - \tau'| \, d\tau' \qquad (98)$$

This equation defines the function $B(\tau)$ accurately within a constant factor which is found when the flux, H, is given. Equation (98) is sometimes called "*Milne's equation*"[8]. The equation represents only a special case of Eq. (61) for $\lambda = 1$ (pure scattering), $\tau_0 = \infty$, $g(\tau) = 0$.

In the theory of stellar atmospheres one also makes a hypothesis about local thermodynamic equilibrium: at every point of a stellar atmosphere the Stefan–Boltzmann law is valid:

$$\rho = aT^4 \qquad (99)$$

[8] E. A. Milne, Radiative Equilibrium in the Outer Layers of a Star, *Monthly Notices of Royal Astronomical Soc.* **81**, 361–375 (1921).

and also the Kirchhoff–Planck law:

$$\frac{\epsilon_\nu}{\alpha_\nu} = B_\nu^*(T) \tag{100}$$

where

$$B_\nu^*(T) = \frac{2h\nu^3}{c^2} \frac{1}{e^{h\nu/kT} - 1} \tag{101}$$

in which the temperature T changes from place to place, the quantity a is Stefan's constant, h is Planck's constant, k is Boltzmann's constant, and c is the velocity of light.

If the function $B(\tau)$ is known, one can easily find the dependence of temperature T on the optical depth τ. Remembering that the integrated density of radiation is equal to

$$\rho(\tau) = \frac{2\pi}{c} \int_0^\pi I(\tau, \theta) \sin \theta \; d\theta \tag{102}$$

and recalling Eq. (95b), we have

$$\rho(\tau) = \frac{4\pi}{c} B(\tau) \tag{103}$$

From Eqs. (99) and (103) it follows that

$$T^4 = \frac{4\pi}{ac} B(\tau) \tag{104}$$

Using the equation of transfer, Eq. (91), and Eq. (101), we can obtain the following expression for the intensity of radiation emerging from the stellar atmosphere with the frequency ν at an angle θ to the normal:

$$I_\nu(0, \theta) = \frac{2h\nu^3}{c^2} \int_0^\infty \frac{e^{-\tau_\nu \sec\theta}}{e^{h\nu/kT} - 1} \sec \theta \; d\tau_\nu \tag{105}$$

where τ_ν is the optical depth for the frequency ν:

$$\tau_\nu = \int_r^\infty \alpha_\nu \; dr \tag{106}$$

If we assume that α_ν/α is constant, then $\tau_\nu = (\alpha_\nu/\alpha)\tau$. Therefore, instead of Eq. (105), we can write:

$$I_\nu(0, \theta) = \frac{2h\nu^3}{c^2} \int_0^\infty \frac{e^{-(\alpha_\nu/\alpha)\tau \sec\theta}}{e^{h\nu/kT} - 1} \frac{\alpha_\nu}{\alpha} \sec \theta \; d\tau \tag{107}$$

In order to perform the integration of this formula we have to remember that the temperature T is connected with τ by means of Eq. (104).

Equation (107) gives the distribution of energy in the continuum of the stellar spectrum at the angular distance θ from the center of the disk. Having found the quantity $I_\nu(0, \theta)$ we can compute the total energy emitted by the star at the frequency ν and per 1 sec as follows:

$$L_\nu = 4\pi r_*^2 \cdot 2\pi \int_0^{\pi/2} I_\nu(0, \theta) \cos\theta \sin\theta \, d\theta \tag{108}$$

Strictly speaking, Eq. (98) is correct only for $\alpha_\nu = \alpha$. We stated this before. If the absorption coefficient depends on frequency, the theory becomes more complex. Mustel[9], Chandrasekhar[10], and others were working on this theory.

8. RADIATIVE TRANSFER IN A STELLAR ATMOSPHERE (SPECTRAL LINE)

Equation (107) giving the intensity of the emergent radiation is not applicable to the frequencies of spectral lines because, for the very high layers where absorption lines are occurring, the assumption of local thermodynamic equilibrium is not correct. Therefore the problem of radiative transfer in respect to frequency of spectral lines should be considered separately.

Here we should assume that in the equation of radiative transfer, Eq. (91), the absorption coefficient λ_ν is the sum of the absorption coefficient κ_ν in the continuum and the absorption coefficient σ_ν in the spectral line:

$$\alpha_\nu = \kappa_\nu + \sigma_\nu \tag{109}$$

The emission coefficient ϵ_ν consists in turn of two parts: the emission coefficient in the continuum which can be represented in the form $\kappa_\nu B_\nu^*(T)$, where $B_\nu^*(T)$ is the Planck function defined by Eq. (101) and the emission coefficient in the spectral line. Assuming that for every frequency there is a pure scattering, we have

$$\epsilon_\nu = \sigma_\nu \int I_\nu \frac{d\omega}{4\pi} + \kappa_\nu B_\nu^*(T) \tag{110}$$

Considering Eqs. (109) and (110), the equation of radiative transfer has the form:

$$\cos\theta \frac{dI_\nu}{dr} = -(\kappa_\nu + \sigma_\nu)I_\nu + \sigma_\nu \int I_\nu \frac{d\omega}{4\pi} + \kappa_\nu B_\nu^*(T) \tag{111}$$

[9] E. R. Mustel, Theory of Radiative Equilibrium in Stellar Atmospheres for the Absorption Coefficient Depending on Frequency, *Trudi GAISH*, Vol. XII, No. 2 (1940).

[10] S. Chandrasekhar, On the Radiative Equilibrium of a Stellar Atmosphere, VII, *Astrophysical J.* **101**, 328 (1945).

Introducing the optical depth for frequency ν as

$$\tau_\nu = \int_r^\infty (\kappa_\nu + \sigma_\nu)\, dr \tag{112}$$

and writing

$$\lambda_\nu = \frac{\sigma_\nu}{\kappa_\nu + \sigma_\nu} \tag{113}$$

we can rewrite Eq. (111) as follows:

$$\left.\begin{aligned}
\cos\theta \frac{dI_\nu(\tau_\nu, \theta)}{d\tau_\nu} &= I_\nu(\tau_\nu, \theta) - B_\nu(\tau_\nu) \\
B_\nu(\tau_\nu) &= \frac{\lambda_\nu}{2} \int_0^\pi I_\nu(\tau_\nu, \theta) \sin\theta\, d\theta + (1 - \lambda_\nu) B_\nu{}^*(T)
\end{aligned}\right\} \tag{114}$$

From the Eqs. (114) and for the condition that $I_\nu(0, \theta) = 0$, with $\theta > \pi/2$, we obtain the following integral equation for the evaluation of $B_\nu(\tau_\nu)$:

$$B_\nu(\tau_\nu) = \frac{\lambda_\nu}{2} \int_0^\infty B_\nu(\tau_\nu') \mathrm{Ei}|\tau_\nu - \tau_\nu'|\, d\tau_\nu' + (1 - \lambda_\nu) B_\nu{}^*(T) \tag{115}$$

Having found the function $B_\nu(\tau_\nu)$, the intensity of the emerging radiation can be computed with the well-known formula:

$$I_\nu(0, \theta) = \int_0^\infty B_\nu(\tau_\nu) e^{-\tau_\nu \sec\theta} \sec\theta\, d\tau_\nu \tag{116}$$

Thus we can determine the contour of an absorption line in the spectrum of a star at an angular distance θ from the center of the disk.

Equation (115) is a separate case of the Eq. (61). Taking into consideration the physical meaning of the quantities entering Eq. (61) we may say that the problem of formation of an absorption line is a problem of the absorption of light in the medium with sources of light situated in it, the radiation coefficient of which is equal to $\kappa_\nu B_\nu{}^*(T)$, with a probability of quantum lifetime for the scattering defined by Eq. (113) and for the spherical indicatrix of scattering.

Eddington[11] was the first to derive the equation of radiative transfer, Eq. (111). It was generalized in some directions by Pannekoek, Strömgren, and others. Instead of Eq. (111), one applies the equation of transfer in which the redistribution of radiation in respect to frequencies within a line is taken into account. The problem of formation of absorption line with redistribution of frequencies will be investigated in Chapter 7.

[11] A. S. Eddington, The Formation of Absorption Lines, *Monthly Notices of Royal Astronomical Soc.* **89**, 620 (1929).

9. Scattering of Light in a One-Dimensional Medium

As an example of the application of the conceptions and equations derived above, let us consider the scattering of light in a one-dimensional medium. In this case the system of equations for radiative transfer and radiative equilibrium is easily solved exactly. As we shall see later, the problem of scattering of light in a medium consisting of plane-parallel layers is approximately reduced to the problem of scattering of light in one-dimensional medium. Consequently, the latter problem possesses a special interest.

Consider now a rectilinear section of length l_0 able to scatter the radiation. If we let $\alpha(l)$ be the absorption coefficient at the distance l from one of the ends of the section, λ be the ratio of the coefficient of scattering to that of absorption—that is, the probability of quantum lifetime during an elementary act of scattering, x be the fraction of energy scattered forward, and if we assume that the radiation of intensity I falls on the element of length dl, the energy absorbed in this element is $I\alpha\, dl$, of which the portion $\lambda\alpha\, dl$ is scattered. The energy scattered forward is $x\lambda I\alpha\, dl$ and the energy scattered backward is equal to $(1-x)\lambda I\alpha\, dl$. The energy $(1-\lambda)I\alpha\, dl$ is really absorbed by the element of length dl.

We transform the geometric distances into optical ones by introducing the optical depth τ and optical thickness τ_0 by means of relations:

$$\tau = \int_0^l \alpha(l)\, dl, \qquad \tau_0 = \int_0^{l_0} \alpha(l)\, dl \qquad (117)$$

Let $I_1(\tau)$ and $I_2(\tau)$ be intensities of radiation occurring at optical depth τ and corresponding, respectively, to increasing and decreasing depths. In our case the equations of radiative transfer have the form:

$$\left. \begin{aligned} \frac{dI_1(\tau)}{d\tau} &= -I_1(\tau) + B_1(\tau) \\[2mm] -\frac{dI_2(\tau)}{d\tau} &= -I_2(\tau) + B_2(\tau) \end{aligned} \right\} \qquad (118)$$

where

$$B_1(\tau) = \frac{\epsilon_1}{\alpha}, \qquad B_2(\tau) = \frac{\epsilon_2}{\alpha} \qquad (119)$$

and ϵ_1 and ϵ_2 are coefficients of radiation.

In order to write the equation of radiative equilibrium one should supply sources of radiation which cause the brightness of the medium.

Let us assume first that the sources of radiation are within the medium. Denoting by $\epsilon_1{}^0 = \alpha B_1{}^0$ and $\epsilon_2{}^0 = \alpha B_2{}^0$ the coefficients of radiation with above-mentioned sources of radiation (that is, coefficients of true radiation), we find for the equation of radiative transfer the following formula:

$$\left.\begin{aligned}
B_1(\tau) &= \lambda[(x I_1 \tau) + (1 - x) I_2(\tau)] + B_1{}^0(\tau) \\
B_2(\tau) &= \lambda[(1 - x) I_1(\tau) + x I_2(\tau)] + B_2{}^0(\tau)
\end{aligned}\right\} \quad (120)$$

We should add to the system of Eqs. (118) and (120) the following boundary conditions:

$$I_1(0) = 0, \qquad I_2(\tau_0) = 0 \qquad (121)$$

If there are outside sources of radiation, they can be determined within boundary conditions; for example, in the case when radiation of intensity I_0 falls on the boundary of the medium $\tau = 0$, we can write $I_1(0) = I_0$ instead of the first boundary condition.

However, one often finds it convenient to separate the radiation coming directly from the outside sources of light and radiation emitted by the medium itself. In the above-mentioned case of the outside radiation of intensity I_0 falling on the boundary $\tau = 0$, the intensity of this radiation will be $I_0 e^{-\tau}$ at the depth τ. Taking the term $I_0 e^{-\tau}$ out of the intensity I in Eq. (120), we obtain

$$\left.\begin{aligned}
B_1(\tau) &= \lambda[x I_1(\tau) + (1 - x) I_2(\tau)] + B_1{}^0(\tau) + \lambda x I_0 e^{-\tau} \\
B_2(\tau) &= \lambda[(1 - x) I_1(\tau) + x I_2(\tau)] + B_2{}^0(\tau) + \lambda(1 - x) I_0 e^{-\tau}
\end{aligned}\right\} \quad (122)$$

Now in Eqs. (118) and (122) we understood by I_1 and I_2 the intensity of radiation emitted by the medium itself, and the boundary conditions have the form of Eq. (121).

Inserting Eqs. (122) into Eqs. (118), we have

$$\left.\begin{aligned}
\frac{dI_1}{d\tau} &= -I_1 + \lambda[x I_1 + (1 - x) I_2] + B_1{}^0 + \lambda x I_0 e^{-\tau} \\
-\frac{dI_2}{d\tau} &= -I_2 + \lambda[(1 - x) I_1 + x I_2] + B_2{}^0 + \lambda(1 - x) I_0 e^{-\tau}
\end{aligned}\right\} \quad (123)$$

From this, first adding term for term in both equations and then subtracting one from the other, we find

$$\left.\begin{aligned}
\frac{d(I_1 - I_2)}{d\tau} &= -(1 - \lambda)(I_1 + I_2) + B_1{}^0 + B_2{}^0 + \lambda I_0 e^{-\tau} \\
\frac{d(I_1 + I_2)}{d\tau} &= -[1 + \lambda(1 - 2x)](I_1 - I_2) + B_1{}^0 - B_2{}^0 \\
&\quad + \lambda(2x - 1) I_0 e^{-\tau}
\end{aligned}\right\} \quad (124)$$

The system of Eqs. (124) is easily solvable in general form for the constants λ and x; however, we shall consider several individual cases instead.

1. *Pure (perfect) scattering.* Assuming in Eqs. (124) that $\lambda = 1$, we have

$$\frac{d(I_1 - I_2)}{d\tau} = B_1{}^0 + B_2{}^0 + I_0 e^{-\tau} \tag{125a}$$

$$\frac{d(I_1 + I_2)}{d\tau} = -2(1-x)(I_1 - I_2) + B_1{}^0 - B_2{}^0 + (2x - 1) I_0 e^{-\tau} \tag{125b}$$

Integrating Eq. (125a) gives

$$I_1 - I_2 = \int_0^\tau (B_1{}^0 + B_2{}^0)\, d\tau - I_0 e^{-\tau} + C_1 \tag{126}$$

where C_1 is an arbitrary constant.

The quantity $I_1 - I_2$ is the flux of radiation. Equation (126) expresses the already known flux integral which is always there in the case of pure scattering (see Sec. 5). Inserting Eq. (126) into Eq. (125b) and integrating, we find

$$I_1 + I_2 = -2(1-x)\left[\int_0^\tau d\tau' \int_0^{\tau'} (B_1{}^0 + B_2{}^0)\, d\tau'' + C_1\tau\right]$$
$$+ \int_0^\tau (B_1{}^0 - B_2{}^0)\, d\tau' - I_0 e^{-\tau} + C_2 \tag{127}$$

where C_2 is a new arbitrary constant.

Equations (126) and (127) in which the constants C_1 and C_2 are defined by the boundary conditions present the entire solution of the problem.

2. *External sources of light.* Assuming that $\tau = 0$, that radiation of intensity I_0 falls on the outside boundary of the medium in which no internal sources are present, and setting $B_1{}^0 = 0$ and $B_2{}^0 = 0$ in Eqs. (124), we obtain

$$\frac{d(I_1 - I_2)}{d\tau} = -(1-\lambda)(I_1 + I_2) + \lambda I_0 e^{-\tau} \tag{128a}$$

$$\frac{d(I_1 + I_2)}{d\tau} = -[1 + \lambda(1 - 2x)](I_1 - I_2) + \lambda(2x - 1) I_0 e^{-\tau} \tag{128b}$$

Differentiating Eq. (128b) with respect to τ and using Eq. (128a), we find

$$\frac{d^2(I_1 + I_2)}{d\tau^2} = k^2(I_1 + I_2) - (1 - k^2) I_0 e^{-\tau} \tag{129}$$

where

$$k^2 = (1-\lambda)[1+\lambda(1-2x)] \qquad (130)$$

An integration of Eq. (129) gives

$$I_1 + I_2 = Ce^{-k\tau} + De^{k\tau} - I_0 e^{-\tau} \qquad (131)$$

where C and D are arbitrary constants. Substituting Eq. (131) into Eq. (128b), we find

$$-Ce^{-k\tau} + De^{k\tau} = -\frac{k}{1-\lambda}(I_1 - I_2 + I_0 e^{-\tau}) \qquad (132)$$

From Eqs. (131) and (132) with boundary conditions of Eq. (121), it follows that

$$I_1(\tau) = I_0 \frac{e^{k(\tau_0-\tau)} - r_0^2 e^{-k(\tau_0-\tau)}}{e^{k\tau_0} - r_0^2 e^{-k\tau_0}} - I_0 e^{-\tau} \qquad (133)$$

$$I_2(\tau) = I_0 r_0 \frac{e^{k(\tau_0-\tau)} - e^{-k(\tau_0-\tau)}}{e^{k\tau_0} - r_0^2 e^{-\tau k_0}} \qquad (134)$$

where we have introduced a new notation:

$$r_0 = \frac{k-1+\lambda}{k+1-\lambda} \qquad (135)$$

Equations (133) and (134) determine the required intensities of radiation $I_1(\tau)$ and $I_2(\tau)$.

Great interest attaches to the intensity of radiation emerging from the medium, that is, $I_1(\tau_0)$ and $I_2(0)$. Equations (133) and (134) give

$$I_1(\tau_0) = I_0 \frac{(1-r_0^2) e^{-k\tau_0}}{1 - r_0^2 e^{-2k\tau_0}} - I_0 e^{-\tau_0} \qquad (136)$$

$$I_2(0) = I_0 r_0 \frac{1 - e^{-2k\tau_0}}{1 - r_0^2 e^{-2k\tau_0}} \qquad (137)$$

In Eq. (137) we see the physical meaning of the quantity r_0. Inserting into the formula $\tau_0 = \infty$, we have

$$I_2(0) = I_0 r_0 \qquad (138)$$

Consequently, the quantity r_0 represents the coefficient of reflection of light by a medium with an infinitely large optical thickness.

A special case is when $\lambda = 1$, for which we turn our attention to Eqs. (126) and (127). Setting in them $B_1^0 = 0$ and $B_2^0 = 0$, we find

$$I_1 - I_2 = -I_0 e^{-\tau} + C_1 \qquad (139)$$

$$I_1 + I_2 = -2(1-x) C_1 \tau - I_0 e^{-\tau} + C_2 \qquad (140)$$

Evaluating the constants C_1 and C_2 from the boundary conditions of Eq. (121), we obtain the required intensities of radiation:

$$I_1(\tau) = I_0 \frac{1 + (1-x)(\tau_0 - \tau)}{1 + (1-x)\tau_0} - I_0 e^{-\tau} \tag{141}$$

$$I_2(\tau) = I_0 \frac{(1-x)(\tau_0 - \tau)}{1 + (1-x)\tau_0} \tag{142}$$

The intensities of radiation emerging from the medium become

$$I_1(\tau_0) = \frac{I_0}{1 + (1-x)\tau_0} - I_0 e^{-\tau_0} \tag{143}$$

$$I_2(0) = I_0 \frac{(1-x)\tau_0}{1 + (1-x)\tau_0} \tag{144}$$

Incidentally, from Eqs. (143) and (144) follows:

$$I_2(0) + I_1(\tau_0) + I_0 e^{-\tau_0} = I_0 \tag{145}$$

This relation expresses the obvious fact that in the case of pure scattering the amount of energy emerging from the medium is equal to the amount of energy falling on it.

3. *Isotropic scattering.* Assuming that the scattering of radiation in a medium occurs with equal probability in all directions, we should write $x = \frac{1}{2}$. Inserting this value of x into Eqs. (133), (134), (141), and (142), we obtain the intensity of radiation for isotropic scattering in a medium illuminated by external sources of radiation.

We consider now the general case when the medium is affected by the internal sources as well as by the external sources of radiation. For simplicity, assume that the internal sources of radiation emit the same amount of energy in both directions. The quantities $B_1{}^0$ and $B_2{}^0$ are equal to each other, and we denote them simply by B_0.

Mindful of previous statements, instead of Eqs. (124) for the isotropic scattering we obtain the following:

$$\frac{d(I_1 - I_2)}{d\tau} = -(1-\lambda)(I_1 + I_2) + 2B_0 + \lambda I_0 e^{-\tau} \tag{146a}$$

$$\frac{d(I_1 + I_2)}{d\tau} = -(I_1 - I_2) \tag{146b}$$

From Eqs. (146) it follows that

$$\frac{d^2(I_1 + I_2)}{d\tau^2} = (1-\lambda)(I_1 + I_2) - 2g(\tau) \tag{147}$$

where

$$g(\tau) = B_0(\tau) + \frac{\lambda}{2}I_0 e^{-\tau} \tag{148}$$

The general solution of Eq. (147) has the form:

$$I_1 + I_2 = \left[\frac{1}{k}\int_0^\tau g(\tau)e^{k\tau}\,d\tau + C\right]e^{-k\tau} + \left[-\frac{1}{k}\int_0^\tau g(\tau)e^{-k\tau}\,d\tau + D\right]e^{k\tau} \tag{149}$$

where C and D are arbitrary constants and $k = \sqrt{1-\lambda}$. Inserting Eq. (149) into Eq. (146b), we find

$$I_1 - I_2 = \left[\int_0^\tau g(\tau)e^{k\tau}\,d\tau + kC\right]e^{-k\tau} + \left[\int_0^\tau g(\tau)e^{-k\tau}\,d\tau - kD\right]e^{k\tau} \tag{150}$$

The constants C and D entering Eqs. (149) and (150) are determined by the boundary conditions of Eq. (121) and are given in the forms:

$$kC = -\frac{(1-k^2)\int_0^{\tau_0} g(\tau)e^{k(\tau_0-\tau)}\,d\tau - (1-k)^2\int_0^{\tau_0} g(\tau)e^{-k(\tau_0-\tau)}\,d\tau}{(1+k)^2 e^{k\tau_0} - (1-k)^2 e^{-k\tau_0}} \tag{151}$$

$$kD = \frac{(1+k)^2\int_0^{\tau_0} g(\tau)e^{k(\tau_0-\tau)}\,d\tau - (1-k^2)\int_0^{\tau_0} g(\tau)e^{-k(\tau_0-\tau)}\,d\tau}{(1+k)^2 e^{k\tau_0} - (1-k)^2 e^{-k\tau_0}} \tag{152}$$

We should note that in the present case of a one-dimensional medium as well as in a three-dimensional medium, the problem of light scattering in the medium can be reduced to a certain integral equation. As is seen from Eqs. (122), the quantities B_1 and B_2 are equal to each other for $x = \frac{1}{2}$ and $B_1{}^0 = B_2{}^0$. Denoting the common meaning by B, we find, from Eqs. (122),

$$B(\tau) = \frac{\lambda}{2}[I_1(\tau) + I_2(\tau)] + B_0(\tau) + \frac{\lambda}{2}I_0 e^{-\tau} \tag{153}$$

The integration of the equations of transfer, Eqs. (118), with the boundary conditions of Eq. (121) and for $B_1 = B_2 = B$ gives

$$\left.\begin{array}{l} I_1(\tau) = \displaystyle\int_0^\tau B(\tau')e^{-(\tau-\tau')}\,d\tau' \\[3mm] I_2(\tau) = \displaystyle\int_\tau^{\tau_0} B(\tau')e^{-(\tau'-\tau)}\,d\tau' \end{array}\right\} \tag{154}$$

Inserting Eqs. (154) into Eq. (153), we receive the following equation for evaluating the function $B(\tau)$:

$$B(\tau) = \frac{\lambda}{2} \int_0^{\tau_0} B(\tau') e^{-|\tau - \tau'|} \, d\tau' + g(\tau) \qquad (155)$$

where we have used Eq. (148).

Equation (155) is analogous to Eq. (61) obtained previously for a three-dimensional medium composed of plane-parallel layers.

The solution of Eq. (155) may be obtained by the substitution of Eq. (149), in which the constants C and D are determined by Eqs. (151) and (152), into Eq. (153).

If internal sources of radiation are absent, then instead of Eq. (155) we have

$$B(\tau) = \frac{\lambda}{2} \int_0^{\tau_0} B(\tau') e^{-|\tau - \tau'|} \, d\tau' + \frac{\lambda}{2} I_0 e^{-\tau} \qquad (156)$$

The solution of this equation has the form:

$$B(\tau) = \lambda I_0 \frac{(1+k) e^{k(\tau_0 - \tau)} - (1-k) e^{-k(\tau_0 - \tau)}}{(1+k)^2 e^{k\tau_0} - (1-k)^2 e^{-k\tau_0}} \qquad (157)$$

For $\lambda = 1$, we find

$$B(\tau) = I_0 \frac{1 + \tau_0 - \tau}{2 + \tau_0} \qquad (158)$$

CHAPTER 2

THE METHODS OF SOLUTION

Many problems in astrophysics, geophysics, and physics are reduced to the solution of the equations of radiative transfer. Generally speaking, solutions of these equations present considerable mathematical difficulties. Therefore, many investigators have dealt with the methods which are applicable to the solution of the above-mentioned equations.

In the present chapter we investigate methods which are frequently used in astrophysics. Such are: method of successive approximations, methods of Schwarzschild–Schuster, Eddington, and Chandrasekhar, and also variational methods.

Ten years ago Ambartsumian developed methods for solution of radiative transfer which are of special interest to astrophysicists. We consider them in Chapter 3. Methods proposed by the author are considered in Chapters 4 and 6.

1. METHOD OF SUCCESSIVE APPROXIMATIONS

We consider the fundamental integral equation in the theory of radiative transfer for planetary atmospheres. In the case of spherical indicatrix of scattering, this equation has the form:

$$B(\tau) = \frac{\lambda}{2} \int_0^{\tau_0} \text{Ei}|\tau - \tau'| B(\tau') \, d\tau' + \frac{\lambda}{4} S e^{-\tau \sec \theta_0} \tag{1}$$

in which the notations have been defined in Chapter 1 (see also Ch. 6).

Equation (1) can be solved in principle by the method of successive approximations. As a first approximation for $B(\tau)$ we take usually the free term of Eq. (1), that is, we write:

$$B_1(\tau) = \frac{\lambda}{4} S e^{-\tau \sec \theta_0} \tag{2}$$

Further, we substitute Eq. (2) into the right-hand side of Eq. (1) and find the second approximation for $B(\tau)$:

$$B_2(\tau) = \frac{\lambda}{4} S e^{-\tau \sec \theta_0} + \frac{\lambda}{2} \int_0^{\tau_0} \text{Ei}|\tau - \tau'| B_1(\tau') \, d\tau' \tag{3}$$

Analogously, we find $B_3(\tau)$ etc.

The physical meaning of such a solution is the following. Accepting Eq. (2) for $B(\tau)$ we assume that the radiation is scattered in the medium only once, that is, we are taking into consideration, as they say, scattering of the *first order*. Substituting Eq. (2) in the integral of Eq. (1), we assume that radiation is scattered in the medium only twice, that is, we are taking into consideration scattering of the *second order*. Therefore, the afore-mentioned method of successive approximations represents successive computation of scattering of the first, second, and higher orders.

Having approximate expressions of the functions $B(\tau)$ we can find approximate expressions for the intensities of radiation scattered in the medium and corresponding coefficients of brightness. For this we use Eqs. (85), (86), and (87) of Chapter 1. Coefficients of brightness due to the scattering of the first order are:

$$\rho_1(\theta, \theta_0) = \frac{\lambda}{4} \frac{1 - e^{-\tau_0(\sec\theta + \sec\theta_0)}}{\cos\theta + \cos\theta_0} \tag{4}$$

$$\sigma_1(\theta, \theta_0) = \frac{\lambda}{4} \frac{e^{-\tau_0\sec\theta} - e^{-\tau_0\sec\theta_0}}{\cos\theta - \cos\theta_0} \tag{5}$$

In Eq. (4), θ denotes an angle of reflection and in Eq. (5) an angle of radiation transmission.

We note that, for an indicatrix of scattering of any other form, we have, instead of Eqs. (4) and (5),

$$\rho_1(\theta, \theta_0, \phi) = \frac{\lambda}{4} x(\gamma_1) \frac{1 - e^{-\tau_0(\sec\theta + \sec\theta_0)}}{\cos\theta + \cos\theta_0} \tag{6}$$

$$\sigma_1(\theta, \theta_0, \phi) = \frac{\lambda}{4} x(\gamma_1) \frac{e^{-\tau_0\sec\theta} - e^{-\tau_0\sec\theta_0}}{\cos\theta - \cos\theta_0} \tag{7}$$

where γ_1 is an angle between the direction of incident radiation and that of radiation scattered in the medium.

Many authors have obtained formulas for the intensities of radiation due to scattering of the first and second order. In 1916 Fesenkov[1] had obtained such a formula for the intensity of radiation scattered by a medium of infinitely large optical thickness with the Rayleigh indicatrix of scattering (phase function). Analogous formulas were found later by Schoenberg[2] and others for different cases. The previously-derived formulas for the coefficients of brightness due to scattering of

[1] V. G. Fesenkov, On the Light Reflection of Turbid Surfaces, *Isv. Russk. Astronomical Soc.* **22**, No. 3 (1916).

[2] E. Schoenberg, Theoretische Photometrie, *Handbuch der Astrophysik* LL/1, Berlin (1929).

the first order are very often applied. Sometimes one uses also the formulas taking into account the first and second order. Therefore, it is interesting to investigate the accuracy of these formulas.

It is obvious that the above-mentioned formulas are the more accurate the less is the average number of scatterings undergone by the quanta in the medium. At the same time the averge number of scatterings depends first of all on the quantity of the parameter λ. If the value of λ is small, that is, the part of the true absorption is great, the quantum suffers on the average a small number of scatterings. This follows mathematically from the fact that the terms of the scattering of the first order are proportional to λ, the terms of the scattering of the second order are proportional to λ^2, and so on. The average number of scatterings will also not be large in the case of small optical thickness of the medium; in other words, the accuracy of Eqs. (4) and (5) is the greater the smaller is the value of λ and τ_0 for the given medium.

TABLE 2.1. COEFFICIENTS OF BRIGHTNESS ρ

τ_0	ρ_1	ρ_2	ρ	ρ'
0.2	0.041	0.052	0.055	0.050
0.4	0.069	0.096	0.113	0.10
0.6	0.087	0.129	0.17	0.15
0.8	0.100	0.153	0.22	0.19
1.0	0.108	0.171	0.27	0.23
1.2	0.114	0.183	0.31	0.27
1.4	0.117	0.192	0.36	0.31
1.6	0.120	1.198	0.40	0.35
1.8	0.122	0.202	0.44	0.38
2.0	0.123	0.205	0.47	0.41
∞	0.125	0.212	1.06	1.00

An idea of the accuracy of Eqs. (4) and (5) in the case ($\lambda = 1$) is given in Tables 2.1 and 2.2. They show values of coefficients of brightness for $\theta_0 = 0$ and $\theta = 0$, and for a medium with a spherical indicatrix of scattering. The first column of each table gives values of the optical thickness of the medium; the second, the coefficients of brightness due to scattering of the first order; the third, the coefficients of brightness due to scattering of the first and second order; the fourth, accurate values of coefficients of brightness; the fifth column will be discussed later.

The tables show that, even for the Earth's atmosphere, the optical thickness of which in the visual part of the spectrum is between 0.2 and 0.4, one should take account of the scattering of higher orders in the solution of some problems. In the case of a medium with great optical thickness, the computation of intensities of radiation with the first, or the first and the second orders only, gives values which are several times greater than the real ones.

TABLE 2.2 COEFFICIENTS OF BRIGHTNESS σ

τ_0	σ_1	σ_2	σ	σ'
0.2	0.041	0.051	0.054	0.050
0.4	0.067	0.093	0.111	0.10
0.6	0.082	0.123	0.16	0.14
0.8	0.090	0.141	0.21	0.18
1.0	0.092	0.150	0.25	0.21
1.2	0.090	0.152	0.28	0.24
1.4	0.086	0.149	0.31	0.27
1.6	0.081	0.143	0.33	0.29
1.8	0.074	0.135	0.35	0.31
2.0	0.068	0.125	0.37	0.32
∞	0	0	0	0

This circumstance compelled us to turn to the solution of integral equations in the theory of scattering of light, obtained by the method of successive approximations rigorously. This has been achieved in the series of works by Kuznetsov for the theory of scattering of light in the Earth's atmosphere.

Kuznetsov[3] examined in detail the question of the convergence of successive approximations, and the technique of the computation of the following approximation if the preceding one is known. As a result he found computationally a solution of Eq. (1) and also a more general equation which takes into account the reflection of light by the Earth's surface. The work of Kuznetsov and of Ovchinskii[4] contains detailed tables of the function $B(\tau)$ for the series of values of the optical thickness of the atmosphere ($\tau_0 = 0.2;\ 0.3;\ 0.4;\ 0.5;\ 0.6$), for zenith distances of the sun ($\theta_0 = 30°,\ 45°,\ 60°,\ 76°$) and for albedo of the Earth's surface ($A = 0,\ 0.1,\ 0.2,\ 0.3,\ 0.8$).

[3] E. S. Kuznetsov, An Application of the Theoretical Formulae of the Non-horizontal Visibility to the Calculation of the Sky Brightness and the Visibility Distance for the Simplest Forms of the Scattering Indicatrix, *Izv. AN SSSR, series geogr.-geophys.* **9**, No. 3 (1945).

[4] E. S. Kuznetsov and B. V. Ovchinskii, Results of a Numerical Solution of the Integral Equation in the Theory of the Light Scattering in the Atmosphere, *Trudi Geophys. Inst. AN SSSR*, No. 4 (1949).

2. Directional Averaging of Radiation Intensities

For the solution of the equations of radiative transfer in astrophysics one very often employs the method based on the averaging of intensities of radiation in respect to direction. As an example we solve by means of this method a problem of radiative transfer in the stellar photosphere. By the "photosphere" of a star we understand a layer which gives out the radiation observed in the continuum of the spectrum.

In the interest of simplicity the coefficient of absorption is assumed to be independent of frequency. Then the integrated intensity of radiation $I(\tau, \theta)$ is determined from the following system of equations [see Ch. 2, Sec. 7, Eq. (95)]:

$$\cos\theta \frac{dI(\tau, \theta)}{d\tau} = I(\tau, \theta) - B(\tau) \tag{8a}$$

$$B(\tau) = \tfrac{1}{2} \int_0^\pi I(\tau, \theta) \sin\theta \, d\theta \tag{8b}$$

At the boundary of the star we have: $I(0, \theta) = 0$ with $\theta > \pi/2$. In addition we assume that the net flux of radiation due to the energy occurring within the star is given.

For the averaging of intensities over the angles we have two methods: one by Schwarzschild[5] and Schuster[6] and the other by Eddington.[7] We shall consider them in detail.

The method of Schwarzschild–Schuster. Let us introduce an average intensity of radiation coming from the bottom up and an average intensity of radiation going in the opposite direction. Denoting these quantities respectively by $I_1(\tau)$ and $I_2(\tau)$, we have

$$I_1(\tau) = \int_0^{\pi/2} I(\tau, \theta) \sin\theta \, d\theta, \qquad I_2(\tau) = \int_{\pi/2}^\pi I(\tau, \theta) \sin\theta \, d\theta \tag{9}$$

Multiplying Eq. (8a) by $\sin\theta \, d\theta$ and integrating over the interval from 0 to $\pi/2$, we obtain

$$\frac{d}{d\tau} \int_0^{\pi/2} I(\tau, \theta) \cos\theta \sin\theta \, d\theta = I_1(\tau) - B(\tau) \tag{10}$$

The integral on the left side of this equation is given approximately in

---

[5] K. Schwarzschild, Über das Gleichgewicht der Sonnenatmosphäre, *Göttinger Nachrichten* **41** (1906).

[6] A. Schuster, Radiation through a Foggy Atmosphere, *Astrophysical J.* **21**, 1 (1905).

[7] A. S. Eddington, *The Internal Constitution of the Stars*, Cambridge University Press (1926).

the form:

$$\int_0^{\pi/2} I(\tau, \theta) \cos \theta \sin \theta \, d\theta = \tfrac{1}{2} I_1(\tau) \tag{11}$$

in other words, we take the average value of intensity of radiation equal to $I_1(\tau)$ outside the integral sign. Then instead of Eq. (10), we have

$$\frac{1}{2} \frac{dI_1(\tau)}{d\tau} = I_1(\tau) - B(\tau) \tag{12}$$

Making the same multiplication and integrating now over the interval from $\tfrac{1}{2}\pi$ to π analogously, we find

$$-\frac{1}{2} \frac{dI_2(\tau)}{d\tau} = I_2(\tau) - B(\tau) \tag{13}$$

We rewrite Eq. (8b) by means of the quantities $I_1(\tau)$ and $I_2(\tau)$ in the form:

$$B(\tau) = \tfrac{1}{2}[I_1(\tau) + I_2(\tau)] \tag{14}$$

Thus we find approximately the system of usual differential equations, Eqs. (12), (13), and (14), instead of the system of integro-differential Eqs. (8).

The obtained system of equations is easier to solve. Adding Eqs. (12) and (13) and using (14), we find

$$I_1(\tau) - I_2(\tau) = F \tag{15}$$

where F is an arbitrary constant. Subtracting Eq. (13) from (12) and using Eq. (15), we obtain

$$I_1(\tau) + I_2(\tau) = 2F\tau + C \tag{16}$$

where C is a new constant.

The boundary condition has in this case the form $I_2(0) = 0$. Having found the quantity $I_2(\tau)$ from Eqs. (15) and (16) and making use of this boundary condition, we have

$$C = F \tag{17}$$

Turning now to the constant F, we see that it is expressed by the flux of radiation which is already given. Indeed, according to the adopted approximation, the radiation flux is equal to

$$H = \int I \cos \theta \, d\omega = 2\pi \left[\int_0^{\pi/2} I \cos \theta \sin \theta \, d\theta + \int_{\pi/2}^{\pi} I \cos \theta \sin \theta \, d\theta \right]$$

$$= \pi(I_1 - I_2) \tag{18}$$

Comparing Eq. (15) with Eq. (18), we find

$$H = \pi F \tag{19}$$

The radiation flux is constant in the photosphere of the star because within it there are neither sources nor reservoirs of energy (see Ch. 1, Sec. 5).

Substituting Eqs. (16) and (17) into Eq. (14), we obtain

$$B(\tau) = F(\tfrac{1}{2} + \tau) \tag{20}$$

Comparing Eq. (20) with Eq. (104) of the first chapter, we find the following expression for temperature T and optical depth τ:

$$T^4 = T_0^4 (1 + 2\tau) \tag{21}$$

where

$$T_0 = \left(\frac{2\pi}{ac} F\right)^{1/4} \tag{22}$$

or the surface temperature of the star.

Knowledge of the function $B(\tau)$ provides also a possibility to compute the integral intensity of radiation leaving the star. For this the following formula can be employed:

$$I(0, \theta) = \int_0^\infty B(\tau) e^{-\tau \sec\theta} \sec\theta \, d\tau \tag{23}$$

Substituting Eq. (20) into Eq. (23), we find

$$I(0, \theta) = F(\tfrac{1}{2} + \cos\theta) \tag{24}$$

Eddington's method. Introducing the quantity

$$\bar{I} = \int I \frac{d\omega}{4\pi} \tag{25}$$

which represents an average intensity of radiation at a fixed point, we may rewrite Eqs. (8a) and (8b) in the form of one equation:

$$\cos\theta \frac{dI(\tau, \theta)}{d\tau} = I(\tau, \theta) - \bar{I}(\tau) \tag{26}$$

Integrating this equation over all solid angles, we find that the radiation flux H is constant. As before, we write $H = \pi F$.

Multiplying Eq. (26) with $\cos\theta \, d\omega$ and integrating over all solid angles, we find

$$\frac{d}{d\tau} \int I \cos^2\theta \, d\omega = H \tag{27}$$

We take the average radiation intensity $\bar{I}$ outside of the integral sign, or we assume approximately

$$\int I \cos^2\theta \, d\omega = \frac{4\pi}{3} I \tag{28}$$

Then Eq. (27) provides

$$\bar{I}(\tau) = \tfrac{3}{4} F\tau + C \tag{29}$$

On the surface of the star, we have

$$\left.\begin{aligned}
\bar{I} &= \tfrac{1}{2} \int_0^{\pi/2} I \sin\theta \, d\theta \\[2mm]
H &= 2\pi \int_0^{\pi/2} I \cos\theta \sin\theta \, d\theta \approx \pi \int_0^{\pi/2} I \sin\theta \, d\theta
\end{aligned}\right\} \tag{30}$$

From this, we find approximately

$$\bar{I} = \frac{H}{2\pi} \qquad \text{for } \tau = 0 \tag{31}$$

With the boundary condition of Eq. (31), we find the constant C:

$$C = \frac{F}{2} \tag{32}$$

According to Eqs. (8) and (25), B is equal to $\bar{I}$; hence, using in addition Eqs. (29) and (32), we obtain

$$B(\tau) = F(\tfrac{1}{2} + \tfrac{3}{4}\tau) \tag{33}$$

Equation (33) provides again a possibility of expressing the temperature T as a function of the optical depth τ, namely:

$$T^4 = T_0^4(1 + \tfrac{3}{2}\tau) \tag{34}$$

Inserting Eq. (33) into Eq. (23), we find an expression for the intensity of radiation leaving the star, as follows:

$$I(0, \theta) = F(\tfrac{1}{2} + \tfrac{3}{4}\cos\theta) \tag{35}$$

It is of interest to compare these approximate formulas for $B(\tau)$ and $I(0, \theta)$ with the rigorous ones (see Sec. 5).

The quantity $I(0, \theta)$ defines the distribution of brightness over the disc of a star. The ratio of brightness at the center of the disc to that at the edge, or $I(0)/I(0, \pi/2)$, is equal to 3, in accordance with Eq. (24) and 2.5 in accordance with Eq. (35); but an exact value of this ratio is 2.9.

Similarly, the quantity $B(\tau)$ for large values of τ is $\approx F\tau$ and $\approx (3/4)F\tau$ corresponding to Eqs. (20) and (33), respectively. The exact theory provides also the last expression. With $\tau = 0$ the above-mentioned formulas provide $B(0) = (\frac{1}{2})F$ in contrast with an accurate value of $B(0) = (\sqrt{3}/4)F$.

It follows then that both methods for averaging radiation intensity in respect to angle provide formulas of approximately the same accuracy.

Methods of Schwarzschild–Schuster and Eddington can also be used in other problems of radiative transfer. In particular we can supply these methods in solving the problem of brightness of a medium illuminated by plane-parallel rays. The brightness coefficients, found in this way by the method of Eddington and for the case of pure scattering, are given in Tables 2.1 and 2.2 marked by ρ' and σ'. Comparing the approximate values of the brightness coefficient with the accurate ones, we see that the method of Eddington provides an accuracy sufficient in many practical applications and for all optical thicknesses.

3. Application of Quadrature Formulas

Recently a method of Chandrasekhar[8] has found wide application in the theory of radiative transfer. The method consists in substituting the integral term of the equation for radiative transfer by the sum of Gauss or, the integro-differential equations of radiative transfer are approximately replaced by the system of linear differential equations with constant coefficients. The method is a generalization of the Schwarzschild–Schuster method, mentioned in the previous section.

Following Chandrasekhar, let us consider the problem of radiative transfer in the atmosphere of a star such that the absorption coefficient does not depend on frequency. In this case Eq. (26) is valid. We rewrite it:

$$\eta \frac{dI(\tau, \eta)}{d\tau} = I(\tau, \eta) - \frac{1}{2} \int_{-1}^{+1} I(\tau, \eta') \, d\eta' \tag{36}$$

where $\eta = \cos \theta$.

The integral sign of Eq. (36) we replace by the sum in accordance with Gauss's formula for numerical quadrature as follows:

$$\int_{-1}^{+1} I(\tau, \eta) \, d\eta \approx \sum_{j=-n}^{n} a_j I(\tau, \eta_j) \tag{37}$$

where $\eta_{-n}, \dots, \eta_{-1}; \eta_1, \dots, \eta_n$ are roots of Legendre polynomial $P_{2n}(\eta)$, and a_j are some weighted coefficients $(a_j = a_{-1})$. Equation (37) is the more accurate the larger is n.

[8] S. Chandrasekhar, *Radiative Transfer*, Oxford University Press (1950) [Russ. Transl. Leningrad (1953)].

In the nth approximation Eq. (36) changes into a system of linear differential equations, of the $2n$th order,

$$\eta_i \frac{dI_i}{d\tau} = I_i - \tfrac{1}{2} \sum_j a_j I_j \qquad (i = \pm 1,..., \pm n) \tag{38}$$

where $I(\tau, \eta_i)$ is denoted as I_i for the sake of abbreviation.

It is easy to see that the functions

$$I_i = \frac{1}{1 + k\eta_i} e^{-k\tau} \qquad (i = \pm 1,..., \pm n) \tag{39}$$

will be special solutions of Eqs. (38). In Eq. (39) the quantity k is defined by the following equation:

$$\tfrac{1}{2} \sum_j \frac{a_j}{1 + k\eta_j} = 1 \tag{40}$$

Because $a_j = a_{-j}$ and $\eta_{-j} = -\eta_j$, we can rewrite Eq. (40) as follows:

$$\sum_{j=1}^{n} \frac{a_j}{1 - k^2 \eta_j^2} = 1 \tag{41}$$

Equation (41) has $2n - 2$ solutions, not equal to zero, which are divided into pairs

$$\pm k_\alpha (\alpha = 1, 2,..., n-1)$$

with $k^2 = 0$ as a solution too. Correspondingly, the system of Eqs. (38) has $2n - 2$ independent solutions of the form of Eq. (39).

It is convincing that the system of Eqs. (38) has also a particular solution:

$$I_i = b(\tau + Q + \eta_i) \qquad (i = \pm 1,..., \pm n) \tag{42}$$

where b and Q are arbitrary constants. Hence, the general solution of Eq. (38) may be rewritten as follows:

$$I_i = b\left[\sum_{\alpha=1}^{n-1} \frac{L_\alpha e^{-k_\alpha \tau}}{1 + k_\alpha \eta_i} + \sum_{\alpha=1}^{n-1} \frac{L_{-\alpha} e^{k_\alpha \tau}}{1 - k_\alpha \eta_i} + \tau + \eta_i + Q \right] \tag{43}$$

$$(i = \pm 1,..., \pm n)$$

where b, $L_{\pm\alpha}$ ($\alpha = 1, 2, ... , n-1$) and Q are $2n$ constants of integration.

The expression for I_i should, in our case, not contain terms which exponentially increase with τ. Therefore, instead of Eq. (43), we have

$$I_i = b\left[\sum_{\alpha=1}^{n-1} \frac{L_\alpha e^{-k_\alpha \tau}}{1 + k_\alpha \tau} + \tau + \eta_i + Q \right] \qquad (i = \pm 1,..., \pm n) \tag{44}$$

No outside radiation falls on the boundary of the star and, therefore,

$$I_{-i} = 0 \quad \text{for } \tau = 0 (i = 1, 2, ..., n) \tag{45}$$

Taking into account Eqs. (45), we obtain n equations

$$\sum_{\alpha=1}^{n-1} \frac{L_\alpha}{1 - k_\alpha \eta_i} - \eta_i + Q = 0 \quad (i = 1, 2, ..., n) \tag{46}$$

which provide determination of the constants L_α $(\alpha = 1, ..., n-1)$ and Q.

The constant b is, however, found from the condition that the radiation flux $H = \pi F$ is given. Writing the quantity F as Gauss's sum:

$$F = 2 \sum_i a_i \eta_i I_i \tag{47}$$

and inserting in it values of I_i from Eq. (44), we find, after some modifications,

$$b = \tfrac{3}{4} F \tag{48}$$

Having found quantities I_i we can compute also the function $B(\tau)$ which is the basic required quantity in the problem. Within the same approximation it is

$$B(\tau) = \tfrac{1}{2} \sum a_i I_i \tag{49}$$

Again, substituting values of I_i from Eqs. (44) into Eq. (49) and remembering Eq. (48), we obtain

$$B(\tau) = \tfrac{3}{4} F \left[\sum_{\alpha=1}^{n-1} L_\alpha e^{-k_\alpha \tau} + \tau + Q \right] \tag{50}$$

Knowledge of the function $B(\tau)$ provides a possibility of computing radiation intensity $I(\tau, \eta)$ emerging at the optical depth τ under any angle arccos η to normal. According to Eqs. (23) and (50), the radiation intensity leaving the star is

$$I(0, \eta) = \tfrac{3}{4} F \left[\sum_{\alpha=1}^{n-1} \frac{L_\alpha}{1 + k_\alpha \eta} + \eta + Q \right] \tag{51}$$

As an example we find now the function $B(\tau)$ in the first approximation. In this case we have $\eta_1 = -\eta_{-1} = 1/\sqrt{3}$, $a_1 = a_{-1} = 1$. Hence, instead of Eq. (38), we have

$$\frac{1}{\sqrt{3}} \frac{dI_1}{d\tau} = I_1 - \tfrac{1}{2}(I_1 + I_{-1})$$

$$-\frac{1}{\sqrt{3}} \frac{dI_{-1}}{d\tau} = I_{-1} - \tfrac{1}{2}(I_1 + I_{-1}) \tag{52}$$

A general solution of this system is given by Eq. (42) with $i = \pm 1$. For the surface of a star we find $Q = 1/\sqrt{3}$.

Therefore, according to Eq. (50), we have

$$B(\tau) = \tfrac{3}{4}F\left(\tau + \frac{1}{\sqrt{3}}\right) \tag{53}$$

It is of interest to remark that this simple formula also gives accurate values of $B(\tau)$ for $\tau = 0$, and not only for its large values, as Eq. (33) does. One may show that this peculiarity of the solution is preserved also for subsequent approximations.

Chandrasekhar has solved many problems of radiative transfer, using the afore-mentioned method. Inasmuch as his results are given in detail in his book,[8] we shall not consider them further.

In conclusion we would remark that the approximate transformation of the integro-differential equation of radiative transfer into a system of linear differential equations can also be made by means of other quadrature formulas and not only by means of the Gauss formula. Kuznetsov[9] suggested expressing the radiation intensity $I(\tau, \eta)$ by means of interpolational polynomial of Lagrange in respect to η. Then, the integral term of the equation of transfer is expressed through values of radiation intensity $I_k(\tau)$ in the "divisions" of interpolation η_k. Having written the equation of transfer for these "divisions," we obtain a system of linear differential equations for finding the quantity $I_k(\tau)$. Number and place of "divisions" of interpolation are arbitrary; therefore, we obtain different forms of the approximate equations for radiative transfer.

4. VARIATIONAL METHODS

Some authors have proposed variational methods for the solution of integral equations of the theory of radiative transfer. These methods are based on constructing a functional which has extreme values by inserting into it a solution of the required equation. Having constructed such a functional, we introduce a certain function similar and chosen with unknown coefficients. These coefficients are found from the condition that the first variation of the functional becomes zero. The function, found in this way, is then accepted as an approximate solution of the integral equation considered.

Let us consider, as before, the problem of radiative transfer in a stellar photosphere. As is known (see Ch. 1, Sec. 7) this problem is reduced to the solution of the integral equation:

[9] E. S. Kuznetsov, A General Method for Formation of Approximate Solutions in Radiative Transfer, *Izv. AN SSSR*, series geogr.-geophys. No. 4 (1951).

$$B(\tau) = \tfrac{1}{2} \int_0^\infty \mathrm{Ei}|\tau - t| B(t)\ dt. \tag{54}$$

Kourganoff[10,11] proposed the following variational method for computing the function $B(\tau)$. In the stellar photosphere the integrated flux of radiation remains the same, or

$$2 \int_0^\pi I(\tau, \theta) \cos\theta \sin\theta\ d\theta = F = \text{const} \tag{55}$$

Expressing $I(\tau, \theta)$ by $B(\tau)$ and inserting it in Eq. (55), we obtain

$$2 \int_\tau^\infty E_2(t - \tau) B(t)\ dt - 2 \int_0^\tau E_2(\tau - t) B(t)\ dt = F \tag{56}$$

where

$$E_n(x) = \int_1^\infty e^{-xz} \frac{dz}{z^n} \tag{57}$$

It is easy to see that the differentiation of Eq. (56) with respect to τ leads to Eq. (54). Consequently, Eq. (54) is satisfied if Eq. (56) is.
   Writing

$$\Phi(\tau) = 2 \int_\tau^\infty E_2(t - \tau) B(t)\ dt - 2 \int_0^\tau E_2(\tau - t) B(t)\ dt \tag{58}$$

we consider the functional

$$\sigma = \int_0^\infty \left[\frac{\Phi(\tau)}{F} - 1 \right]^2 d\tau \tag{59}$$

If the function $B(\tau)$ of Eq. (58) is a solution of Eq. (54), then, $\sigma = 0$. If $B(\tau)$ is another function, $\sigma > 0$. Thus, the solution of Eq. (54) provides the minimal value of the functional.
   Let us introduce a new function $q(\tau)$ instead of $B(\tau)$ by means of the relation

$$B(\tau) = \tfrac{3}{4} F[\tau + q(\tau)] \tag{60}$$

and let us find $q(\tau)$ in the form

$$q(\tau) = A_0 + A_2 E_2(\tau) + A_3 E_3(\tau) + \ldots + A_n E_n(\tau) \tag{61}$$

Then σ will be a function of $A_0, A_2, \ldots, A_n$. For finding these coefficients $A_0, A_2, \ldots, A_n$ we have a system of linear algebraic equations obtained from the minimum of the functional Eq. (59):

[10] V. Kourganoff, Sur la constance du flux intégré dans les atmosphère stellaires et la résolution de l'equation de transfert, *Comptes Rendus* **225**, 491 (1947).
   [11] V. Kourganoff, with the collaboration of I. W. Busbridge, *Basic Problems in Transfer Problems*, Oxford University Press (1952).

$$\frac{\partial \sigma}{\partial A_0} = 0, \qquad \frac{\partial \sigma}{\partial A_2} = 0, ..., \frac{\partial \sigma}{\partial A_n} = 0 \tag{62}$$

Substituting these coefficients into Eq. (61), we obtain an approximate solution of the problem, the best "on the average" for the chosen form of the function $q(\tau)$.

Let us have an example $q(\tau) = A_0$:

$$B(\tau) = \tfrac{3}{4} F(\tau + A_0) \tag{63}$$

Inserting Eq. (63) into Eq. (59), we find

$$\sigma = \tfrac{9}{4}[J_{33} A_0{}^2 - 2 J_{34} A_0 + J_{44}] \tag{64}$$

where

$$J_{nm} = \int_0^\infty E_n(\tau) E_m(\tau) \, d\tau \tag{65}$$

From the condition of minimum for σ, we obtain

$$A_0 = \frac{J_{34}}{J_{33}} = 0.719 \tag{66}$$

Kourganoff has obtained accurate values of the required function $B(\tau)$ by using the afore-mentioned method and setting n equal consecutively to 2, 3, 4, 5, 6.

There are other variational methods proposed for the solution of Eq. (54) and based on the use of the functionals differing from Eq. (59). One such method was that of Marshak,[12] Davison,[13] and Le Caine.[14] It is interesting to remark that this method was originally proposed for solution of the problem of neutron diffusion.

Substituting Eq. (60) into Eq. (54), we obtain the following non-homogeneous equation for determination of the function $q(\tau)$:

$$q(\tau) = \tfrac{1}{2} \int_0^\infty \mathrm{Ei}|\tau - t| q(t) \, dt + f_0(\tau) \tag{67}$$

where

$$f_0(\tau) = \tfrac{1}{2} E_3(\tau) \tag{68}$$

We can show that if $q(\tau)$ satisfies Eq. (67), we have an extreme functional

$$\frac{\displaystyle\int_0^\infty q(\tau) \left[q(\tau) - \tfrac{1}{2} \int_0^\infty \mathrm{Ei}|\tau - t| q(t) \, dt \right] d\tau}{\left[\displaystyle\int_0^\infty q(\tau) f_0(\tau) \, d\tau \right]^2} \tag{69}$$

[12] R. F. Marshak, The Variational Method for Asymptotic Neutron Densities, *Phys. Rev.* **71**, 688 (1947).

[13] B. Davison, A Remark on the Variational Method, *Phys. Rev.* **71**, 694 (1947).

[14] J. Le Caine, Application of a Variational Method to Milne's Problem, *Phys. Rev.* **72**, 564 (1947).

This very functional was used in the works of the afore-mentioned authors; Eq. (61) served for the function $q(\tau)$.

Recently Su Shu Huang[15] employed another functional for the solution of Eq. (67). He has shown that the functional

$$\int_0^\infty q(\tau)\left[(q\tau)-\tfrac{1}{2}\int_0^\infty q(t)\,\mathrm{Ei}|\tau - t|\,dt\right]d\tau - \int_0^\infty q(\tau)E_3(\tau)\,d\tau \qquad (70)$$

will be stationary when $q(\tau)$ is a solution of Eq. (67), and for an approximate computation of $q(\tau)$, Eq. (61) was taken with $n = 5$.

Su Shu Huang, using functionals analogous to those in Eq. (70), has also given an approximate solution to the problem of absorption line contours in stellar spectra and the problem of diffuse reflection in a medium with infinitely large optical thickness.

Menzel and Sen[16] developed a method similar to the variational methods mentioned above. Their method consists in representing the required function as a sum of the type in Eq. (61) and determining the coefficients from a condition that the given integral equation will, on the average, be best satisfied for different weighted functions. By this method the authors have solved a number of problems in the theory of radiative transfer in stellar atmospheres.

5. Methods of Precise Solution

There are great difficulties in finding exact solutions of the integral equations in the theory of radiative transfer in analytical form. Up to the present time such solutions were found only for the case of the spherical indicatrix of scattering in a medium with an infinitely large optical thickness. The method is based on application of Fourier integrals.

Hopf[17] gave an exact solution of the integral equation, Eq. (54). Incidentally, he was the first who found the relation

$$B(0) = \frac{\sqrt{3}}{4}F \qquad (71)$$

For an asymptotic value of the function $q(\tau)$, he derived the formula

$$q_\infty = \frac{1}{\pi}\int_0^{\pi/2}\left(\frac{3}{\sin^2\alpha} - \frac{\mathrm{tg}\,\alpha}{\alpha - \mathrm{tg}\,\alpha}\right)d\alpha \qquad (72)$$

[15] Su Shu Huang, The Variational Method for Problems of Radiative Transfer, *Astrophysical J.*, **117**, 211 (1953).

[16] D. H. Menzel and H. K. Sen, Transfer of Radiation, *Astrophysical J.* **110**, 1 (1949); **113**, 482 (1951).

[17] E. Hopf, Mathematical Problems of Radiative Equilibrium, *Cambridge Tracts* **31**, (1934).

Computations give $q_\infty = 0.710$.

Fok[18] derived an exact solution of the equation

$$B(\tau) = \int_0^\infty K|\tau - t|B(t)\, dt + g(\tau) \qquad (73)$$

with rather general assumptions regarding the kernel of the free term. From it and with

$$K(\tau) = \frac{\lambda}{2}\text{Ei}\tau, \qquad g(\tau) = \frac{\lambda}{4}Se^{-\tau/\xi} \qquad (74)$$

one derives an expression for the function $B(\tau)$ in the problem of luminescence of a medium with infinitely large optical thickness illuminated by parallel rays, or the solution of (1) for the case of $\tau_0 = \infty$.

We observe that the intensity of the emergent radiation was found by Fok to be

$$I(0, \eta, \zeta) = \frac{\lambda}{4}S\frac{\phi(\eta)\phi(\zeta)}{\eta + \zeta}\zeta \qquad (75)$$

and that the function $\phi(\zeta)$ was determined by the formula

$$\lg \phi(\zeta) = -\frac{1}{2\pi}\int_{-\infty}^{+\infty}\lg\left(1 - \lambda\frac{\text{arctg}\, u}{u}\right)\frac{\zeta\, du}{1 + \zeta^2 u^2} \qquad (76)$$

Here ϕ and η are cosines of angles formed by the incident and reflected radiation respectively.

Ambartsumian (see Ch. 3) also derived Eq. (75) for the quantity $I(0, \eta, \zeta)$ at the same time as Fok.

[18] V. A. Fok, On Certain Integral Equations in Mathematical Physics, *Mathem. sbor.* **14** (56), No. 1–2 (1944).

CHAPTER 3

METHOD OF ADDITION OF LAYERS

The previously mentioned methods permit us a determination of the function $B(\tau, \theta, \phi)$. Having found the function, we can compute also radiation intensitites at any optical depth by means of some integration. In particular, we find intensities of the emerging radiation. Thus, for determination of these intensities we have to determine the function $B(\tau, \theta, \phi)$ beforehand; in other words, we have to know the march of light (light regime) in the medium.

However, in many practical applications it is necessary to know only intensities of the emerging radiation, or the corresponding brightness coefficients. The question therefore arises whether it is not possible to find brightness coefficients without knowing the function $B(\tau, \theta, \phi)$ and to write down equations which determine directly these quantities which are most interesting in practice. The answer to this question was given by Ambartsumian.[1]

He showed that equations for computing brightness coefficients can easily be derived from the fundamental integral equation in the theory of light scattering. At the same time he developed another method for deriving the afore-mentioned equations, a method which is independent of the usual equations of radiative transfer and radiative equilibrium employed in the theory of light scattering.

The second method of Ambartsumian was originally applied to the problem of the reflection of light diffused in a medium with infinitely large optical thickness. He used the following "invariance" principle: the reflecting property of the medium does not change if one adds a layer of infinitely small optical thickness to the given medium. The equation for brightness coefficients was found as a result of the analysis of processes occurring in the additional layer.

Generally speaking, this method consists of mental addition of two layers of some optical thickness. Equations for computation of brightness coefficients are found by means of relations between emergent radiation intensities and radiation intensities on the boundary of two layers.

---

[1] V. A. Ambartsumian, One-Dimensional Case in the Problem of a Scattering and Absorbing Medium with a Finite Optical Thickness, *Akad. Nauk Armen. SSR*, No. 1–2 (1944).

Both methods of Ambartsumian clarify the structure of brightness coefficients. He succeeded in expressing these complicated functions of several arguments through some auxiliary functions which depend only on one argument. The auxiliary functions themselves are found by a system of functional equations.

The methods of Ambartsumian as well as his functional equations are very important in the present theory of light scattering and we analyze them in this chapter.

1. ONE-DIMENSIONAL MEDIUM

We begin our analysis of the theory of Ambartsumian with the problem of light scattering in a one-dimensional medium and, during the solution of this problem, we clarify the application of the method of "adding layers."

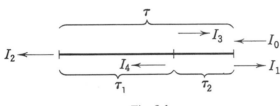

Fig. 3.1

Let us have one-dimensional medium of optical thickness τ, illuminated from one side by radiation of intensity I_0. Assuming that the probability of the quantum lifetime during an elementary act of scattering in the medium is λ, and the probability of scattering inward and outward is equal to x and $1-x$, respectively, let us find the radiation intensity reflected and transmitted by the medium.

In solving this problem we divide the medium into two slabs with optical thickness τ_1 and τ_2 and introduce radiation intensities I_3 and I_4 on the boundary between two layers in addition to I_1, the intensity of the reflected light, and I_2, the intensity of the transmitted light (Fig. 3.1).

We denote the required reflection and transmission coefficients by r and q, respectively. Then, by definition, we have

$$I_1 = r(\tau_1 + \tau_2)I_0 \tag{1}$$

$$I_2 = q(\tau_1 + \tau_2)I_0 \tag{2}$$

Further, we can write

$$I_1 = r(\tau_2)I_0 + q(\tau_2)I_3 \tag{3}$$

$$I_2 = q(\tau_1)I_4 \tag{4}$$

$$I_3 = r(\tau_1)I_4 \tag{5}$$

$$I_4 = q(\tau_2)I_0 + r(\tau_2)I_3 \tag{6}$$

The last three equations provide

$$I_2 = \frac{q(\tau_1)q(\tau_2)}{1 - r(\tau_1)r(\tau_2)}I_0 \tag{7}$$

$$I_3 = \frac{r(\tau_1)q(\tau_2)}{1 - r(\tau_1)r(\tau_2)}I_0 \tag{8}$$

Inserting Eq. (7) into Eq. (2), we find

$$q(\tau_1 + \tau_2) = \frac{q(\tau_1)q(\tau_2)}{1 - r(\tau_1)r(\tau_2)} \tag{9}$$

Moreover, Eqs. (1), (3), and (8) provide

$$r(\tau_1 + \tau_2) = r(\tau_2) + \frac{q^2(\tau_2)r(\tau_1)}{1 - r(\tau_1)r(\tau_2)} \tag{10}$$

Two functional equations, Eqs. (9) and (10), serve now for determination of the unknown functions $r(\tau)$ and $q(\tau)$.

First we solve the obtained equations for the case of pure scattering. In this case,

$$r(\tau) = 1 - q(\tau) \tag{11}$$

Inserting Eq. (11) into Eq. (9), we obtain one functional equation for computing the quantity $q(\tau)$:

$$q(\tau_1 + \tau_2) = \frac{q(\tau_1)\,q(\tau_2)}{q(\tau_1) + q(\tau_2) - q(\tau_1)q(\tau_2)} \tag{12}$$

This equation we rewrite as

$$\frac{1}{q(\tau_1 + \tau_2)} - 1 = \frac{1}{q(\tau_1)} - 1 + \frac{1}{q(\tau_2)} - 1$$

Hence we see that the quantity

$$1/q(\tau) - 1$$

should be a linear uniform function of τ. Denoting it by $a\tau$, we find

$$q(\tau) = \frac{1}{1 + a\tau} \tag{13}$$

This is the required solution of the functional equation, Eq. (12).

To determine the constant a, we should analyze the transmission of radiation by a layer of a small optical thickness. With small τ, we have, instead of Eq. (13),

$$q(\tau) = 1 - a\tau \tag{14}$$

On the other hand, the quantity $q(\tau)$ can be found from the following considerations. If radiation of intensity I_0 falls on the medium the absorbed energy will be $I_0\tau$ for small τ. We have agreed already that the back reflected fraction of the absorbed energy is $1-x$. Hence the intensity of the reflected radiation will be $(1-x)I_0\tau$. Consequently, $r(\tau) = (1-x)\tau$, and hence

$$q(\tau) = 1 - (1-x)\tau \tag{15}$$

Comparing Eqs. (14) and (15), we find that

$$a = 1 - x \tag{16}$$

and inserting this value of a in Eq. (13), we obtain finally

$$q(\tau) = \frac{1}{1 + (1-x)\tau} \tag{17}$$

Let us solve Eqs. (9) and (10) for a general case when not only scattering but also true absorption of radiation occurs in the medium.

We assume here that the optical thickness of one of the layers, into which the medium is divided, is infinitely small. This permits us to transform the functional equations, Eqs. (9) and (10), into differential equations.

Before this we write expressions for the coefficients of reflection and transmission of light by a medium of small optical thickness. Similar expressions for pure scattering have already been given. For any value of λ and for the optical thickness $d\tau$, we then derive analogously:

$$r = \lambda(1-x)\,d\tau \tag{18}$$

$$q = 1 - (1 - \lambda x)\,d\tau \tag{19}$$

Replacing τ_1 and τ_2 by $d\tau$ and τ, respectively, in Eqs. (9) and (10) and employing Eqs. (18) and (19), we find

$$q(\tau + d\tau) = \frac{q(\tau)[1 - (1 - \lambda x)\,d\tau]}{1 - r(\tau)\lambda(1-x)\,d\tau}$$

$$r(\tau + d\tau) = r(\tau) + \frac{q^2(\tau)\lambda(1-x)\,d\tau}{1 - r(\tau)\lambda(1-x)\,d\tau}$$

or, neglecting the terms in $d\tau^2$,

$$\frac{dq(\tau)}{d\tau} = \lambda(1-x)q(\tau)r(\tau) - (1-\lambda x)q(\tau) \tag{20}$$

$$\frac{dr(\tau)}{d\tau} = \lambda(1-x)q^2(\tau) \tag{21}$$

These differential equations can be solved without difficulty. Dividing Eq. (20) by Eq. (21), we have

$$q\,dq = r\,dr - \frac{1-\lambda x}{\lambda(1-x)}dr \tag{22}$$

Integrating this equation with the condition for $q = 1$ and $r = 0$ (which corresponds to $\tau = 0$), we obtain

$$1 + r^2 - \frac{2(1-\lambda x)}{\lambda(1-x)}r = q^2 \tag{23}$$

Thus we have received an interesting interrelationship between the coefficients r and q.

Denoting the roots of the three-term quadratic on the left side of Eq. (23) by r_0 and $1/r_0$, we have another expression instead of Eq. (23):

$$(r_0 - r)\left(\frac{1}{r_0} - r\right) = q^2 \tag{24}$$

Assuming $r_0 \leqslant 1$, we have $r = r_0$ for $q = 0$. But $q = 0$ for $\tau = \infty$. Hence r_0 represents the reflection coefficient of a medium with infinitely large optical thickness. We note that Eq. (24) can be derived directly from Eq. (10) for $\tau_1 = \infty$ and $\tau_2 = \tau$.

By means of Eq. (24), Eq. (21) can be rewritten as follows:

$$\frac{dr}{(r_0 - r)\left(\dfrac{1}{r_0} - r\right)} = \lambda(1-x)\,d\tau \tag{25}$$

Integrating this equation with $r = 0$ and $\tau = 0$, we find

$$r = r_0\frac{1 - e^{-2k\tau}}{1 - r_0^2 e^{-2k\tau}} \tag{26}$$

where

$$k = \frac{\lambda}{2}(1-x)\frac{1 - r_0^2}{r_0} \tag{27}$$

Inserting Eq. (26) into Eq. (24), we obtain

$$q = \frac{(1 - r_0^2) e^{-k\tau}}{1 - r_0^2 e^{-2k\tau}} \qquad (28)$$

Equations (26) and (28) determine the required quantities r and q.

Now we assume that the medium has an infinitely large optical thickness and it is required to find the reflecting property of the medium by means of the previously formulated "invariance principle."

Fig. 3.2

Let us add a layer of small optical thickness to the medium under consideration (Fig. 3.2), and let us assume that the properties of both mediums are identical. Then, it is obvious that an addition of this (small) layer will not change the reflection coefficient of the medium.

In order to determine this reflection coefficient, denoted here by r_0, we have to find the radiation intensity reflected by the medium with the additional layer and set this intensity equal to the radiation intensity reflected by the original medium, or to the quantity $r_0 I_0$.

It is simple to show that the radiation intensity reflected by the medium with the additional layer consists of the following parts if we neglect the quantities of order $\Delta\epsilon^2$:

1. Radiation intensity transmitted by the additional layer, reflected by the medium and again transmitted by the layer:

$$I_0(1 - \Delta\tau) r_0 (1 - \Delta\tau)$$

2. Radiation intensity scattered backward by the additional layer:

$$I_0 \Delta\tau\lambda(1 - x)$$

3. Radiation intensity scattered forward by the layer and reflected by the medium:

$$I_0 \Delta\tau\lambda x r_0$$

4. Radiation intensity reflected by the medium and scattered by the layer:

$$I_0 r_0 \Delta\tau\lambda x$$

5. Radiation intensity reflected by the medium, scattered backward by the layer and again reflected by the medium:

$$I_0 r_0 \Delta\tau\lambda(1 - x) r_0$$

Adding these quantities together and setting them all equal to $I_0 r_0$, we have

$$I_0 r_0 = I_0(1 - \Delta\tau)r_0(1 - \Delta\tau) + I_0\Delta\tau\lambda(1 - x) + I_0\Delta\tau\lambda x r_0$$
$$+ I_0 r_0\Delta\tau\lambda x + I_0 r_0\Delta\tau\lambda(1 - x)r_0$$

Hence,

$$r_0^2 - 2\frac{1 - \lambda x}{\lambda(1 - x)}r_0 + 1 = 0 \tag{29}$$

which is the required equation for determining r_0.

It goes without saying that results derived in this section could have been obtained in the usual way by employing the equations of radiative transfer and radiative equilibrium (see Ch. 1, Sec. 9). The point was, however, that here we were interested not so much in the results as in the method.

2. Diffuse Light Reflection

Let us apply this method to the problem of diffuse light reflection by a plane layer of infinitely large optical thickness, and start with an assumption that the indicatrix of scattering is spherical.[2]

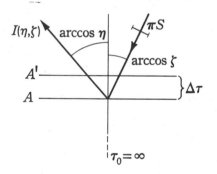

Fig. 3.3

Let πS be the small area illuminated perpendicularly by the parallel rays, ζ the cosine of the angle of incident rays, η the cosine of the angle of reflected rays, $I(\eta, \zeta)$, the intensity of reflected light, and $\Delta\tau$ (Fig. 3.3) the additional layer of small optical thickness.

Since the reflecting property of the medium with infinitely large optical thickness does not change by addition of the small layer, we can equate the radiation intensity reflected by the new boundary of the medium to the original intensity. This provides an equation for computing the quantity $I(\eta, \zeta)$ directly.

[2] V. A. Ambartsumian, On the Question of a Diffuse Light Reflection in a Turbid Medium, *DAN SSSR* **38**, No. 8 (1943).

Denoting the new boundary of the medium by A' and the original one by A and neglecting the terms in $\Delta\tau^2$, we can, as in the one-dimensional case, find an expression for radiation intensity reflected by the boundary A' taking into account only the following processes:

1. Radiation from external sources, diminished by absorption in the additional layer, falls on the boundary A, then is reflected and finally leaves the medium, being diminished again on the way out. Evidently the intensity of the emerging radiation will be equal to

$$I(\eta, \zeta)\left(1 - \frac{\Delta\tau}{\zeta}\right)\left(1 - \frac{\Delta\tau}{\eta}\right)$$

2. The additional layer scatters a fraction of the direct radiation incident on it in the given direction, which is defined by η. The corresponding radiation intensity is then

$$\frac{\lambda}{4}S\frac{\Delta\tau}{\eta}$$

3. A fraction of direct radiation scattered by the additional layer is thrown toward the boundary A and partially reflected by it. The expression for this intensity is

$$\frac{\lambda}{2}\Delta\tau \int_0^1 I(\eta, \eta')\frac{d\eta'}{\eta'}$$

4. Direct radiation is first reflected by the boundary A and then it is scattered by the additional layer in a given direction. The intensity of this radiation is equal to

$$\frac{\lambda}{2}\frac{\Delta\tau}{\eta} \int_0^1 I(\eta', \zeta)\, d\eta'$$

5. Direct radiation is first reflected by the surface A, then it is scattered backward by the additional layer, and finally it is again reflected by the surface A. As a result of this threefold process, we have

$$\lambda\Delta\tau \int_0^1 \frac{I(\eta, \eta'')}{S}\frac{d\eta''}{\eta''} \int_0^1 I(\eta', \zeta)\, d\eta'$$

Adding these expressions and making them all equal to $I(\eta, \zeta)$, we find the required equation:

$$I(\eta, \zeta)\left(\frac{1}{\eta} + \frac{1}{\zeta}\right) = \frac{\lambda}{4}S\frac{1}{\eta} + \frac{\lambda}{2}\int_0^1 I(\eta, \eta')\frac{d\eta'}{\eta'}$$

$$+ \frac{\lambda}{2\eta}\int_0^1 I(\eta', \zeta)\, d\eta' + \lambda \int_0^1 \frac{I(\eta, \eta'')}{S}\frac{d\eta''}{\eta''}\int_0^1 I(\eta', \zeta)\, d\eta' \tag{30}$$

In order to simplify this equation we express the radiation intensity $I(\eta, \zeta)$ by the brightness coefficient $\rho(\eta, \zeta)$ as follows:

$$I(\eta, \zeta) = S\rho(\eta, \zeta)\zeta \tag{31}$$

Then, instead of Eq. (30), we have

$$\rho(\eta, \zeta)(\eta + \zeta) = \frac{\lambda}{4}\left[1 + 2\eta \int_0^1 \rho(\eta, \eta')\,d\eta'\right]\left[1 + 2\zeta \int_0^1 \rho(\eta', \zeta)\,d\eta'\right] \tag{32}$$

It is easy to see that if the function $\rho(\eta, \zeta)$ satisfies Eq. (32), the function $\rho(\zeta, \eta)$ will also satisfy it. Thus for a permitted uniqueness of the solution of Eq. (32), we should have

$$\rho(\eta, \zeta) = \rho(\zeta, \eta) \tag{33}$$

or the brightness coefficient should be a symmetrical function of both angles, that of incidence and that of reflection. As stated in Chapter 1, Section 6, this conclusion follows also from physical considerations.

We conclude from the symmetrical property of the function $\rho(\eta, \zeta)$ that on the right side of Eq. (32) we have a product of some function, depending only on η, and a function of the same kind, depending only on ζ; writing

$$\phi(\eta) = 1 + 2\eta \int_0^1 \rho(\eta, \eta')\,d\eta' \tag{34}$$

we find that the brightness coefficient is defined by a formula:

$$\rho(\eta, \zeta) = \frac{\lambda}{4}\frac{\phi(\eta)\phi(\zeta)}{\eta + \zeta} \tag{35}$$

In other words, we have expressed the function $\rho(\eta, \zeta)$ of two arguments as a function $\phi(\eta)$ of only one argument. As for this function $\phi(\eta)$, it is defined by the equation

$$\phi(\eta) = 1 + \frac{\lambda}{2}\eta\phi(\eta) \int_0^1 \frac{\phi(\eta')}{\eta + \eta'}\,d\eta' \tag{36}$$

which is obtained by inserting Eq. (35) into Eq. (34).

Equation (36) can be solved numerically without any difficulty. Table 3.1 shows results of the solution for some values of the parameter λ.

If the function $\phi(\eta)$ is known for given value of λ, Eq. (35) easily provides values of the brightness coefficient $\rho(\eta, \zeta)$ for any other combination of angles of incidence and reflection. As an example we give in Table 3.2 values of the brightness coefficient $\rho(\eta, \zeta)$ for the case of pure scattering ($\lambda = 1$).

The problem of diffuse light reflection by a plane layer with an infinitely large optical thickness, and for any other indicatrix of scattering $x(\gamma)$, can be solved in the same manner as in the case of the spherical indicatrix of scattering.[3]

In the case of any other indicatrix of scattering the brightness coefficient depends, generally speaking, not only on the angles of incidence and reflection, but also on the difference of azimuth between the reflected and incident rays. This coefficient we denote by $\rho(\eta, \zeta, \phi - \phi_0)$, and remembering that the cosine of the angle between the two directions with arccos η', ϕ' and arccos ζ, ϕ_0 is equal to

$$\cos \gamma' = \eta' \zeta + \sqrt{(1 - \eta'^2)(1 - \zeta^2)} \cos(\phi' - \phi_0) \qquad (37)$$

we shall express the scattering indicatrix $x(\gamma')$ in the form $x(\eta', \zeta, \phi' - \phi_0)$.

TABLE 3.1. VALUES OF THE FUNCTION $\phi(\eta)$

η \ λ	0.4	0.5	0.6	0.7	0.8	0.9	1.0
0	1.00	1.00	1.00	1.00	1.00	1.00	1.00
0.1	1.06	1.07	1.09	1.11	1.14	1.17	1.25
0.2	1.09	1.11	1.15	1.18	1.23	1.29	1.45
0.3	1.11	1.14	1.19	1.24	1.30	1.39	1.64
0.4	1.13	1.17	1.22	1.28	1.36	1.48	1.83
0.5	1.14	1.19	1.25	1.32	1.41	1.56	2.01
0.6	1.15	1.20	1.27	1.35	1.46	1.63	2.19
0.7	1.16	1.22	1.29	1.38	1.50	1.69	2.38
0.8	1.17	1.23	1.31	1.40	1.54	1.75	2.55
0.9	1.18	1.24	1.32	1.42	1.57	1.80	2.73
1.0	1.18	1.25	1.34	1.44	1.60	1.85	2.91

TABLE 3.2. BRIGHTNESS COEFFICIENTS ρ (η, ζ) FOR THE CASE OF PURE SCATTERING

η \ ζ	0	0.1	0.2	0.3	0.4	0.5	0.6	0.7	0.8	0.9	1.0
0	∞	3.12	1.81	1.37	1.14	1.01	0.91	0.85	0.80	0.76	0.73
0.1	3.12	1.95	1.51	1.28	1.14	1.05	0.98	0.93	0.88	0.85	0.83
0.2	1.81	1.51	1.32	1.19	1.11	1.04	0.99	0.96	0.93	0.90	0.88
0.3	1.37	1.28	1.19	1.13	1.07	1.03	1.00	0.98	0.95	0.93	0.92
0.4	1.14	1.14	1.11	1.07	1.05	1.02	1.00	0.99	0.97	0.96	0.95
0.5	1.01	1.05	1.04	1.03	1.02	1.01	1.00	1.00	0.99	0.98	0.98
0.6	0.91	0.98	0.99	1.00	1.00	1.00	1.00	1.00	1.00	1.00	1.00
0.7	0.85	0.93	0.96	0.98	0.99	1.00	1.00	1.01	1.01	1.01	1.02
0.8	0.80	0.88	0.93	0.95	0.97	0.99	1.00	1.01	1.02	1.02	1.03
0.9	0.76	0.85	0.90	0.93	0.96	0.98	1.00	1.01	1.02	1.03	1.04
1.0	0.73	0.83	0.88	0.92	0.95	0.98	1.00	1.02	1.03	1.04	1.06

[3] V. A. Ambartsumian, On the Problem of a Diffuse Light Reflection, *JETF* **13**, Bulletins 9–10 (1943).

Employing the invariance of brightness coefficient in respect to the addition of a layer with a small optical thickness $\Delta\tau$, we obtain the following equation for finding the quantity $\rho(\eta, \zeta, \phi - \phi_0)$:

$$(\eta + \zeta)\rho(\eta, \zeta, \phi - \phi_0) = \frac{\lambda}{4}x(-\eta, \zeta, \phi - \phi_0)$$

$$+ \frac{\lambda}{4\pi}\zeta \int_0^{2\pi} d\phi' \int_0^1 x(\eta, \eta', \phi - \phi')\rho(\eta', \zeta, \phi' - \phi_0)\, d\eta'$$

$$+ \frac{\lambda}{4\pi}\eta \int_0^{2\pi} d\phi' \int_0^1 \rho(\eta, \eta', \phi - \phi')x(\eta', \zeta, \phi' - \phi_0)\, d\eta'$$

$$+ \frac{\lambda}{4\pi^2}\eta\zeta \int_0^{2\pi} d\phi' \int_0^1 \rho(\eta, \eta', \phi - \phi')\, d\eta'$$

$$\times \int_0^{2\pi} d\phi'' \int_0^1 x(-\eta', \eta'', \phi' - \phi_0)\rho(\eta'', \zeta, \phi'' - \phi_0)\, d\eta'' \qquad (38)$$

Equation (38) is a general form of Eq. (32).

We assume that the scattering indicatrix $x(\gamma)$ is expanded in series with Legendre polynomials:

$$x(\gamma) = \sum_{i=0}^{n} x_i P_i(\cos\gamma) \qquad (39)$$

The theorem of sum of spherical functions permits us to present the function $x(\gamma)$ in the form

$$x(\eta, \zeta, \phi - \phi_0) = \sum_{m=0}^{n} q_m(\eta, \zeta) \cos m(\phi - \phi_0) \qquad (40)$$

where

$$q_m(\eta, \zeta) = \sum_{i=m}^{n} c_{im} P_i^m(\eta) P_i^m(\zeta) \qquad (41)$$

$$c_{i0} = x_i, \qquad c_{im} = 2x_i \frac{(i-m)!}{(i+m)!} \qquad (42)$$

The brightness coefficient is also given in the form of a series analogous to Eq. (40):

$$\rho(\eta, \zeta, \phi - \phi_0) = \sum_{m=0}^{n} f_m(\eta, \zeta) \cos m(\phi - \phi_0) \qquad (43)$$

Inserting Eqs. (40) and (43) into (38), integrating in respect to ϕ' and ϕ'', and equalizing coefficients with $\cos m(\phi - \phi_0)$ in both parts of the equation, we find

$$(\eta + \zeta)f_m(\eta, \zeta) = \frac{\lambda}{4}q_m(-\eta, \zeta) + \frac{2}{2-\delta_{0m}} \int_0^1 q_m(\eta, \eta')f_m(\eta', \zeta) \, d\eta'$$

$$+ \frac{2}{2-\delta_{0m}} \int_0^1 q_m(\eta', \zeta)f_m(\eta, \eta') \, d\eta'$$

$$+ \frac{4}{(2-\delta_{0m})^2} \int_0^1 f_m(\eta, \eta') \, d\eta' \int_0^1 q_m(-\eta', \eta'')f_m(\eta'', \zeta) \, d\eta'' \qquad (44)$$

where $\delta_{00} = 1$ and $\delta_{0m} = 0$ for $m > 0$. In this way we obtain a separate functional equation for determination of each function $f_m(\eta, \zeta)$.

Inserting now Eq. (41) into Eq. (44), we find, after some transformations, the following equation:

$$(\eta + \zeta)f_m(\eta, \zeta) = \frac{\lambda}{4} \sum_{i=m}^{n} (-1)^{i+m}c_{im}$$

$$\times \left[P_i^m(\eta) + 2\frac{(-1)^{i+m}}{2-\delta_{0m}} \int_0^1 f_m(\eta, \eta') P_i^m(\eta') \, d\eta' \right]$$

$$\times \left[P_i^m(\zeta) + 2\frac{(-1)^{i+m}}{2-\delta_{0m}} \int_0^1 f_m(\eta', \eta) P_i^m(\eta') \, d\eta' \right] \qquad (45)$$

Since the function $f_m(\eta, \zeta)$ is symmetrical, Eq. (45) can be written in the form

$$f_m(\eta, \zeta) = \frac{\lambda}{4} \sum_{i=m}^{n} (-1)^{i+m}\frac{c_{im}\phi_i^m(\eta)\phi_i^m(\zeta)}{\eta + \zeta} \qquad (46)$$

where

$$\phi_i^m(\eta) = P_i^m(\eta) + 2\frac{(-1)^{i+m}}{2-\delta_{0m}} \int_0^1 f_m(\eta, \eta') P_i^m(\eta') \, d\eta' \qquad (47)$$

In other words, the functions $f_m(\eta, \zeta)$ depending on two arguments can be expressed as functions $\phi_i^m(\eta)$ depending only on one argument.

Combining Eq. (46) with Eq. (47), we receive a system of functional equations for determination of the auxiliary functions $\phi_i^m(\eta)$:

$$\phi_i^m(\eta) = P_i^m(\eta)$$

$$+ \frac{\lambda}{2} \sum_{k=m}^{n} (-1)^{i+k}x_k\frac{(k-m)!}{(k+m)!}\eta \int_0^1 \frac{\phi_k^m(\eta)\phi_k^m(\eta')}{\eta + \eta'}P_i^m(\eta') \, d\eta' \qquad (48)$$

$$(i = m, m+1,..., n)$$

The number of equations is $n-m+1$ for given m.

We observe, therefore, that the brightness coefficient is represented by $n+1$ functions $f_m(\eta, \zeta)$ for the scattering indicatrix of the form given in Eq. (39). Each function $f_m(\eta, \zeta)$ is, in turn, expressed by $n - m + 1$ functions $\phi_i{}^m(\eta)$. Thus, to find the function $\rho(\eta, \zeta, \phi - \phi_0)$ for a given n, we have to find $(n+1)(n+2)/2$ auxiliary functions $\phi_i{}^m(\eta)$.

For an example consider the simplest case of the spherical indicatrix of scattering:

$$x(\gamma) = 1 + x_1 \cos \gamma \tag{49}$$

Here the brightness coefficient is equal to

$$\rho(\eta, \zeta, \phi - \phi_0) = f_0(\eta, \zeta) + f_1(\eta, \zeta) \cos(\phi - \phi_0) \tag{50}$$

and the functions $f_0(\eta, \zeta)$ and $f_1(\eta, \zeta)$ according to Eq. (46) have the following forms:

$$f_0(\eta, \zeta) = \frac{\lambda}{4} \frac{\phi_0{}^0(\eta)\phi_0{}^0(\zeta) - x_1\phi_1{}^0(\eta)\phi_1{}^0(\zeta)}{\eta + \zeta} \tag{51}$$

$$f_1(\eta, \zeta) = \frac{\lambda}{4} x_1 \frac{\phi_1{}^1(\eta)\phi_1{}^1(\zeta)}{\eta + \zeta} \tag{52}$$

The auxiliary functions $\phi_0{}^0(\eta)$ and $\phi_1{}^0(\zeta)$ are computed from the system of equations:

$$\phi_0{}^0(\eta) = 1 + \frac{\lambda}{2}\eta\phi_0{}^0(\eta) \int_0^1 \frac{\phi_0{}^0(\eta')}{\eta + \eta'} \, d\eta' - \frac{\lambda}{2}x_1\eta\phi_1{}^0(\eta) \int_0^1 \frac{\phi_1{}^0(\eta')}{\eta + \eta'} \, d\eta' \tag{53a}$$

$$\phi_1{}^0(\eta) = \eta - \frac{\lambda}{2}\eta\phi_0{}^0(\eta) \int_0^1 \frac{\phi_0{}^0(\eta')}{\eta + \eta'}\eta' \, d\eta' + \frac{\lambda}{2}x_1\eta\phi_1{}^0(\eta) \int_0^1 \frac{\phi_1{}^0(\eta')}{\eta + \eta'}\eta' \, d\eta' \tag{53b}$$

but the auxiliary function $\phi_1{}^1(\eta)$, from the equation

$$\phi_1{}^1(\eta) = \sqrt{1 - \eta^2} + \frac{\lambda}{4}x_1\eta\phi_1{}^1(\eta) \int_0^1 \frac{\phi_1{}^1(\eta')}{\eta + \eta'} \, d\eta' \tag{54}$$

Equations (53) and (54) are easy to solve by the method of successive approximations.

We observe that from Eqs. (53) follows a simple relation between $\phi_0{}^0(\eta)$ and $\phi_1{}^0(\eta)$; the relation can be used in the solution of the system. To find this relation, we make the following substitution in the second of Eqs. (53):

$$\frac{\eta'}{\eta + \eta'} = 1 - \frac{\eta}{\eta + \eta'}$$

Then

$$\phi_1{}^0(\eta) = \eta - \frac{\lambda}{2}\eta\phi_0{}^0(\eta) \int_0^1 \phi_0{}^0(\eta') \, d\eta' + \frac{\lambda}{2}x_1\eta\phi_1{}^0(\eta) \int_0^1 \phi_1{}^0(\eta') \, d\eta'$$

$$+ \frac{\lambda}{2}\eta^2\phi_0{}^0(\eta) \int_0^1 \frac{\phi_0{}^0(\eta')}{\eta + \eta'} \, d\eta' - \frac{\lambda}{2}x_1\eta^2\phi_1{}^0(\eta) \int_0^1 \frac{\phi_1{}^0(\eta')}{\eta + \eta'} \, d\eta'$$

The last two members are, according to Eq. (53a), equal to

$$\eta[\phi_0{}^0(\eta) - 1]$$

Thus, introducing

$$\alpha = \int_0^1 \phi_0{}^0(\eta)\, d\eta, \qquad \beta = \int_0^1 \phi_1{}^0(\eta)\, d\eta$$

we find

$$\phi_1{}^0(\eta) = \frac{[1 - (\lambda/2)\alpha]\eta\phi_0{}^0(\eta)}{1 - (\lambda/2) x_1 \beta \eta} \tag{55}$$

Tables 3.3, 3.4 and 3.5 .show values of the auxiliary functions $\phi_0{}^0(\eta)$, $\phi_1{}^0(\eta)$ and $\phi_1{}^1(\eta)$ for a scattering indicatrix $x(\gamma) = 1 + \cos \gamma$ and for different values of the parameter λ.

TABLE 3.3. FUNCTION $\phi_0{}^0(\eta)$ FOR THE INDICATRIX $x(\gamma) = 1 + \cos \gamma$

η \ λ	0.4	0.5	0.6	0.7	0.8	0.9	1.0
0	1.00	1.00	1.00	1.00	1.00	1.00	1.00
0.1	1.05	1.07	1.09	1.11	1.13	1.17	1.25
0.2	1.08	1.11	1.14	1.17	1.22	1.28	1.45
0.3	1.10	1.13	1.17	1.22	1.28	1.37	1.64
0.4	1.11	1.15	1.19	1.25	1.32	1.44	1.83
0.5	1.12	1.16	1.21	1.27	1.36	1.50	2.01
0.6	1.12	1.16	1.22	1.29	1.39	1.54	2.19
0.7	1.12	1.17	1.23	1.30	1.41	1.60	2.38
0.8	1.12	1.17	1.23	1.31	1.43	1.64	2.55
0.9	1.12	1.17	1.23	1.32	1.44	1.67	2.73
1.0	1.12	1.17	1.23	1.32	1.45	1.70	2.91

TABLE 3.4. FUNCTION $\phi_1{}^0(\eta)$ FOR THE INDICATRIX $x(\gamma) = 1 + \cos \gamma$

η \ λ	0.4	0.5	0.6	0.7	0.8	0.9	1.0
0	0	0	0	0	0	0	0
0.1	0.08	0.08	0.07	0.06	0.05	0.04	0
0.2	0.17	0.16	0.15	0.14	0.12	0.09	0
0.3	0.26	0.25	0.24	0.22	0.19	0.15	0
0.4	0.36	0.34	0.32	0.30	0.27	0.21	0
0.5	0.46	0.44	0.42	0.39	0.35	0.28	0
0.6	0.56	0.54	0.51	0.48	0.43	0.35	0
0.7	0.65	0.64	0.61	0.57	0.52	0.43	0
0.8	0.76	0.73	0.71	0.67	0.61	0.51	0
0.9	0.86	0.84	0.81	0.77	0.70	0.59	0
1.0	0.96	0.94	0.91	0.87	0.80	0.67	0

TABLE 3.5. FUNCTION $\phi_1{}^1(\eta)$ FOR THE INDICATRIX $x(\gamma) = 1 + \cos \gamma$

η \ λ	0.4	0.5	0.6	0.7	0.8	0.9	1.0
0	1.00	1.00	1.00	1.00	1.00	1.00	1.00
0.1	1.02	1.02	1.03	1.03	1.04	1.04	1.05
0.2	1.01	1.02	1.03	1.03	1.04	1.05	1.06
0.3	0.99	1.00	1.01	1.02	1.03	1.04	1.05
0.4	0.95	0.96	0.98	0.99	1.00	1.01	1.02
0.5	0.90	0.92	0.93	0.94	0.95	0.96	0.98
0.6	0.84	0.85	0.86	0.87	0.88	0.90	0.91
0.7	0.75	0.76	0.77	0.78	0.79	0.80	0.82
0.8	0.63	0.64	0.65	0.66	0.67	0.68	0.69
0.9	0.46	0.47	.0.47	0.48	0.49	0.49	0.50
1.0	0	0	0	0	0	0	0

It is interesting that for $\lambda = 1$ the function $\phi_0{}^0(\eta)$ is identical with the function $\phi(\eta)$ for the spherical scattering indicatrix, but $\phi_1{}^0(\eta) = 0$; it is still more interesting that this is true for any value of x; we can convince ourselves simply by looking at Eqs. (53). In other words, the brightness coefficient averaged over the azimuth and for the scattering indicatrix

$$x(\gamma) = 1 + x_1 \cos \gamma$$

is exactly the same for the case of pure scattering as for that of a spherical indicatrix.

3. ALBEDO OF THE MEDIUM

In practical applications it is important to know not so much about the intensity of radiation emerging along different directions as about the total energy emerging per unit area and unit time. This energy, expressed as a fraction of energy per unit of surface and time and coming from the external sources, is called, as is well known, the *albedo* of the medium. We denote it by A.

Let us express the albedo by means of the brightness coefficient ρ. If the intensity of emergent radiation is $I(\eta, \zeta, \phi)$ the amount of energy emergent per unit of area and time and within the solid angle $d\omega$ will be

$$I(\eta, \zeta, \phi)\eta \; d\omega$$

and the total energy emerging through the same area and in the same time is

$$E = \int_0^{2\pi} d\phi \int_0^1 I(\eta, \zeta, \phi)\eta \; d\eta \tag{56}$$

Expressing the radiation intensity $I(\eta, \zeta, \phi)$ through the brightness coefficient $\rho(\eta, \zeta, \phi)$, we have

$$E = S\zeta \int_0^{2\pi} d\phi \int_0^1 \rho(\eta, \zeta, \phi)\eta \, d\eta \tag{57}$$

On the other hand, the amount of energy falling on unit area per unit time is

$$E_0 = \pi S\zeta \tag{58}$$

By definition albedo is $A = E/E_0$. Thus, from Eqs. (57) and (58), we find

$$A(\zeta) = \frac{1}{\pi} \int_0^{2\pi} d\phi \int_0^1 \rho(\eta, \zeta, \phi)\eta \, d\eta \tag{59}$$

In the case of the spherical indicatrix, we simplify Eq. (59) by writing

$$A(\zeta) = 2 \int_0^1 \rho(\eta, \zeta)\eta \, d\eta \tag{60}$$

We observe that for the constant coefficient of brightness

$$A = \rho$$

For a medium with infinitely large optical thickness we can easily obtain a simple formula expressing albedo $A(\zeta)$ by means of the aforementioned auxiliary functions.

Inserting the expression of brightness coefficient according to Eq. (35) into Eq. (60), we find for the spherical indicatrix of scattering:

$$A(\zeta) = \frac{\lambda}{2} \int_0^1 \frac{\phi(\eta)\phi(\zeta)}{\eta + \zeta}\eta \, d\eta$$

$$I = \frac{\lambda}{2}\phi(\zeta) \int_0^1 \phi(\eta) \, d\eta - \frac{\lambda}{2}\zeta\phi(\zeta) \int_0^1 \frac{\phi(\eta)}{\eta + \zeta} a\eta$$

Using Eq. (36), which defines the function $\phi(\eta)$, we can rewrite the preceding equation as

$$A(\zeta) = 1 - \phi(\zeta)\left[1 - \frac{\lambda}{2} \int_0^1 \phi(\eta) \, d\eta\right]$$

But the integral

$$\alpha_0 = \int_0^1 \phi(\eta) \, d\eta$$

can be easily found from the very same Eq. (36). Integrating both sides of this equation:

$$\int_0^1 \phi(\eta)\, d\eta = 1 + \frac{\lambda}{2} \int_0^1 \int_0^1 \frac{\phi(\eta)\phi(\eta')}{\eta + \eta'} \eta\, d\eta\, d\eta'$$

$$= 1 + \frac{\lambda}{2} \int_0^1 \phi(\eta)\, d\eta \int_0^1 \phi(\eta')\, d\eta' - \frac{\lambda}{2} \int_0^1 \int_0^1 \frac{\phi(\eta)\phi(\eta')}{\eta + \eta'} \eta'\, d\eta\, d\eta'$$

from which emerges the following quadratic equation for computing α_0:

$$(\lambda/4)\alpha_0^2 - \alpha_0 + 1 = 0$$

This equation provides

$$\alpha_0 = (2/\lambda)(1 - \sqrt{1 - \lambda})$$

The sign before the radical is "minus", as $\alpha_0 = 1$ for $\lambda = 0$. Thus, finally the albedo is

$$A(\zeta) = 1 - \phi(\zeta)\sqrt{1 - \lambda} \tag{61}$$

For the simplest nonspherical indicatrix $x(\gamma) = 1 + x_1 \cos \gamma$ the albedo $A(\zeta)$ is found by inserting Eq. (50) into Eq. (59). Doing this, we have

$$A(\zeta) = \frac{\lambda}{2} \int_0^1 \frac{\phi_0{}^0(\eta)\phi_0{}^0(\zeta) - x_1\phi_1{}^0(\eta)\phi_1{}^0(\zeta)}{\eta + \zeta} \eta\, d\eta$$

or, remembering Eq. (53)b),

$$A(\zeta) = 1 - \frac{1}{\zeta}\phi_1{}^0(\zeta) \tag{62}$$

We may remark that Eq. (62) is transformed into Eq. (61) if we transform the function $\phi_1{}^0(\zeta)$ into $\phi_0{}^0(\zeta)$ by means of Eq. (55), putting $x_1 = 0$.

Tables 3.6 and 3.7 contain albedo values of a plane layer with infinitely large optical thickness and for the scattering indicatrix $x(\gamma) = 1 + x_1 \cos \gamma$ with $x_1 = 0$ (spherical indicatrix) and with $x_1 = 1$.

In planetary astronomy one uses, in addition to the albedo of a plane layer, the so-called *spherical albedo*. This quantity is the ratio of energy reflected by the whole planet to the energy received by the planet from the sun. With the plane albedo known, one can easily compute the spherical albedo.

The energy received by the planet from the sun is $\pi R^2 \pi S$, where R is radius of the planet (Fig. 3.4). On the other hand, the energy reflected by the planet will be

$$2\pi \int_0^R A(\zeta)\pi\, Sr\, dr$$

where r is the distance of the chosen point on the disk of the planet from the centre of the visible disk.

But $rdr = R^2 \zeta d\zeta$.

TABLE 3.6. PLANE ALBEDO $A(\zeta)$ FOR THE SPHERICAL INDICATRIX

λ ζ	0.4	0.5	0.6	0.7	0.8	0.9	1.0
0	0.23	0.29	0.37	0.45	0.55	0.68	1.00
0.1	0.18	0.24	0.31	0.39	0.49	0.63	1.00
0.2	0.16	0.21	0.28	0.35	0.45	0.59	1.00
0.3	0.14	0.19	0.25	0.32	0.42	0.56	1.00
0.4	0.13	0.17	0.23	0.30	0.39	0.53	1.00
0.5	0.12	0.16	0.21	0.28	0.37	0.51	1.00
0.6	0.11	0.15	0.20	0.26	0.35	0.49	1.00
0.7	0.10	0.14	0.19	0.25	0.33	0.47	1.00
0.8	0.10	0.13	0.17	0.23	0.31	0.45	1.00
0.9	0.09	0.12	0.16	0.22	0.30	0.43	1.00
1.0	0.08	0.12	0.15	0.21	0.29	0.41	1.00

TABLE 3.7. PLANE ALBEDO $A(\zeta)$ FOR THE INDICATRIX $x(\gamma) = 1 + \cos \gamma$

λ ζ	0.4	0.5	0.6	0.7	0.8	0.9	1.0
0	0.22	0.28	0.36	0.43	0.53	0.66	1.00
0.1	0.17	0.23	0.29	0.36	0.46	0.59	1.00
0.2	0.14	0.19	0.25	0.32	0.41	0.55	1.00
0.3	0.12	0.16	0.22	0.28	0.37	0.51	1.00
0.4	0.10	0.14	0.19	0.25	0.34	0.48	1.00
0.5	0.09	0.12	0.17	0.22	0.31	0.45	1.00
0.6	0.08	0.11	0.15	0.20	0.28	0.42	1.00
0.7	0.07	0.09	0.13	0.18	0.26	0.39	1.00
0.8	0.06	0.08	0.12	0.16	0.24	0.37	1.00
0.9	0.05	0.07	0.10	0.15	0.22	0.35	1.00
1.0	0.04	0.06	0.09	0.13	0.20	0.33	1.00

Hence, the last expression can be written:

$$2\pi R^2 \cdot \pi S \int_0^1 A(\zeta)\zeta \, d\zeta$$

Denoting the spherical albedo by A^*, we then obtain

$$A^* = 2 \int_0^1 A(\zeta)\zeta \, d\zeta \qquad (63)$$

Table 3.8 contains values of spherical albedo for a medium with infinitely large optical thickness and for the scattering indicatrix $x(\gamma) = 1 + x_1 \cos \gamma$; Tables 3.6 and 3.7 and Eq. (63) were used in computation of these values.

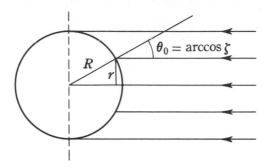

Fig. 3.4

Formulas and tables given in this and previous sections may be employed in the study of planetary atmospheres with large optical thickness, e.g., atmospheres of Venus, Jupiter, and Saturn, as has been done by Ambartsumian,[4] Barabashev,[5] and others.

TABLE 3.8. SPHERICAL ALBEDO A^*

x_1 \ λ	0.4	0.5	0.6	0.7	0.8	0.9	1.0
0	0.11	0.15	0.19	0.26	0.34	0.48	1.00
0.5	0.09	0.13	0.17	0.23	0.31	0.45	1.00
1.0	0.07	0.10	0.14	0.20	0.28	0.41	1.00

4. THE DIFFUSE REFLECTION AND TRANSMISSION OF LIGHT

We shall now consider the problem of luminescence of a plane layer with finite optical thickness, τ_0. As before we assume that the layer is illuminated by parallel rays. The problem is to find the intensity of radiation as well as that of diffusely reflected and diffusely transmitted light.

[4] V. A. Ambartsumian, On the Light Scattering in Planetary Atmospheres, *Russian Astronomical J.* **19**, No. 5 (1942).

[5] N. P. Barabashev, Photometric Results on Saturn, *Trudi Astr. Obs. HGU* **1**(9) (1950).

In solving this problem we could apply the following "invariance principle": an additional small layer with small optical thickness $\Delta\tau$ on both sides of the medium does not change the reflecting and transmitting properties of the medium. But we prefer to avail ourselves of another method derived by Ambartsumian in the theory of light scattering.[4] Both methods of Ambartsumian lead to the same functional equations for determination of the required radiation intensities.

Our starting equation is the fundamental integral equation in the theory of light scattering. For the sake of simplicity, consider the case of spherical indicatrix of scattering. The equation is (see Ch. 1, Sec. 6)

$$B(\tau, \zeta) = \frac{\lambda}{2} \int_0^{\tau_0} \mathrm{Ei}|\tau - t| B(t, \zeta) \, dt + \frac{\lambda}{4} S e^{-\tau/\zeta} \tag{64}$$

Here the dependence of the quantity B on the cosine of the angle formed by the external incident radiation ζ is clearly indicated.

Rewriting Eq. (64) in the form

$$B(\tau, \zeta) = \frac{\lambda}{2} \int_0^{\tau} \mathrm{Ei}(\tau - t) B(t, \zeta) \, dt + \frac{\lambda}{2} \int_{\tau}^{\tau_0} \mathrm{Ei}(t - \tau) B(t, \zeta) \, dt + \frac{\lambda}{4} S e^{-\tau/\zeta}$$

and putting $\tau - t = x$ in the first integral and $t - \tau = x$ in the second one, we find

$$B(\tau, \zeta) = \frac{\lambda}{2} \int_0^{\tau} \mathrm{Ei}\, x B(\tau - x, \zeta) \, dx + \frac{\lambda}{2} \int_0^{\tau_0 - \tau} \mathrm{Ei}\, x B(\tau + x, \zeta) \, dx + \frac{\lambda}{4} S e^{-\tau/\zeta} \tag{65}$$

Differentiating this equation in respect to τ, we obtain

$$B'(\tau, \zeta) = \frac{\lambda}{2} \int_0^{\tau_0} \mathrm{Ei}|\tau - t| B'(t, \zeta) \, dt - \frac{\lambda S}{4\zeta} e^{-\tau/\zeta}$$

$$+ \frac{\lambda}{2} B(0, \zeta) \mathrm{Ei}\, \tau - \frac{\lambda}{2} B(\tau_0, \zeta) \mathrm{Ei}(\tau_0 - \tau)$$

or, remembering the definition of the function $\mathrm{Ei}\tau$,

$$B'(\tau, \zeta) = \frac{\lambda}{2} \int_0^{\tau_0} \mathrm{Ei}|\tau - t| B'(t, \zeta) \, dt - \frac{\lambda S}{4\zeta} e^{-\tau/\zeta} + \frac{\lambda}{2} B(0, \zeta) \int_0^1 e^{-\tau/\zeta'} \frac{d\zeta'}{\zeta'}$$

$$- \frac{\lambda}{2} B(\tau_0, \zeta) \int_0^1 e^{-(\tau_0 - \tau)/\zeta'} \frac{d\zeta'}{\zeta'} \tag{66}$$

We observe that Eq. (66) has the same kernel as the starting equation Eq. (64), and differs only by a free term. But the free term of Eq. (66) is in reality a superposition of terms similar to those of the free term in Eq. (64). Because both equations are linear, this means that the solution of Eq. (66) is a superposition of solutions of Eq. (26), namely:

$$B'(\tau, \zeta) = -\frac{1}{\zeta}B(\tau, \zeta) + \frac{2}{S}B(0, \zeta)\int_0^1 B(\tau, \zeta')\frac{d\zeta'}{\zeta'}$$

$$-\frac{2}{S}B(\tau_0, \zeta)\int_0^1 B(\tau_0 - \tau, \zeta')\frac{d\zeta'}{\zeta'} \tag{67}$$

This is an important relation between the function $B(\tau, \zeta)$ and its derivative in respect to τ.

By means of Eq. (67) we can easily derive functional equations for evaluating the brightness coefficients $\rho(\eta, \zeta)$ and $\sigma(\eta, \zeta)$ which are defined as:

$$\left.\begin{aligned}
S\rho(\eta, \zeta)\zeta &= \int_0^{\tau_0} B(\tau, \zeta)e^{-\tau/\eta}\frac{d\tau}{\eta} \\
S\sigma(\eta, \zeta)\zeta &= \int_0^{\tau_0} B(\tau, \zeta)e^{-(\tau_0-\tau)/\eta}\frac{d\tau}{\eta}
\end{aligned}\right\} \tag{68}$$

Multiplying both sides of Eq. (67) by $e^{-\tau/\eta}d\tau/\eta$, integrating with respect to τ in the interval $0, \pi$, and remembering Eqs. (68), we find

$$S\rho(\eta, \zeta)(\eta + \zeta) = B(0, \zeta)[1 + 2\eta\int_0^1 \rho(\eta, \zeta')\ d\zeta']$$

$$-B(\tau_0, \zeta)[e^{-\tau_0/\eta} + 2\eta\int_0^1 \sigma(\eta, \zeta')\ d\zeta'] \tag{69}$$

Multiplying Eq. (67) by $e^{-(\tau_0-\tau)/\eta}d\tau/\eta$ and integrating, we find analogously

$$S\sigma(\eta, \zeta)(\eta - \zeta) = B(0, \zeta)[e^{-\tau_0/\eta} + 2\eta\int_0^1 \sigma(\eta, \zeta')\ d\zeta']$$

$$-B(\tau_0, \zeta)[1 + 2\eta\int_0^1 \rho(\eta, \zeta')\ d\zeta'] \tag{70}$$

But the quantities $B(0, \zeta)$ and $B(\tau_0, \zeta)$ can be easily expressed by means of functions $\rho(\eta, \zeta)$ and $\sigma(\eta, \zeta)$. Indeed, from Eq. (64) follows:

$$B(0, \zeta) = \frac{\lambda}{2}\int_0^{\tau_0} B(t, \zeta)\ dt \int_0^1 e^{-t/\eta'}\frac{d\eta'}{\eta'} + \frac{\lambda}{4}S$$

$$= \frac{\lambda}{2}\int_0^1 d\eta'\int_0^{\tau_0} B(t, \zeta)e^{-t/\eta'}\frac{dt}{\eta'} + \frac{\lambda}{4}S$$

$$= \frac{\lambda}{4}S[1 + 2\zeta\int_0^1 \rho(\eta', \zeta)\ d\eta'] \tag{71}$$

and

$$B(\tau_0, \zeta) = \frac{\lambda}{2} \int_0^{\tau_0} B(t, \zeta) \, dt \int_0^1 e^{-(\tau_0 - t)/\eta'} \frac{d\eta'}{\eta'} + \frac{\lambda}{4} S e^{-\tau_0/\zeta}$$

$$= \frac{\lambda}{2} \int_0^1 d\eta' \int_0^{\tau_0} B(t, \zeta) e^{-(\tau_0 - t)/\eta'} \frac{dt}{\eta'} + \frac{\lambda}{4} S e^{-\tau_0/\zeta}$$

$$= \frac{\lambda}{4} S \left[e^{-\tau_0/\zeta} + 2\zeta \int_0^1 \sigma(\eta', \zeta) \, d\eta' \right] \tag{72}$$

Instead of Eqs. (69) and (70), we therefore have

$$\rho(\eta, \zeta)(\eta + \zeta) = \frac{\lambda}{4} [1 + 2\zeta \int_0^1 \rho(\eta', \zeta) \, d\eta'][1 + 2\eta \int_0^1 \rho(\eta, \zeta') \, d\zeta']$$

$$- \frac{\lambda}{4} [e^{-\tau_0/\zeta} + 2\zeta \int_0^1 \sigma(\eta', \zeta) \, d\eta'][e^{-\tau_0/\eta} + 2\eta \int_0^1 \sigma(\eta', \zeta) \, d\eta'] \tag{73}$$

and

$$\sigma(\eta, \zeta)(\eta - \zeta) = \frac{\lambda}{4} [1 + 2\zeta \int_0^1 \rho(\eta', \zeta) \, d\eta'][e^{-\tau_0/\eta} + 2\eta \int_0^1 \sigma(\eta, \zeta') \, d\zeta']$$

$$- \frac{\lambda}{4} [e^{-\tau_0/\zeta} + 2\zeta \int_0^1 \sigma(\eta', \zeta) \, d\eta'][1 + 2\eta \int_0^1 \rho(\eta, \zeta') \, d\zeta'] \tag{74}$$

Because the brightness coefficients are symmetrical in respect to η and ζ, we can rewrite Eqs. (73) and (74) as follows:

$$\rho(\eta, \zeta) = \frac{\lambda}{4} \frac{\phi(\zeta)\phi(\eta) - \psi(\zeta)\psi(\eta)}{\eta + \zeta} \tag{75}$$

$$\sigma(\eta, \zeta) = \frac{\lambda}{4} \frac{\phi(\zeta)\psi(\eta) - \psi(\zeta)\phi(\eta)}{\eta - \zeta} \tag{76}$$

where

$$\phi(\eta) = 1 + 2\eta \int_0^1 \rho(\eta, \zeta') \, d\zeta' \tag{77}$$

$$\psi(\eta) = e^{-\tau_0/\eta} + 2\eta \int_0^1 \sigma(\eta, \zeta') \, d\zeta' \tag{78}$$

Equations (77) and (78) define the structure of the brightness coefficients. Substituting Eqs. (75) and (76) into Eqs. (77) and (78), respectively, we obtain the following equations for determination of the auxiliary functions $\phi(\eta)$ and $\psi(\eta)$:

$$\phi(\eta) = 1 + \frac{\lambda}{2} \eta \int_0^1 \frac{\phi(\zeta)\phi(\eta) - \psi(\zeta)\psi(\eta)}{\eta + \zeta} \, d\zeta \tag{79}$$

$$\psi(\eta) = e^{-\tau_0/\eta} + \frac{\lambda}{2} \eta \int_0^1 \frac{\phi(\zeta)\psi(\eta) - \psi(\zeta)\phi(\eta)}{\eta - \zeta} \, d\zeta \tag{80}$$

Equations (75) and (76) and Eqs. (79) and (80) are the required ones. From them, as a special case, follow Eqs. (35) and (36) for the case $\tau_0 = \infty$.

We note that zero moments of the functions $\phi(\eta)$ and $\psi(\eta)$ are simply connected with each other. To find this connection we integrate both sides of Eq. (79) in respect to η:

$$\int_0^1 \phi(\eta) \, d\eta = 1 + \frac{\lambda}{2} \int_0^1 \int_0^1 \frac{\eta \phi(\zeta) \phi(\eta)}{\eta + \zeta} \, d\eta d\zeta - \frac{\lambda}{2} \int_0^1 \int_0^1 \frac{\eta \psi(\zeta) \psi(\eta)}{\eta + \zeta} \, d\eta d\zeta \quad (81)$$

But

$$\int_0^1 \int_0^1 \frac{\eta \phi(\zeta) \phi(\eta)}{\eta + \zeta} \, d\eta d\zeta = [\int_0^1 \phi(\eta) \, d\eta]^2 - \int_0^1 \int_0^1 \frac{\zeta \phi(\zeta) \phi(\eta)}{\eta + \zeta} \, d\eta d\zeta$$

$$= \tfrac{1}{2} [\int_0^1 \phi(\eta) \, d\eta]^2$$

Introducing

$$\int_0^1 \phi(\eta) \, d\eta = \alpha_0, \qquad \int_0^1 \psi(\eta) \, d\eta = \beta_0 \qquad (82)$$

we have

$$\alpha_0 = 1 + \frac{\lambda}{4}(\alpha_0^2 - \beta_0^2) \qquad (83)$$

instead of Eq. (81); for $\lambda = 1$ this relation becomes

$$\alpha_0 + \beta_0 = 2 \qquad (84)$$

The system of Eqs. (79) and (80) can be solved numerically. However, we should remember that for the case of pure scattering, the solution of this system is not unique. It is easily shown that if $\phi(\eta)$ and $\psi(\eta)$ are solutions of the system of Eqs. (79) and (80) for $\lambda = 1$, the function

$$\phi(\eta) + C\eta[\phi(\eta) + \psi(\eta)]$$
$$\psi(\eta) - C\eta[\phi(\eta) + \psi(\eta)]$$

is also a solution of the system. Here C is an arbitrary constant. In order to remove the indeterminacy one can use the integral flux and the so-called K-integral (see Ch. 1., Sec. 5).

For determination of the brightness coefficients $\rho(\eta, \zeta)$, $\sigma(\eta, \zeta)$, and auxiliary functions $\phi(\eta)$ and $\psi(\eta)$, it is interesting that we can derive other equations different from the above-mentioned. Knowing that these quantities depend not only on variables η and ζ but also on the optical thickness of the layer τ_0, let us derive equations for expression of the required quantities depending on different values of τ_0.

We start, as before, from the fundamental integral equation in the theory of light scattering and rewrite it, underlining the dependence of B on τ_0:

$$B(\tau, \zeta, \tau_0) = \frac{\lambda}{2} \int_0^{\tau_0} \mathrm{Ei}|\tau - t| B(t, \zeta, \tau_0) \, dt + \frac{\lambda}{4} S e^{-\tau/\zeta} \tag{85}$$

we can rewrite it again:

$$B(\tau_0 - \tau, \zeta, \tau_0) = \frac{\lambda}{2} \int_0^{\tau_0} \mathrm{Ei}|\tau - t| B(\tau_0 - t, \zeta, \tau_0) \, dt + \frac{\lambda}{4} S e^{-(\tau_0 - \tau)/\zeta} \tag{86}$$

Differentiating Eqs. (85) and (86) in respect to τ_0, we find

$$\frac{\partial B(\tau, \zeta, \tau_0)}{\partial \tau_0} = \frac{\lambda}{2} \int_0^{\tau_0} \mathrm{Ei}|\tau - t| \frac{\partial B(t, \zeta, \tau_0)}{\partial \tau_0} \, dt + \frac{\lambda}{2} \mathrm{Ei}(\tau_0 - \tau) B(\tau_0, \zeta, \tau_0) \tag{87}$$

$$\frac{\partial B(\tau_0 - \tau, \zeta, \tau_0)}{\partial \tau_0} = \frac{\lambda}{2} \int_0^{\tau_0} \mathrm{Ei}|\tau - t| \frac{\partial B(\tau_0 - t, \zeta, \tau_0)}{\partial \tau_0} \, dt$$

$$+ \frac{\lambda}{2} \mathrm{Ei}(\tau_0 - \tau) B(0, \zeta, \tau_0) - \frac{\lambda}{4\zeta} e^{-(\tau_0 - \tau)/\zeta} \tag{88}$$

In solving Eqs. (87) and (88) by means of Eqs. (85) and (86), we apply the superposition principle:

$$\frac{\partial B(\tau, \zeta, \tau_0)}{\partial \tau_0} = \frac{2}{S} B(\tau_0, \zeta, \tau_0) \int_0^1 B(\tau_0 - \tau, \eta', \tau_0) \frac{d\eta'}{\eta'} \tag{89}$$

$$\frac{\partial B(\tau_0 - \tau, \zeta, \tau_0)}{\partial \tau_0} = \frac{2}{S} B(0, \zeta, \tau_0) \int_0^1 B(\tau_0 - \tau, \eta', \tau_0) \frac{d\eta'}{\eta'} - \frac{1}{\zeta} B(\tau_0 - \tau, \zeta, \tau_0) \tag{90}$$

Turning now to Eq. (68) which defines brightness coefficients ρ and σ, we rewrite them

$$\left. \begin{aligned} S\rho(\eta, \zeta, \tau_0)\zeta &= \int_0^{\tau_0} B(\tau, \zeta, \tau_0) e^{-\tau/\eta} \frac{d\tau}{\eta} \\ S\sigma(\eta, \zeta, \tau_0)\zeta &= \int_0^{\tau_0} B(\tau_0 - \tau, \zeta, \tau_0) e^{-\tau/\eta} \frac{d\tau}{\eta} \end{aligned} \right\} \tag{91}$$

and differentiating with respect to τ_0, we obtain

$$S \frac{\partial \rho}{\partial \tau_0} \zeta = \int_0^{\tau_0} \frac{\partial B(\tau, \zeta, \tau_0)}{\partial \tau_0} e^{-\tau/\eta} \frac{d\tau}{\eta} + B(\tau_0, \zeta, \tau_0) e^{-\tau_0/\eta} \frac{1}{\eta} \tag{92}$$

$$S \frac{\partial \sigma}{\partial \tau_0} \zeta = \int_0^{\tau_0} \frac{\partial B(\tau_0 - \tau, \zeta, \tau_0)}{\partial \tau_0} e^{-\tau/\eta} \frac{d\tau}{\eta} + B(0, \zeta, \tau_0) e^{-\tau_0/\eta} \frac{1}{\eta} \tag{93}$$

Substituting Eqs. (89) and (90) into Eqs. (92) and (93), respectively, we have

$$S\frac{\partial \rho}{\partial \tau_0}\zeta = \frac{2}{S}B(\tau_0, \zeta, \tau_0)\int_0^{\tau_0} e^{-\tau/\eta}\frac{d\tau}{\eta}\int_0^1 B(\tau_0-\tau, \eta', \tau_0)\frac{d\eta'}{\eta'}$$

$$+ B(\tau_0, \zeta, \tau_0)e^{-\tau_0/\eta}\frac{1}{\eta}$$

$$S\frac{\partial \sigma}{\partial \tau_0}\zeta = \frac{2}{S}B(0, \zeta, \tau_0)\int_0^{\tau_0} e^{-\tau/\eta}\frac{d\tau}{\eta}\int_0^1 B(\tau_0-\tau, \eta', \tau_0)\frac{d\eta'}{\eta'}$$

$$-\frac{1}{\zeta}\int_0^{\tau_0} B(\tau_0-\tau, \zeta, \tau_0)e^{-\tau/\eta}\frac{d\tau}{\eta} + B(0, \zeta, \tau_0)e^{-\tau_0/\eta}\frac{1}{\eta}$$

or, recollecting Eqs. (91),

$$S\frac{\partial \rho}{\partial \tau_0}\zeta = B(\tau_0, \zeta, \tau_0)\left[2\int_0^1 \sigma(\eta, \eta', \tau_0)\,d\eta' + \frac{1}{\eta}e^{-\tau_0/\eta}\right] \tag{94}$$

$$S\frac{\partial \sigma}{\partial \tau_0}\zeta = B(0, \zeta, \tau_0)\left[2\int_0^1 \sigma(\eta, \eta', \tau_0)\,d\eta' + \frac{1}{\eta}e^{-\tau_0/\eta}\right] - S\sigma(\eta, \zeta, \tau_0) \tag{95}$$

However, Eqs. (85) and (86) give, for $\tau = 0$,

$$\left.\begin{array}{l} B(0, \zeta, \tau_0) = \dfrac{\lambda}{4}S[1 + 2\zeta\displaystyle\int_0^1 \rho(\eta', \zeta, \tau_0)\,d\eta'] \\[3mm] B(\tau_0, \zeta, \tau_0) = \dfrac{\lambda}{4}S[e^{-\tau_0/\zeta} + 2\zeta\displaystyle\int_0^1 \sigma(\eta', \zeta, \tau_0)\,d\eta' \end{array}\right\} \tag{96}$$

Therefore, denoting

$$B(0, \zeta, \tau_0) = \frac{\lambda}{4}S\phi(\tau_0, \zeta), \qquad B(\tau_0, \zeta, \tau_0) = \frac{\lambda}{4}S\psi(\tau_0, \zeta) \tag{97}$$

we find, instead of Eqs. (94) and (95),

$$\frac{\partial \rho}{\partial \tau_0}\eta\zeta = \frac{\lambda}{4}\psi(\tau_0, \zeta)\psi(\tau_0, \eta) \tag{98}$$

$$\frac{\partial \sigma}{\partial \tau_0}\eta\zeta = \frac{\lambda}{4}\phi(\tau_0, \zeta)\psi(\tau_0, \eta) - \eta\sigma(\eta, \zeta, \tau_0) \tag{99}$$

Hence,

$$\rho(\eta, \zeta, \tau_0)\eta\zeta = \frac{\lambda}{4}\int_0^{\tau_0} \psi(t_0, \eta)\psi(t_0, \zeta)\,dt_0 \tag{100}$$

$$\sigma(\eta, \zeta, \tau_0)\eta\zeta = \frac{\lambda}{4}\int_0^{\tau_0} e^{-(\tau_0-t_0)/\zeta}\phi(t_0, \zeta)\psi(t_0, \eta)\,dt_0 \tag{101}$$

Inserting Eqs. (100) and (101) into Eqs. (96) and remembering Eq. (97) we find:

$$\phi(\tau_0, \zeta) = 1 + \frac{\lambda}{2} \int_0^{\tau_0} \psi(t_0, \zeta)\, dt_0 \int_0^1 \psi(t_0, \eta') \frac{d\eta'}{\eta'} \tag{102}$$

$$\psi(\tau_0, \zeta) = e^{-\tau_0/\zeta}\left[1 + \frac{\lambda}{2} \int_0^{\tau_0} e^{t_0/\zeta}\phi(t_0, \zeta)\, dt_0 \int_0^1 \psi(t_0, \eta') \frac{d\eta'}{\eta'}\right] \tag{103}$$

In this way we have derived new Eqs. (102) and (103) for finding of auxiliary functions ϕ and ψ and new Eqs. (100) and (101) expressing brightness coefficients ρ and σ by means of auxiliary functions.

The system of Eqs. (102) and (103) can be easily solved numerically by proceeding step by step from the small values of τ_0 to the larger ones. In this way we compute values of the functions ϕ and ψ for the case of pure scattering and give them in Tables 3.9 and 3.10 with an accuracy of one-two units of the last digit.

TABLE 3.9. VALUES OF THE FUNCTION $\phi(\tau_0, \eta)$, FOR $\lambda = 1$

η / τ_0	0	0.1	0.2	0.3	0.4	0.5	0.6	0.7	0.8	0.9	1.0
0	1.00	1.00	1.00	1.00	1.00	1.00	1.00	1.00	1.00	1.00	1.00
0.1	1.00	1.11	1.13	1.14	1.15	1.15	1.15	1.16	1.16	1.16	1.16
0.2	1.00	1.14	1.20	1.22	1.23	1.24	1.25	1.25	1.26	1.26	1.26
0.3	1.00	1.16	1.23	1.27	1.30	1.31	1.32	1.33	1.34	1.34	1.35
0.4	1.00	1.17	1.26	1.31	1.35	1.37	1.39	1.40	1.42	1.42	1.43
0.5	1.00	1.18	1.28	1.34	1.39	1.42	1.44	1.46	1.48	1.49	1.50
0.6	1.00	1.18	1.29	1.36	1.42	1.46	1.49	1.51	1.53	1.55	1.56
0.7	1.00	1.18	1.30	1.38	1.47	1.50	1.54	1.56	1.58	1.60	1.61
0.8	1.00	1.19	1.31	1.40	1.49	1.53	1.58	1.60	1.63	1.65	1.67
0.9	1.00	1.19	1.32	1.42	1.49	1.56	1.61	1.64	1.67	1.70	1.72
1.0	1.00	1.19	1.33	1.43	1.51	1.58	1.63	1.67	1.70	1.74	1.76

TABLE 3.10. VALUES OF THE FUNCTION $\psi(\tau_0, \eta)$, FOR $\lambda = 1$

η / τ_0	0	0.1	0.2	0.3	0.4	0.5	0.6	0.7	0.8	0.9	1.0
0	0	1.00	1.00	1.00	1.00	1.00	1.00	1.00	1.00	1.00	1.00
0.1	0	0.46	0.73	0.85	0.92	0.97	1.00	1.02	1.04	1.05	1.06
0.2	0	0.24	0.53	0.71	0.82	0.90	0.95	0.99	1.03	1.05	1.07
0.3	0	0.15	0.40	0.59	0.72	0.83	0.90	0.96	1.01	1.04	1.07
0.4	0	0.10	0.31	0.50	0.65	0.76	0.86	0.93	0.99	1.02	1.06
0.5	0	0.09	0.25	0.43	0.59	0.71	0.81	0.89	0.95	1.01	1.05
0.6	0	0.07	0.21	0.37	0.53	0.66	0.72	0.85	0.92	0.98	1.04
0.7	0	0.07	0.18	0.33	0.48	0.61	0.71	0.81	0.89	0.96	1.02
0.8	0	0.06	0.16	0.30	0.43	0.57	0.68	0.78	0.86	0.94	1.00
0.9	0	0.06	0.15	0.27	0.40	0.53	0.64	0.75	0.83	0.92	0.99
1.0	0	0.06	0.14	0.25	0.37	0.50	0.61	0.72	0.81	0.90	0.97

5. The Determination of the Function $B(\tau, \zeta)$

In the previous sections we considered the problem of finding the intensity of emergent radiation. However, often it is interesting to find intensities of internal radiation. It appears that, having solved the first problem, the second one can be greatly simplified. In other words, we obtain another method for finding the light pattern within the medium.

Here we deal with the question of light pattern within a plane layer with infinitely large optical thickness. We assume first that the problem of diffuse reflection of light by plane layer is known. Consider isotropic scattering, for simplicity's sake.

We know that computation of radiation intensities, inside as well as outside the medium, is reduced to computation of the function $B(\tau, \zeta)$.

Usually this function is found from the fundamental integral equation in the theory of light scattering. However, if we know the function $\phi(\zeta)$, which was introduced in the problem of diffuse light scattering and expressed by Eq. (36), we can derive another integral equation for computing the function $B(\tau, \zeta)$.

In the foregoing section we derived Eq. (67) connecting the function $B(\tau, \zeta)$ and its derivative with respect to τ_0. For $\tau_0 = \infty$ this relation becomes

$$B'(\tau, \zeta) = -\frac{1}{\zeta}B(\tau, \zeta) + \frac{2}{S}B(0, \zeta)\int_0^1 B(\tau, \zeta')\frac{d\zeta'}{\zeta'} \qquad (104)$$

Availing ourselves of the known notation

$$B(0, \zeta) = \frac{\lambda}{4}S\phi(\zeta) \qquad (105)$$

and introducing a new notation

$$2\int_0^1 B(\tau, \zeta')\frac{d\zeta'}{\zeta'} = S\Phi(\tau) \qquad (106)$$

we can rewrite Eq. (104) as

$$B'(\tau, \zeta) = -\frac{1}{\zeta}B(\tau, \zeta) + \frac{\lambda}{4}S\phi(\zeta)\Phi(\tau) \qquad (107)$$

Solving Eq. (107) with respect to $B(\tau, \zeta)$, we find

$$B(\tau, \zeta) = \frac{\lambda}{4}S\phi(\zeta)e^{-\tau/\zeta}[1 + \int_0^\tau e^{t/\zeta}\Phi(t)\,dt] \qquad (108)$$

This formula permits us to find the function $B(\tau, \zeta)$ if the function $\Phi(\tau)$ is known. But the equation for $\Phi(\tau)$ can be easily derived from the same Eq. (108). Multiplying both sides by $1/\zeta$ and integrating with respect to ζ in the interval from 0 to 1, we have

$$\Phi(\tau) = K(\tau) + \int_0^\tau \Phi(t) K(\tau - t) \, dt \tag{109}$$

where

$$K(\tau) = \frac{\lambda}{2} \int_0^1 e^{-\tau/\zeta} \phi(\zeta) \frac{d\zeta}{\zeta} \tag{110}$$

We have thus reduced the computation of the function $B(\tau, \zeta)$ to the computation of the function $\Phi(\tau)$, which is defined by an integral equation of Volterra kind.

It is important that, for the deeper layers ($\tau \gg 1$), Eq. (104) provide an accurate asymptotic expression of the function $B(\tau, \zeta)$. We shall find this expression in the form

$$B(\tau, \zeta) = C(\zeta) e^{-k\tau} \tag{111}$$

where $C(\zeta)$ is an unknown function of ζ, and k is an unknown constant. The fact that with $\tau \gg 1$ the function $B(\tau, \zeta)$ is represented by Eq. (111) follows from physical considerations: relative directional distribution of radiation intensities should not depend on τ in the layers of the medium.

Substituting Eq. (111) into Eq. (104) and recollecting Eq. (105), we find

$$-kC(\zeta) = -\frac{1}{\zeta} C(\zeta) + \frac{\lambda}{2} \phi(\zeta) \int_0^1 C(\zeta') \frac{d\zeta'}{\zeta'}$$

hence,

$$C(\zeta) = A \frac{\phi(\zeta) \zeta}{1 - k\zeta} \tag{112}$$

where

$$A = \frac{\lambda}{2} \int_0^1 C(\zeta') \frac{d\zeta'}{\zeta'} \tag{113}$$

Multiplying both sides of Eq. (112) with $\lambda/2\zeta$, integrating with respect to ζ in the interval from 0 to 1, and remembering Eq. (113), we obtain the following equation for computing the constant k:

$$\frac{\lambda}{2} \int_0^1 \frac{\phi(\zeta)}{1 - k\zeta} \, d\zeta = 1 \tag{114}$$

It is easily shown that the relation between λ and k can be established even without the function $\phi(\zeta)$. For this one employs the equation which defines the function $\phi(\zeta)$:

$$\phi(\eta) = 1 + \frac{\lambda}{2}\eta\phi(\eta) \int_0^1 \frac{\phi(\zeta)}{\eta + \zeta} d\zeta \tag{115}$$

Multiplying both sides of Eq. (115) by $(\lambda/2)[1/(1 - k\eta)]$ and integrating with respect to η in interval from 0 to 1, we find

$$\frac{\lambda}{2}\int_0^1 \frac{\phi(\eta)}{1 - k\eta} d\eta = -\frac{\lambda}{2k}\lg(1 - k) + \frac{\lambda^2}{4}\int_0^1 \frac{\phi(\eta)}{1 - k\eta}\eta \, d\eta \int_0^1 \frac{\phi(\zeta)}{\eta + \zeta} d\zeta$$

or

$$\frac{\lambda}{2}\int_0^1 \frac{\phi(\eta)}{1 - k\eta} d\eta = -\frac{\lambda}{2k}\lg(1 - k) + \frac{\lambda^2}{4}\int_0^1 \frac{\phi(\eta)}{1 - k\eta} d\eta \int_0^1 \frac{\phi(\zeta)}{1 + k\zeta} d\zeta$$

$$-\frac{\lambda^2}{4}\int_0^1 \frac{\phi(\zeta)}{1 + k\zeta}\zeta \, d\zeta \int_0^1 \frac{\phi(\eta)}{\eta + \zeta} d\eta$$

From this it follows that, if Eq. (114) is correct, the following relation must be correct too:

$$1 = -\frac{\lambda}{2k}\lg(1 - k) + \frac{\lambda}{2}\int_0^1 \frac{d\zeta}{1 + k\zeta}\left[\phi(\zeta) - \frac{\lambda}{2}\phi(\zeta)\zeta \int_0^1 \frac{\phi(\eta)}{\eta + \zeta} d\eta\right]$$

which, if we remember Eq. (115), becomes

$$\frac{\lambda}{2k}\lg\frac{1 + k}{1 - k} = 1 \tag{116}$$

The function $B(\tau, \zeta)$ can therefore be rewritten in the following form

$$B(\tau, \zeta) = A\frac{\phi(\zeta)\zeta}{1 - k\zeta}e^{-k\tau} \tag{117}$$

where k is defined by Eq. (116).

Table 3.11 contains values of k depending on λ.

TABLE 3.11. VALUES OF k AND λ FOR SPHERICAL SCATTERING INDICATRIX

k	0	0.05	0.10	0.15	0.20	0.25	0.30	0.35	0.40	0.45	0.50
λ	1.000	0.999	0.997	0.992	0.987	0.979	0.969	0.958	0.944	0.928	0.910

k		0.55	0.60	0.65	0.70	0.75	0.80	0.85	0.90	0.95	1.00
λ		0.890	0.866	0.838	0.807	0.771	0.728	0.677	0.611	0.519	0

The constant A entering Eq. (117) cannot be found from Eq. (104), but we can evaluate it from the following considerations.

Consider integral equation of the first order:

$$B(\tau) = \frac{\lambda}{2} \int_{-\infty}^{+\infty} B(t)\,\mathrm{Ei}|\tau - t|\, dt \qquad (118)$$

We can easily convince ourselves that the solution of this equation is a function of $e^{-k\tau}$ where k is defined by Eq. (116). Therefore we can write the following identity:

$$e^{-k\tau} = \frac{\lambda}{2} \int_0^\infty e^{-kt}\mathrm{Ei}|\tau - t|\, dt + \frac{\lambda}{2} \int_0^\infty e^{kt}\mathrm{Ei}(\tau + t)\, dt \qquad (119)$$

But

$$\int_0^\infty e^{kt}\mathrm{Ei}(\tau + t)\, dt = \int_0^\infty e^{kt}\, dt \int_0^1 e^{-(\tau + t)/\zeta} \frac{d\zeta}{\zeta}$$

$$= \int_0^1 e^{-\tau/\zeta} \frac{d\zeta}{\zeta} \int_0^1 e^{kt - (t/\zeta)}\, dt = \int_0^1 e^{\tau/\zeta} \frac{d\zeta}{1 - k\zeta}$$

It follows that, instead of Eq. (119), we may write:

$$e^{-k\tau} = \frac{\lambda}{2} \int_0^\infty e^{-kt}\mathrm{Ei}|\tau - t|\, dt + \frac{\lambda}{2} \int_0^1 e^{-\tau/\zeta} \frac{d\zeta}{1 - k\zeta} \qquad (120)$$

Comparing Eq. (120) with the following fundamental integral equation in theory of light scattering

$$B(\tau, \zeta) = \frac{\lambda}{2} \int_0^\infty B(t, \zeta)\,\mathrm{Ei}|\tau - t|\, dt + \frac{\lambda}{4} S e^{-\tau/\zeta} \qquad (121)$$

we see that the function $e^{-k\tau}$ can be expressed as a superposition of solutions of Eq. (121), namely:

$$e^{-k\tau} = \frac{2}{S} \int_0^1 \frac{B(\tau, \zeta)}{1 - k\zeta}\, d\zeta \qquad (122)$$

The function $B(\tau, \zeta)$ should satisfy Eq. (122) for all τ, including the case with very large values of τ. Then the function $B(\tau, \zeta)$ is expressed by Eq. (117). Substituting Eq. (117) into Eq. (122), we find:

$$A \int_0^1 \frac{\phi(\zeta)\zeta\, d\zeta}{(1 - k\zeta)^2} = \frac{S}{2} \qquad (123)$$

This is the required equation for computing A. After the quantity A has been found, one can feel that our problem of finding the function $B(\tau, \zeta)$ in deep layers of the medium is solved.

Thus we have shown that the function $\phi(\zeta)$ permits us to compute values of $B(\tau, \zeta)$ on the boundary of the medium by means of Eq. (105)

and also in the deep layers of the medium by means of Eq. (117). The values of $B(\tau, \zeta)$ for intermediate regions can be computed by means of Eq. (109).

6. MARCH OF LIGHT IN DEEP LAYERS

Evaluation of the light pattern within a medium with an arbitrary scattering indicatrix may be made by means of the same method which was employed in the previous section for the case of the spherical scattering indicatrix. In particular, one can also obtain an asymptotic expression of the function B in the deep layers. However, if we are interested in accuracy up to a constant factor, we can find this expression much more simply.[6]

Consider the basic integral equation in theory of light scattering with an arbitrary scattering indicatrix. For $\tau_0 = \infty$ this equation has the form:

$$B(\tau, \eta, \phi) = \frac{\lambda}{4\pi} \int_0^\tau dt \int_0^1 \frac{d\eta'}{\eta'} \int_0^{2\pi} e^{-(\tau-t)/\eta'} x(\gamma) B(t, \eta', \phi') \, d\phi'$$

$$- \frac{\lambda}{4\pi} \int_\tau^\infty dt \int_{-1}^0 \frac{d\eta'}{\eta'} \int_0^{2\pi} e^{-(\tau-t)/\eta'} x(\gamma) B(t, \eta', \phi') \, d\phi' + \frac{\lambda}{4} x(\gamma_1) S e^{-\tau/\zeta}$$

$$(124)$$

Let us make the following assumptions concerning the light pattern within a medium: (1) direct radiation is negligible as compared with diffused radiation; (2) radiation intensity does not depend on azimuth; (3) relative angular distribution of radiation intensity does not depend on optical depth. It goes without saying that we could prove the existence of these properties of the medium; we are content, however, that these properties follow out of physical considerations.

We rewrite Eq. (124) as follows. First we neglect the free term on account of the first of the above-mentioned properties, then we replace the lower limit 0 by $-\infty$ in the first integral; as a result we have

$$B(\tau, \eta, \phi) = \frac{\lambda}{4\pi} \int_{-\infty}^\tau dt \int_0^1 \frac{d\eta'}{\eta'} \int_0^{2\pi} e^{-(\tau-t)/\eta'} x(\gamma) B(t, \eta', \phi') \, d\phi'$$

$$- \frac{\lambda}{4\pi} \int_\tau^\infty dt \int_{-1}^0 \frac{d\eta'}{\eta'} \int_0^{2\pi} e^{-(\tau-t)/\eta'} x(\gamma) B(t, \eta', \phi') \, d\phi' \qquad (125)$$

[6] V. A. Ambartsumian, A New Method of Finding a Light Scattering in a Turbid Medium, *Izv. AN SSSR, series geogr.-geoph.* **3** (1942).

The second property permits us to assume that B is independent of ϕ. Then, instead of Eq. (125), we find

$$B(\tau, \eta) = \frac{\lambda}{2} \int_{-\infty}^{\tau} dt \int_{0}^{1} e^{-(\tau-t)/\eta'} B(t, \eta') p(\eta, \eta') \frac{d\eta'}{\eta'}$$
$$- \frac{\lambda}{2} \int_{\tau}^{\infty} dt \int_{-1}^{0} e^{-(\tau-t)/\eta'} B(t, \eta') p(\eta, \eta') \frac{d\eta'}{\eta'} \qquad (126)$$

where

$$p(\eta, \eta') = \frac{1}{2\pi} \int_{0}^{2\pi} x(\gamma) \, d\phi' \qquad (127)$$

The third property allows us to write

$$B(\tau, \eta) = a(\tau) b(\eta)$$

or, since the zero point of optical depth is arbitrary,

$$B(\tau, \eta) = b(\eta) e^{-k\tau} \qquad (128)$$

where k is a constant. Substituting Eq. (128) into Eq. (126), we have

$$b(\eta) = \frac{\lambda}{2} \int_{-1}^{+1} \frac{p(\eta, \eta') b(\eta')}{1 - k\eta'} \, d\eta' \qquad (129)$$

Therefore, we find that in deep layers the quantity $B(\tau, \eta)$ is given by Eq. (128) and the function $b(\eta)$ by Eq. (129). Because Eq. (129) has a solution differing from zero for a given λ and only for a definite value of k, the required value of the constant k is found from the condition of solubility of this equation.

Using Eq. (128) and the equation of radiative transfer, we derive the following expression for radiation intensity in the deep layers of the medium:

$$I(\tau, \eta) = \frac{b(\eta)}{1 - k\eta} e^{-k\tau} \qquad (130)$$

Turning now to Eq. (129), we observe that the kernel of this equation is unsymmetrical because the function $p(\eta, \eta')$ is symmetrical. But we can easily make the equation symmetrical. For this, we introduce a new function, instead of $b(\eta)$,

$$h(\eta) = \frac{b(\eta)}{\sqrt{1 - k\eta}} \qquad (131)$$

Then, instead of Eq. (129), we have

$$h(\eta) = \frac{\lambda}{2} \int_{-1}^{+1} \frac{p(\eta, \eta') h(\eta')}{\sqrt{(1 - k\eta)(1 - k\eta')}} \, d\eta' \qquad (132)$$

with a symmetrical kernel.

Analysis of Eq. (132) may be made in the usual manner, but we are now not interested in this; we should like to emphasize its two properties.

1. For a given scattering indicatrix values of k decrease with the increasing of λ.

2. For pure scattering, $\lambda = 1$, and for an arbitrary scattering indicatrix, $k = 0$.

We can easily show the correctness of the last property. For that we first convince ourselves that the solution of Eq. (129) with $\lambda = 1$ will be $b(\eta) = 1$ and $k = 0$. Then, inserting these values in Eq. (129), and remembering Eq. (127), we obtain

$$\frac{1}{4\pi} \int_0^{2\pi} d\phi' \int_0^1 x(\gamma) \, d\eta' = 1$$

which is an identity on account of normalization of the scattering indicatrix.

We assume, as before, that the scattering indicatrix is expanded in series with Legendre polynomials:

$$x(\gamma) = \sum_{i=0}^n x_i P_i(\cos \gamma) \tag{133}$$

Then, recollecting Eq. (40), we find

$$p(\eta, \eta') = \sum_{i=0}^n x_i P_i(\eta) P_i(\eta') \tag{134}$$

In other words, expressing the scattering indicatrix in the form of Eq. (133), we found that the kernel of the integral equation, Eq. (129), became degenerate and, consequently, the equation considered can be solved without any difficulty.

In Eqs. (129) and (134), we see that the function $b(\eta)$ can be expanded into a series

$$b(\eta) = \sum_{i=0}^n b_i P_i(\eta) \tag{135}$$

where b_i are some coefficients. Inserting Eqs. (134) and (135) into Eq. (129), we receive the following system of linear algebraic equations for computing the coefficients b_i:

$$b_i = \frac{\lambda}{2} x_i \sum_{j=0}^n b_j \int_{-1}^{+1} \frac{P_j(\eta') P_i(\eta')}{1 - k\eta'} \, d\eta' \qquad (i = 0, 1, ..., n) \tag{136}$$

Making the determinant of this system equal to zero, we find the value of the parameter k.

Let us find a solution of Eq. (129) for some particular case of the scattering indicatrix.

In the case of the spherical scattering indicatrix, $[x(\gamma) = 1]$, Eqs. (135) and (136) give

$$b(\eta) = b_0 = \text{const}$$

and

$$\frac{\lambda}{2} \int_{-1}^{+1} \frac{d\eta'}{1 - k\eta'} = 1$$

The last relation is Eq. (116) for determination of k.

In the case of the simplest, nonspherical scattering indicatrix,

$$x(\gamma) = 1 + x_1 \cos \gamma$$

the function $b(\eta)$ has the form

$$b(\eta) = b_0 + b_1 \eta \tag{137}$$

By finding the coefficients b_0 and b_1 from Eq. (136), we obtain a system of two linear homogeneous equations:

$$\left.\begin{aligned}
b_0 &= \lambda\left[\frac{b_0}{2k}\lg\frac{1+k}{1-k} - b_1\left(\frac{1}{k} - \frac{1}{2k^2}\lg\frac{1+k}{1-k}\right)\right] \\
b_1 &= -\lambda x_1\left(\frac{1}{k} - \frac{1}{2k^2}\lg\frac{1+k}{1-k}\right)\left(b_0 + \frac{b_1}{k}\right)
\end{aligned}\right\} \tag{138}$$

In order to make these equations simultaneous it is necessary that the determinant of the system of Eqs. (138) shall equal zero. This condition leads to

$$\frac{\lambda}{2k}\left(1 + x_1\frac{1-\lambda}{k^2}\right)\lg\frac{1+k}{1-k} - \lambda x_1\frac{1-\lambda}{k^2} = 1 \tag{139}$$

which defines the required k; after this, we find the ratio b_1/b_0 by employing Eqs. (138).

TABLE 3.12. λ VALUES DEPENDING ON k AND x; THE CASE OF THE SCATTERING INDICATRIX $x(\gamma) = 1 + x_1 \cos \gamma$

x_1 \ k	0.2	0.3	0.4	0.5	0.6	0.7	0.8	0.9	0.95
0	0.99	0.97	0.94	0.91	0.87	0.81	0.73	0.61	0.52
0.2	0.99	0.97	0.94	0.90	0.86	0.79	0.71	0.59	0,49
0.4	0.98	0.96	0.94	0.90	0.85	0.78	0.69	0.56	0.47
0.6	0.98	0.96	0.93	0.89	0.83	0.76	0.67	0.54	0,44
0.8	0.98	0.96	0.92	0.88	0.82	0.75	0.65	0.52	0.41
1.0	0.98	0.96	0.92	0.87	0.81	0.73	0.63	0.49	0.39

Tables 3.12 and 3.13 contain the results of computations with Eq. (129) and for the adopted scattering indicatrix values of λ and b_1/b_0 as functions of x_1 and k.

TABLE 3.13. b_1/b_0 VALUES DEPENDING ON k AND x; THE CASE OF THE SCATTERING INDICATRIX $x(\gamma) = 1 + x_1 \cos \gamma$

k x_1	0.2	0.3	0.4	0.5	0.6	0.7	0.8	0.9	0.95
0	0	0	0	0	0	0	0	0	0
0.2	0.02	0.02	0.03	0.04	0.05	0.06	0.07	0.09	0.10
0.4	0.03	0.05	0.06	0.08	0.10	0.13	0.15	0.20	0.22
0.6	0.06	0.08	0.11	0.14	0.17	0.21	0.25	0.31	0.35
0.8	0.09	0.10	0.15	0.20	0.23	0.29	0.35	0.44	0.49
1.0	0.10	0.13	0.21	0.26	0.31	0.38	0.46	0.56	0.63

In the above-considered case the radiation intensity is expressed in the form

$$I(\tau, \eta) = \frac{b_0 + b_1 \eta}{1 - k\eta} e^{-k\tau} \tag{140}$$

It follows, in particular, that the ratio of the intensity of the rising radiation, with $\eta = -1$, to that of the descending radiation, with $\eta = 1$, is

$$\frac{I(\tau, -1)}{I(\tau, +1)} = \frac{b_0 - b_1}{b_0 + b_1} \cdot \frac{1 - k}{1 + k} \tag{141}$$

Tables 3.12 and 3.13 permit us to evaluate this ratio. For example, with $x_1 = 0.6$ and $\lambda = 0.93$, Table 3.12 delivers $k = 0.4$; further, Table 3.13 provides $b_1/b_0 = 0.11$. Hence, $I(\tau, -1)/I(\tau, +1) = 0.35$.

Analogously, we can solve Eq. (129) for more complicated scattering indicatrices. However, if the number of terms in the Legendre polynomial expansion of the scattering indicatrix is great, the computations become rather cumbersome. Therefore, earlier another method was proposed[7] which manipulates Eq. (129) much more quickly. At the same time tables of auxiliary quantities were given for the solution of Eq. (129) and also the results of solution for a scattering indicatrix of the form:

$$x(\gamma) = C(1 \pm \cos \gamma)^n \tag{142}$$

and for different values of the parameter η.

[7] V. V. Sobolev, On the March of Light in Deep Layers of a Turbid Medium, *Izv. AN SSSR, series geogr.-geophys.* **8**, No. 5 (1944).

7. Diffuse Reflection and Transmission of Light in a Medium of Infinitely Large Optical Thickness

In Section 4 of this chapter we obtained the results which permit us to find the brightness coefficient of a plane layer of any optical thickness. But the solution of Eqs. (79) and (80), which define auxiliary functions, becomes difficult for large values of τ_0. Yet, in practice, we meet these cases very often. That is why it is interesting that one can obtain simple asymptotic formulas of the reflection and transmission coefficients for large values of τ_0 and that the solutions are the more accurate the larger is τ_0.

To derive the above-mentioned formulas we shall avail ourselves of the fact that the light pattern in the deep layers of the medium is known to us.

The integral equation defining the function $B(\tau, \zeta)$ we can rewrite, for the case of large optical thickness, in the form

$$B(\tau, \zeta) = \frac{\lambda}{2} \int_0^{\tau_0} B(t, \zeta) \mathrm{Ei}|\tau - t|\, dt + \frac{\lambda}{2} \int_{\tau_0}^{\infty} B(t, \zeta) \mathrm{Ei}(t - \tau)\, dt + \frac{\lambda}{4} e^{-\tau/\zeta} \tag{143}$$

Here we have assumed that $S = 1$ and $0 \leqslant \tau \leqslant \tau_0$. The second integral of this equation can be again rewritten as

$$\int_{\tau_0}^{\infty} B(t, \zeta) \mathrm{Ei}(t - \tau)\, dt = \int_{\tau_0}^{\infty} B(t, \zeta)\, dt \int_0^1 e^{-(t-\tau)/\eta} \frac{d\eta}{\eta}$$

$$= \int_0^1 e^{-(\tau_0 - \tau)/\eta}\, d\eta \int_{\tau_0}^{\infty} B(t, \zeta) e^{-(t-\tau_0)/\eta} \frac{dt}{\eta}$$

$$= \int_0^1 e^{-(\tau_0 - \tau)/\eta} I(\tau_0, -\eta, \zeta)\, d\eta \tag{144}$$

where $I(\tau_0, -\eta, \zeta)$ is radiation intensity passing upward at the optical depth τ_0 at an angle $\arccos(-\eta)$ to the internal normal.

Keeping in mind Eq. (144) and comparing Eq. (143) with Eq. (85), which defines the function $B(\tau, \zeta, \tau_0)$ for a medium with finite optical thickness τ_0 and $S = 1$, we see that the free term of Eq. (143) is a superposition of the free terms of Eq. (85). Hence,

$$B(\tau, \zeta) = B(\tau, \zeta, \tau_0) + 2 \int_0^1 I(\tau_0, -\eta, \zeta) B(\tau_0 - \tau, \eta, \tau_0)\, d\eta \tag{145}$$

Let us apply Eq. (145) to a case when $\tau_0 \gg 1$. At large optical depth the function $B(\tau, \zeta)$ is given by Eq. (117) and hence

$$I(\tau_0, -\eta, \zeta) = \frac{A}{1 + k\eta} \frac{\phi(\zeta)\zeta}{1 - k\zeta} e^{-k\tau_0} \tag{146}$$

Inserting Eq. (146) into Eq. (145), we obtain

$$B(\tau, \zeta) = B(\tau, \zeta, \tau_0) + 2A\frac{\phi(\zeta)\zeta}{1 - k\zeta}e^{-k\tau_0}\int_0^1 B(\tau_0 - \tau, \zeta', \tau_0)\frac{d\zeta'}{1 + k\zeta'} \quad (147)$$

Denoting the reflection coefficient and the transmission coefficient by $\rho(\eta, \zeta, \tau_0)$ and $\sigma(\eta, \zeta, \tau_0)$, respectively, for a plane layer with optical thickness τ_0, multiplying Eq. (147) by $e^{-(\tau/\eta)}d\tau/\eta$ and integrating with respect to τ in the interval from 0 to τ_0, we find

$$\rho(\eta, \zeta) = \rho(\eta, \zeta, \tau_0) + 2A\frac{\phi(\zeta)}{1 - k\zeta}e^{-k\tau_0}\int_0^1 \sigma(\eta, \zeta', \tau_0)\frac{\zeta' \, d\zeta'}{1 + k\zeta'} \quad (148)$$

where $\rho(\eta, \zeta)$ as before, is the reflection coefficient for a plane layer with infinitely large optical thickness, and the term of the order $e^{-[k+(1/\eta)]\tau_0}$ is neglected. Further, multiplying Eq. (147) by $e^{-(\tau_0-\tau)/\eta}d\tau/\eta$, integrating with respect to τ in the interval from 0 to τ, and again using the function $B(\tau, \zeta)$ of Eq. (117), we obtain

$$\frac{A}{1 - k\eta}\frac{\phi(\zeta)}{1 - k\zeta}e^{-k\tau_0} = \sigma(\eta, \zeta, \tau_0)$$
$$+ 2A\frac{\phi(\zeta)}{1 - k\zeta}e^{-k\tau_0}\int_0^1 \rho(\eta, \zeta', \tau_0)\frac{\zeta' \, d\zeta'}{1 + k\zeta'} \quad (149)$$

We observe that the second term on the right side of Eq. (148) is small in comparison with the first one. Therefore, for the first approximation, we can rewrite Eq. (148) as

$$\rho(\eta, \zeta, \tau_0) = \rho(\eta, \zeta) \quad (150)$$

Substituting Eq. (150) into Eq. (149), we have

$$\sigma(\eta, \zeta, \tau_0) = A\frac{\phi(\zeta)}{1 - k\zeta}e^{-k\tau_0}\left[\frac{1}{1 - k\eta} - 2\int_0^1 \rho(\eta, \zeta')\frac{\zeta' \, d\zeta'}{1 + k\zeta'}\right] \quad (151)$$

Remembering the quantity $\rho(\eta, \zeta)$ in Eq. (35) and the quantity $\phi(\eta)$ in Eq. (36), we easily can rewrite this relation:

$$\sigma(\eta, \zeta, \tau_0) = A\frac{\phi(\eta)}{1 - k\eta}\frac{\phi(\zeta)}{1 - k\zeta}e^{-k\tau_0}\left[1 - \frac{\lambda}{2}\int_0^1 \frac{\phi(\zeta')}{1 + k\zeta'} \, d\zeta'\right] \quad (152)$$

Inserting Eq. (152) into Eq. (148), we obtain an expression for $\rho(\eta, \zeta, \tau_0)$ as a second approximation:

$$\rho(\eta, \zeta, \tau_0) = \rho(\eta, \zeta) - 2A^2\frac{\phi(\eta)}{1 - k\eta}\frac{\phi(\zeta)}{1 - k\zeta}e^{-2k\tau_0}$$
$$\times\left[1 - \frac{\lambda}{2}\int_0^1 \frac{\phi(\zeta')}{1 + k\zeta'} \, d\zeta'\right]\int_0^1 \frac{\phi(\zeta')}{1 - k^2\zeta'^2}\zeta' \, d\zeta' \quad (153)$$

Equations (152) and (153) represent the required asymptotic expressions for the brightness coefficients $\rho(\eta, \zeta, \tau_0)$ and $\sigma(\eta, \zeta, \tau_0)$ and for large optical thickness. We remind ourselves here that the quantity A of these formulas is defined by Eq. (123).

A special interest attaches to the case of pure scattering: $\lambda = 1$ and $k = 0$. Since in this case it is true that

$$\int_0^1 \phi(\zeta) \, d\zeta = 2$$

from Eq. (152) we obtain $\sigma(\eta, \zeta, \tau_0) = 0$. This means that in finding $\sigma(\eta, \zeta, \tau_0)$, we should take into consideration not only the first term but also the second one.

For $\lambda = 1$, Eqs. (148) and (149) become

$$\rho(\eta, \zeta, \tau_0) = \rho(\eta, \zeta) - 2A\phi(\zeta) \int_0^1 \sigma(\eta, \zeta', \tau_0)\zeta' \, d\zeta' \tag{154}$$

$$\sigma(\eta, \zeta, \tau_0) = A\phi(\zeta)[1 - 2\int_0^1 \rho(\eta, \zeta', \tau_0)\zeta' \, d\zeta'] \tag{155}$$

Inserting Eq. (154) into Eq. (155), we derive

$$\sigma(\eta, \zeta, \tau_0) = 2A\phi(\zeta) \int_0^1 \sigma(\eta, \zeta', \tau_0)\zeta' \, d\zeta' \tag{156}$$

But the quantities $\rho(\eta, \zeta, \tau_0)$ and $\sigma(\eta, \zeta, \tau_0)$ must be symmetrical functions of η and ζ; consequently, it must be that

$$\rho(\eta, \zeta, \tau_0) = \rho(\eta, \zeta) - 2A\phi(\zeta)\phi(\eta)f(\tau_0) \tag{157}$$

$$\sigma(\eta, \zeta, \tau_0) = 2A\phi(\zeta)\phi(\eta)f(\tau_0) \tag{158}$$

where $f(\tau_0)$ is a function of τ_0, as yet unknown.

In finding $f(\tau_0)$, we employ the following artificial method. It is easy to show that

$$\int_0^{\tau_0} \text{Ei}|\tau - t| t \, dt = 2\tau + \int_0^1 e^{-\tau/\zeta}\zeta \, d\zeta - \int_0^1 e^{-(\tau_0-\tau)/\zeta}(\tau_0 + \zeta) \, d\zeta \tag{159}$$

This means that the solution of the following integral equation

$$B(\tau) = \tfrac{1}{2}\int_0^{\tau_0} \text{Ei}|\tau - t| B(t) \, dt - \tfrac{1}{2} \int_0^1 e^{-\tau/\zeta}\zeta \, d\zeta$$

$$+ \tfrac{1}{2} \int_0^1 e^{-(\tau_0-\tau)/\zeta}(\tau_0 + \zeta) \, d\zeta \tag{160}$$

will be $B(\tau) = \tau$.

Comparing Eq. (160) with the equation which defines the function $B(\tau, \zeta, \tau_0)$:

$$B(\tau, \zeta, \tau_0) = \tfrac{1}{2} \int_0^{\tau_0} \text{Ei}|\tau - t| B(t, \zeta, \tau_0) \, dt + \tfrac{1}{4} e^{-\tau/\zeta} \qquad (161)$$

and knowing that the free term of Eq. (160) is a superposition of the free terms of Eq. (161), we find

$$\tau = -2 \int_0^1 B(\tau, \zeta, \tau_0) \zeta \, d\zeta + 2 \int_0^1 B(\tau_0 - \tau, \zeta, \tau_0)(\tau_0 + \zeta) \, d\zeta \qquad (162)$$

Putting $\tau = 0$ into Eq. (162), we derive

$$\int_0^1 B(0, \zeta, \tau_0) \zeta \, d\zeta = \int_0^1 B(\tau_0, \zeta, \tau_0)(\tau_0 + \zeta) \, d\zeta \qquad (163)$$

This is the required equation for computing the function $f(\tau_0)$ because the quantities $B(0, \zeta, \tau_0)$ and $B(\tau_0, \zeta, \tau_0)$ can easily be expressed by means of this function.

Integrating Eq. (158) with respect to ζ and in the interval, 0, 1, and remembering Eq. (78) without the term $e^{-\tau_0/\zeta}$ and Eq. (97), we find

$$B(\tau_0, \eta, \tau_0) = 2A\phi(\eta)\eta f(\tau_0) \qquad (164)$$

Further, with Eq. (147) and for $\tau = 0$, we derive

$$B(0, \zeta, \tau_0) = B(0, \zeta) - 2A\phi(\zeta)\zeta \int_0^1 B(\tau_0, \zeta', \tau_0) \, d\zeta' \qquad (165)$$

A substitution of Eq. (164) into Eq. (165) gives

$$B(0, \zeta, \tau_0) = B(0, \zeta) - 2A\phi(\zeta)\zeta f(\tau_0) \qquad (166)$$

where Eq. (123) was employed, which defines A.

Using again Eqs. (164) and (166), we obtain from Eq. (163):

$$2Af(\tau_0) = \frac{\displaystyle\int_0^1 B(0, \zeta) \, d\zeta}{\displaystyle 2\int_0^1 \phi(\zeta)\zeta^2 \, d\zeta + \tau_0 \int_0^1 \phi(\zeta) \, \zeta \, d\zeta} \qquad (167)$$

or since $B(0, \zeta) = \tfrac{1}{4}\phi(\zeta)$,

$$2Af(\rho_0) = \frac{1}{4} \frac{1}{\tau_0 + \gamma} \qquad (168)$$

where we have introduced

$$\gamma = 2\frac{\displaystyle\int_0^1 \phi(\zeta)\zeta^2 \, d\zeta}{\displaystyle\int_0^1 \phi(\zeta)\zeta \, d\zeta} \tag{169}$$

Hence, $\gamma = 1.42$.

Finally, inserting Eq. (168) into Eqs. (157) and (158), we derive the following expressions for determination of the reflection and transmission coefficient in the case of the pure scattering:

$$\rho(\eta, \zeta, \tau_0) = \rho(\eta, \zeta) - \frac{1}{4}\frac{\phi(\eta)\phi(\zeta)}{\tau_0 + \gamma} \tag{170}$$

$$\sigma(\eta, \zeta, \tau_0) = \frac{1}{4}\frac{\phi(\eta)\phi(\zeta)}{\tau_0 + \gamma} \tag{171}$$

These formulas are the more accurate the greater is τ_0, as has been stated before.

8. DIRECTIONAL DISTRIBUTION OF DIFFUSELY-TRANSMITTED RADIATION

Previously we have derived formulas for radiation intensities, diffusely transmitted by a medium of a large optical thickness and for the spherical scattering indicatrix. Analogously, we can find formulas corresponding to any other form of the scattering indicatrix. But the process is complicated. If, however, we are interested only in the relative angular distribution of the diffusely transmitted radiation, the process is much more simple.[8]

Equation (152) shows that the relative angular distribution of the diffusely transmitted radiation does not depend on the optical depth, nor on the direction of the descending radiation. This is obviously true for any form of the scattering indicatrix, not only for a spherical one. Moreover, for any form of the scattering indicatrix, the intensity of radiation diffusely transmitted by a medium with large optical depth does not depend on the azimuth (Sec. 6). We denote this intensity by $I(\eta)$ and we shall find it with an accuracy of a constant factor.

The quantity $I(\eta)$ can be very simply found by the method of addition of layers with a small optical thickness $\Delta\tau$, discussed in detail in Section 2.

[8] V. A. Ambartsumian, Light Diffusion in a Scattering Medium of a Large Optical Thickness, *DAN SSSR* **43**, No. 3 (1944).

Adding a layer of thickness $\Delta\tau$ to the lower boundary of the medium, we find that the intensity of radiation passing the new boundary will be equal to $I(\eta)(1-k\Delta\tau)$, where k is a constant. On the other hand, the same intensity can be found by taking into account all changes caused by the additional layer.

First of all, the layer weakens the radiation in a given direction. Correspondingly, the radiation intensity will be

$$I(\eta)\left(1-\frac{\Delta\tau}{\eta}\right)$$

Further, the layer scatters the radiation coming from the old boundary in the same direction. The intensity of this radiation will be

$$\frac{\lambda}{2\eta}\Delta\tau \int_0^1 I(\eta')p(\eta,\eta')\,d\eta'$$

where the quantity $p(\eta,\eta')$ is defined by Eq. (127).

Finally, the layer scatters the radiation toward the old boundary and this radiation is diffusely reflected from it in the direction η. The intensity of this radiation is

$$\lambda\Delta\tau \int_0^1 f_0(\eta,\eta'')\,d\eta'' \int_0^1 I(\eta')p(-\eta'',\eta')\,d\eta'$$

where $f_0(\eta,\eta'')$ is the brightness coefficient averaged over azimuth and for a layer of infinitely large optical thickness.

Therefore, we obtain

$$I(\eta)(1-k\Delta\tau) = I(\eta)\left(1-\frac{\Delta\tau}{\eta}\right)+\frac{\lambda}{2\eta}\Delta\tau \int_0^1 I(\eta')p(\eta,\eta')\,d\eta'$$

$$+\lambda\Delta\tau \int_0^1 f_0(\eta,\eta'')\,d\eta'' \int_0^1 I(\eta')p(-\eta'',\eta')\,d\eta' \qquad (172)$$

Hence

$$I(\eta)(1-k\eta) = \frac{\lambda}{2} \int_0^1 I(\eta')p(\eta,\eta')\,d\eta'$$

$$+\lambda\eta \int_0^1 f_0(\eta,\eta'')\,d\eta'' \int_0^1 I(\eta')p(-\eta'',\eta')\,d\eta' \qquad (173)$$

Equation (173) can be rewritten as

$$I(\eta)(1-k\eta) = \frac{\lambda}{2} \int_0^1 K(\eta,\eta')I(\eta')\,d\eta' \qquad (174)$$

where

$$K(\eta, \eta') = p(\eta, \eta') + 2\eta \int_0^1 f_0(\eta, \eta'') p(-\eta'', \eta') \, d\eta'' \qquad (175)$$

The latter expression can be greatly simplified, first by inserting Eq. (134) into Eq. (175):

$$K(\eta, \eta') = \sum_{i=0}^n x_i P_i(\eta')[P_i(\eta) + 2(-1)^i \eta \int_0^1 f_0(\eta, \eta'') P_i(\eta'') \, d\eta''] \qquad (176)$$

and, second, by concluding from Eq. (47) that

$$\phi_i^0(\eta) = P_i(\eta) + 2(-1)^i \eta \int_0^1 f_0(\eta, \eta'') P_i(\eta'') \, d\eta'' \qquad (177)$$

$$K(\eta, \eta') = \sum_{i=0}^n x_i P_i(\eta') \phi_i^0(\eta) \qquad (178)$$

Inserting Eq. (178) into Eq. (174), we find

$$I(\eta) = \frac{\lambda}{2} \sum_{i=0}^n \frac{x_i c_i \phi_i^0(\eta)}{1 - k\eta} \qquad (179)$$

where

$$c_i = \int_0^1 I(\eta) P_i(\eta) \, d\eta \qquad (180)$$

In order to find constant c_i, we multiply Eq. (171) by $P_j(\eta)$ and integrate with respect to η in the interval 0,1; the result is

$$c_j = \frac{\lambda}{2} \sum_{i=0}^n a_{ij} x_i c_i \qquad (181)$$

where

$$a_{ij} = \int_0^1 \frac{\phi_i^0(\eta) P_j(\eta) \, d\eta}{1 - k\eta} \qquad (182)$$

The constants c_i can therefore be found from the system of algebraic Eqs. (181) of the first degree. The value of k is found from the conditions of solving this system.

Equation (179) provides the final solution of the problem. We see that the intensity of the diffusely transmitted radiation by a layer of infinitely large optical thickness is rendered by the same functions $\phi_i^0(\eta)$ which were derived earlier in the problem of the diffuse reflection of light.

Consider the two simplest cases of Eq. (179) as an example.

For the spherical scattering indicatrix, we obtain from Eq. (179):

$$I(\eta) = C \frac{\phi_0^0(\eta)}{1 - k\eta} \qquad (183)$$

where $C = (\lambda/2)c_0$, and Eqs. (181) and (182) give the following equation for computing k:

$$1 = \frac{\lambda}{2} \int_0^1 \frac{\phi_0{}^0(\eta)}{1 - k\eta} \, d\eta \qquad (184)$$

As has been shown in Section 5 of this chapter, Eq. (184) can be transformed into the form of Eq. (116). In other words, Eq. (183) is found in accordance with Eq. (152).

For a scattering indicatrix of the form $x(\gamma) = 1 + x_1 \cos \gamma$, Eq. (179) gives

$$I(\eta) = \frac{\lambda}{2} \frac{c_0\phi_0{}^0(\eta) + x_1 c_1 \phi_1{}^0(\eta)}{1 - k\eta} \qquad (185)$$

but from Eqs. (181) and (182) we find

$$c_0 = c_0\frac{\lambda}{2} \int_0^1 \frac{\phi_0{}^0(\eta)}{1 - k\eta} \, d\eta + c_1\frac{\lambda}{2}x_1 \int_0^1 \frac{\phi_1{}^0(\eta)}{1 - k\eta} \, d\eta \qquad (186)$$

$$c_1 = c_0\frac{\lambda}{2} \int_0^1 \frac{\phi_0{}^0(\eta)}{1 - k\eta}\eta \, d\eta + c_1\frac{\lambda}{2}x_1 \int_0^1 \frac{\phi_1{}^0(\eta)}{1 - k\eta}\eta \, d\eta \qquad (187)$$

which serve for determination of c_1/c_0 and k.

Assuming that there is pure scattering, $\lambda = 1$, and remembering Section 2 where we have shown that the function $\phi_0{}^0(\eta)$ is the same for all values of x_1, and is equal to $\phi_0{}^0(\eta)$ for the spherical indicatrix, but $\phi_1{}^0(\eta) = 0$, and $k = 0$, for $\lambda = 1$, we obtain

$$I(\eta) = C\phi_0{}^0(\eta) \qquad (188)$$

Thus, for the case of pure scattering, the intensity of the radiation diffusely transmitted by a medium with very large optical thickness is the same for all indicatrices of the form $x(\gamma) = 1 + x_1 \cos \gamma$ and is defined by Eq. (188).

This result is important for the problem of brightness distribution over the cloudy sky. As a first approximation we replace the real indicatrix by an indicatrix of the form $x = 1 + x_1 \cos \gamma$, for example, we neglect higher terms of the Legendre polynomials in the expansion. Assuming, then, that the clouds produce pure scattering, we find that the brightness distribution over an overcast sky will be represented by Eq. (188). According to this formula, the ratio of the brightness at the zenith to that at the horizon is equal to 2.9, which value agrees well with the observations.

With this we conclude our investigation of the theory of Ambartsumian. Chandrasekhar developed this theory by employing the invariance principle.

chapter 4

THE LINEAR INTEGRAL EQUATIONS FOR BRIGHTNESS COEFFICIENTS

We stated previously that one of the most important problems in theory of light scattering is the determination of intensities of radiation diffusely reflected and transmitted by a plane layer. In Chapter 3 we discussed methods which permit us to determine these intensities, or the corresponding brightness coefficients, without the knowledge of the function B. It was also possible to clarify the structure of brightness coefficients, or to express these functions of several arguments by means of auxiliary functions which depend on only one argument; the auxiliary functions themselves appear to be functional equations of relatively simple kind.

Now we propose still another method to determine intensities of radiation diffusely reflected and transmitted by a plane layer. This method consists of derivation of linear integral equations which determine brightness coefficients directly. These equations may easily be obtained from the equation of radiative transfer and that of radiative equilibrium.[1-4]

Moreover, we shall show that the auxiliary functions introduced previously also satisfy the linear integral equations. From some point of view these equations have a great advantage over the functional equations derived previously.

The point is that the linear integral equations for brightness coefficients, and for auxiliary functions as well, become very simple in the case of a plane layer with infinitely large optical thickness: they are transformed into equations with a Cauchy-like kernel which have a finite solution.

[1] V. V. Sobolev, On the Brightness Coefficients of a Plane Layer of a Turbid Medium, *DAN SSSR* **6**, No. 5 (1948).

[2] V. V. Sobolev, On the Diffuse Reflection and Transmission of Light by a Plane Layer of the Turbid Medium, *DAN SSSR* **69**, No. 3 (1949).

[3] V. V. Sobolev, On the Problem of the Diffuse Reflection and Transmission of Light, *DAN SSSR* **69**, No. 4 (1949).

[4] V. V. Sobolev, On the Brightness Distribution over the Disk of a Star, *Russian Astronomical J.* **26**, No. 1 (1949).

1. The Integral Equations for the Brightness Coefficients

Consider a plane layer with the optical thickness τ_0, illuminated by parallel rays. Assuming at first that the scattering indicatrix is spherical, we have the equations of radiative transfer and radiative equilibrium as follows:

$$\eta' \frac{dI(\tau, \eta', \zeta)}{d\tau} = B(\tau, \zeta) - I(\tau, \eta', \zeta) \tag{1}$$

$$B(\tau, \zeta) = \frac{\lambda}{2} \int_{-1}^{+1} I(\tau, \eta', \zeta)\, d\eta' + \frac{\lambda}{4} Se^{-\tau/\zeta} \tag{2}$$

where ζ is the cosine of the incident external radiation and η is the cosine of an angle formed by the direction of scattered radiation and that of the internal normal.

Our problem is to find the intensity of diffusely reflected radiation $I(0, -\eta, \zeta)$ and the intensity of diffusely transmitted radiation $I(\tau_0, \eta, \zeta)$. We know that these quantities are connected with the quantity $B(\tau, \zeta)$ and the brightness coefficients $\rho(\eta, \zeta)$ and $\sigma(\eta, \zeta)$ by means of the following relations:

$$S\rho(\eta, \zeta)\zeta = I(0, -\eta, \zeta) = \int_0^{\tau_0} B(\tau, \zeta) e^{-\tau/\eta} \frac{d\tau}{\eta} \tag{3}$$

$$S\sigma(\eta, \zeta)\zeta = I(\tau_0, \eta, \zeta) = \int_0^{\tau_0} B(\tau, \zeta) e^{-(\tau_0-\tau)/\eta} \frac{d\tau}{\eta} \tag{4}$$

To obtain equations for computing brightness coefficients we proceed as follows. We first multiply Eq. (2) by $e^{-\tau/\eta} d\tau/\eta$, then by $e^{-(\tau_0-\tau)/\eta} d\tau/\eta$ and integrate it with respect to τ in an interval, $0, \tau_0$. Recollecting Eqs. (3) and (4), we find

$$S\rho(\eta, \zeta)\zeta = \frac{\lambda}{2} \int_{-1}^{+1} d\eta' \int_0^{\tau_0} I(\tau, \eta', \zeta) e^{-\tau/\eta} \frac{d\tau}{\eta} + \frac{\lambda}{4} S\rho_1(\eta, \zeta)\zeta \tag{5}$$

$$S\sigma(\eta, \zeta)\zeta = \frac{\lambda}{2} \int_{-1}^{+1} d\eta' \int_0^{\tau_0} I(\tau, \eta', \zeta) e^{-(\tau_0-\tau)/\eta} \frac{d\tau}{\eta} + \frac{\lambda}{4} S\sigma_1(\eta, \zeta)\zeta \tag{6}$$

where

$$\rho_1(\eta, \zeta) = \frac{\lambda}{4} \frac{1 - e^{-\tau_0[(1/\eta)+(1/\zeta)]}}{\eta + \zeta}, \qquad \sigma_1(\eta, \zeta) = \frac{\lambda}{4} \frac{e^{-\tau_0/\eta} - e^{-\tau_0/\zeta}}{\eta - \zeta} \tag{7}$$

are the brightness coefficients for scattering of the first order.

Using now the equation of radiative transfer we can express the integrals

$$\int_0^{\tau_0} I(\tau, \eta', \zeta) e^{-\tau/\eta} \frac{d\tau}{\eta} \quad \text{and} \quad \int_0^{\tau_0} I(\tau, \eta', \zeta) e^{-(\tau_0-\tau)/\eta} \frac{d\tau}{\eta}$$

by means of the same brightness coefficients $\rho(\eta, \zeta)$ and $\sigma(\eta, \zeta)$. Indeed, multiplying Eq. (1) first by $e^{-\tau/\eta} d\tau/\eta$, then by $e^{-(\tau_0-\tau)/\eta} d\tau/\eta$ and integrating it in respect to τ over the interval, $0, \tau_0$, we have

$$\frac{\eta'}{\eta} I(\tau_0, \eta', \zeta) e^{-\tau_0/\eta} - \frac{\eta'}{\eta} I(0, \eta', \zeta) + \frac{\eta'}{\eta} \int_0^{\tau_0} I(\tau, \eta', \zeta) e^{-\tau/\eta} \frac{d\tau}{\eta}$$

$$= I(0, -\eta, \zeta) - \int_0^{\tau_0} I(\tau, \eta', \zeta) e^{-\tau/\eta} \frac{d\tau}{\eta} \tag{8}$$

$$\frac{\eta'}{\eta} I(\tau_0, \eta', \zeta) - \frac{\eta'}{\eta} I(0, \eta', \zeta) e^{-\tau_0/\eta} - \frac{\eta'}{\eta} \int_0^{\tau_0} I(\tau, \eta', \zeta) e^{-(\tau_0-\tau)/\eta} \frac{d\tau}{\eta}$$

$$= I(\tau_0, \eta, \zeta) - \int_0^{\tau_0} I(\tau, \eta', \zeta) e^{-(\tau_0-\tau)/\eta} \frac{d\tau}{\eta} \tag{9}$$

or, remembering Eqs. (3) and (4),

$$(\eta + \eta') \int_0^{\tau_0} I(\tau, \eta', \zeta) e^{-\tau/\eta} \frac{d\tau}{\eta}$$

$$= [\eta\rho(\eta, \zeta) + \eta'\rho(-\eta', \zeta) - \eta'\sigma(\eta', \zeta) e^{-\tau_0/\eta}] S\zeta \tag{10}$$

$$(\eta - \eta') \int_0^{\tau_0} I(\tau, \eta', \zeta) e^{-(\tau_0-\tau)/\eta} \frac{d\tau}{\eta}$$

$$= [\eta\sigma(\eta, \zeta) - \eta'\sigma(\eta', \zeta) + \eta'\rho(-\eta', \zeta) e^{-\tau_0/\eta}] S\zeta \tag{11}$$

where $\rho(-\eta', \zeta) = 0$ for $\eta' > 0$ and $\sigma(\eta', \zeta) = 0$ for $\eta' < 0$.

Inserting Eq. (10) into Eq. (5) and Eq. (11) into Eq. (6), we obtain

$$\rho(\eta, \zeta)\left(1 - \frac{\lambda}{2}\eta \lg\frac{1+\eta}{1-\eta}\right) = \frac{\lambda}{2} \int_0^1 \frac{\rho(\eta', \zeta)}{\eta' - \eta}\eta' \, d\eta'$$

$$-\frac{\lambda}{2}e^{-\tau_0/\eta} \int_0^1 \frac{\sigma(\eta', \zeta)}{\eta' + \zeta}\eta' \, d\eta' + \rho_1(\eta, \zeta) \tag{12}$$

$$\sigma(\eta, \zeta)\left(1 - \frac{\lambda}{2}\eta \lg\frac{1+\eta}{1-\eta}\right) = \frac{\lambda}{2} \int_0^1 \frac{\sigma(\eta', \zeta)}{\eta' - \eta}\eta' \, d\eta'$$

$$-\frac{\lambda}{2}e^{-\tau_0/\eta} \int_0^1 \frac{\rho(\eta', \zeta)}{\eta' + \zeta}\eta' \, d\eta' + \sigma_1(\eta, \zeta) \tag{13}$$

This is the required system of linear integral equations for $\rho(\eta, \zeta)$ and $\sigma(\eta, \zeta)$.

We emphasize that in Eqs. (12) and (13) only the quantity η is an independent variable while the quantities τ_0 and ζ are only parameters.

Assuming now a nonspherical indicatrix of light scattering by a plane layer, we have instead of Eqs. (1) and (2):

$$\eta' \frac{dI(\tau, \eta', \zeta, \phi - \phi_0)}{d\tau} = B(\tau, \eta', \zeta, \phi - \phi_0) - I(\tau, \eta', \zeta, \phi - \phi_0) \quad (14)$$

$$B(\tau, \eta, \zeta, \phi - \phi_0) = \frac{\lambda}{4\pi} \int_0^{2\pi} d\phi' \int_{-1}^{+1} I(\tau, \eta', \zeta, \phi' - \phi_0) x(\eta, \eta', \phi - \phi') \, d\eta'$$

$$+ \frac{\lambda}{4} Sx(\eta, \zeta, \phi - \phi_0) e^{-\tau/\zeta} \quad (15)$$

Here the quantity $x(\eta, \eta', \phi - \phi')$ denotes an indicatrix $x(\gamma)$ with

$$\cos\gamma = \eta\eta' + \sqrt{(1 - \eta^2)(1 - \eta'^2)} \cos(\phi - \phi') \quad (16)$$

Let us introduce "the generalized brightness coefficients" $F(\eta, \eta', \zeta, \phi - \phi_0)$ and $G(\eta, \eta', \zeta, \phi - \phi_0)$ defined as

$$SF(\eta, \eta', \zeta, \phi - \phi_0)\zeta = \int_0^{\tau_0} B(\tau, -\eta', \zeta, \phi - \phi_0) e^{-\tau/\eta} \frac{d\tau}{\eta} \quad (17)$$

$$SG(\eta, \eta', \zeta, \phi - \phi_0)\zeta = \int_0^{\tau_0} B(\tau, \eta', \zeta, \phi - \phi_0) e^{-(\tau_0 - \tau)/\eta} \frac{d\tau}{\eta} \quad (18)$$

It is obvious that the required coefficients are also defined by the following relations:

$$\left. \begin{array}{l} \rho(\eta, \zeta, \phi - \phi_0) = F(\eta, \eta, \zeta, \phi - \phi_0) \\ \sigma(\eta, \zeta, \phi - \phi_0) = G(\eta, \eta, \zeta, \phi - \phi_0) \end{array} \right\} \quad (19)$$

Proceeding in the same manner as in the case of the spherical indicatrix we derive the following equations for computing F and G:

$$F(\eta'', \eta, \zeta, \phi - \phi_0)$$
$$= \frac{\lambda}{4\pi} \int_0^{2\pi} d\phi' \int_{-1}^{+1} \frac{\eta'' F(\eta'', \eta', \zeta, \phi' - \phi_0) - \eta' F(\eta', \eta', \zeta, \phi' - \phi_0)}{\eta'' - \eta'}$$
$$\times x(\eta, \eta', \phi - \phi') \, d\eta' - \frac{\lambda}{4\pi} e^{-\tau_0/\eta''} \int_0^{2\pi} d\phi' \int_0^1 \frac{\eta'}{\eta'' + \eta'}$$
$$\times \sigma(\eta', \zeta, \phi' - \phi_0) x(\eta, -\eta', \phi - \phi') \, d\eta'$$
$$+ x(-\eta, \zeta, \phi - \phi_0) \rho_1(\eta'', \zeta) \quad (20)$$

$$G(\eta'', \eta, \zeta, \phi - \phi_0)$$

$$= \frac{\lambda}{4\pi} \int_0^{2\pi} d\phi' \int_{-1}^{+1} \frac{\eta'' G(\eta'', \eta', \zeta, \phi' - \phi_0) - \eta' G(\eta', \eta', \zeta, \phi' - \phi_0)}{\eta'' - \eta'}$$

$$\times x(\eta, \eta', \phi - \phi') \, d\eta' - \frac{\lambda}{4\pi} e^{-\tau_0/\eta''} \int_0^{2\pi} d\phi' \int_0^1 \frac{\eta'}{\eta'' + \eta'}$$

$$\times \rho(\eta', \zeta, \phi' - \phi_0) x(\eta, -\eta', \phi - \phi') \, d\eta'$$

$$+ x(\eta, \zeta, \phi - \phi_0) \sigma_1(\eta'', \zeta) \tag{21}$$

where $F(\eta', \eta', \zeta, \phi' - \phi_0) = 0$ and $G(\eta', \eta', \zeta, \phi' - \phi_0) = 0$ for $\eta' < 0$.

As before, we now assume that the indicatrix is expanded in series with Legendre polynomials:

$$x(\gamma) = \sum_{i=0}^{n} x_i P_i(\cos \gamma) \tag{22}$$

In such a case, we have

$$x(\eta, \eta', \phi - \phi') = \sum_{m=0}^{n} \cos m(\phi - \phi') \sum_{i=m}^{n} c_{im} P_i^m(\eta) P_i^m(\eta') \tag{23}$$

where

$$c_{i0} = x_i, \qquad c_{im} = 2x_i \frac{(i-m)!}{(i+m)!} \tag{24}$$

We wish now to find expressions for F and G in the form:

$$\left. \begin{aligned} F(\eta'', \eta, \zeta, \phi - \phi_0) &= \sum_{m=0}^{n} \cos m(\phi - \phi_0) \sum_{i=m}^{n} u_i^m(\eta'', \zeta) P_i^m(\eta) \\ G(\eta'', \eta, \zeta, \phi - \phi_0) &= \sum_{m=0}^{n} \cos m(\phi - \phi_0) \sum_{i=m}^{n} v_i^m(\eta'', \zeta) P_i^m(\eta) \end{aligned} \right\} \tag{25}$$

where $u_i^m(\eta, \zeta)$ and $v_i^m(\eta, \zeta)$ are functions not yet defined.

Inserting Eqs. (23) and (25) in Eqs. (20) and (21), respectively, we find

$$u_i^m(\eta, \zeta) = \frac{\lambda}{2} x_i \frac{(i-m)!}{(i+m)!}$$

$$\times \sum_{j=m}^{n} \left[\int_{-1}^{+1} \frac{\eta u_j^m(\eta, \zeta) - \eta' u_j^m(\eta', \zeta)}{\eta - \eta'} P_i^m(\eta') P_j^m(\eta') \, d\eta' \right.$$

$$\left. - e^{-\tau_0/\eta} \int_0^1 \frac{\eta'}{\eta + \eta'} v_j^m(\eta', \zeta) P_i^m(-\eta') P_j^m(\eta') d\eta' \right]$$

$$+ c_{im} P_i^m(-\zeta) \rho_1(\eta, \zeta) \tag{26}$$

$$v_i{}^m(\eta, \zeta) = \frac{\lambda}{2} x_i \frac{(i-m)!}{(i+m)!}$$

$$\times \sum_{j=m}^{n} \left[\int_{-1}^{+1} \frac{\eta\, v_j{}^m(\eta, \zeta) - \eta'\, v_j{}^m(\eta', \zeta)}{\eta - \eta'} P_i{}^m(\eta') P_j{}^m(\eta')\, d\eta' \right.$$

$$\left. - e^{-\tau_0/\eta} \int_0^1 \frac{\eta'}{\eta + \eta'} u_j{}^m(\eta', \zeta) P_i{}^m(-\eta') P_j{}^m(\eta')\, d\eta' \right]$$

$$+ c_{im} P_i{}^m(\zeta)\sigma_1(\eta, \zeta) \tag{27}$$

In other words, for each m we have a separate system of linear integral equations which determine $u_i{}^m(\eta, \zeta)$ and $v_i{}^m(\eta, \zeta)$.

According to Eqs. (19) and (25), the brightness coefficients may be expressed by means of the functions $u_i{}^m(\eta, \zeta)$ and $v_i{}^m(\eta, \zeta)$, as follows:

$$\rho(\eta, \zeta, \phi - \phi_0) = \sum_{m=0}^{n} \rho_m(\eta, \zeta) \cos m(\phi - \phi_0) \tag{28a}$$

$$\sigma(\eta, \zeta, \phi - \phi_0) = \sum_{m=0}^{n} \sigma_m(\eta, \zeta) \cos m(\phi - \phi_0) \tag{28b}$$

where

$$\rho_m(\eta, \zeta) = \sum_{i=m}^{n} u_i{}^m(\eta, \zeta) P_i{}^m(\eta) \tag{29a}$$

$$\sigma_m(\eta, \zeta) = \sum_{i=m}^{n} v_i{}^m(\eta, \zeta) P_i{}^m(\eta) \tag{29b}$$

It is easy to find equations which define directly the quantities $\rho_m(\eta, \zeta)$ and $\sigma_m(\eta, \zeta)$. For this we transform Eqs. (26) and (27) into

$$u_i{}^m(\eta, \zeta) = \frac{\lambda}{2} x_i \frac{(i-m)!}{(i+m)!} \left[\int_{-1}^{+1} \frac{\eta\rho_m(\eta, \zeta) - \eta'\rho_m(\eta', \zeta)}{\eta - \eta'} P_i{}^m(\eta') d\eta' \right.$$

$$- \sum_{j=m}^{n} u_j{}^m(\eta, \zeta) \int_{-1}^{+1} \frac{P_j{}^m(\eta) - P_j{}^m(\eta')}{\eta - \eta'} P_i{}^m(\eta')\, d\eta'$$

$$\left. - e^{-\tau_0/\eta} \int_0^1 \frac{\eta'}{\eta + \eta'} \sigma_m(\eta', \zeta) P_i{}^m(-\eta')\, d\eta' \right]$$

$$+ c_{im} P_i{}^m(-\zeta)\rho_1(\eta, \zeta) \tag{30}$$

$$v_i{}^m(\eta, \zeta) = \frac{\lambda}{2} x_i \frac{(i-m)!}{(i+m)!} \left[\int_{-1}^{+1} \frac{\eta\sigma_m(\eta, \zeta) - \eta'\sigma_m(\eta', \zeta)}{\eta - \eta'} P_i{}^m(\eta')\, d\eta' \right.$$

$$- \sum_{j=m}^{n} v_j{}^m(\eta, \zeta) \int_{-1}^{+1} \frac{P_j{}^m(\eta) - P_j{}^m(\eta')}{\eta - \eta'} P_i{}^m(\eta')\, d\eta'$$

$$\left. - e^{-\tau_0/\eta} \int_0^1 \frac{\eta'}{\eta + \eta'} \rho_m(\eta', \zeta) P_i{}^m(-\eta')\, d\eta' \right]$$

$$+ c_{im} P_i{}^m(\zeta)\sigma_1(\eta, \zeta) \tag{31}$$

These equations may be considered as systems of linear algebraic equations of the functions $u_i{}^m(\eta, \zeta)$ and $v_i{}^m(\eta, \zeta)$. By finding these functions from Eqs. (30) and (31) and inserting them into Eq. (29) we, in reality, obtain for each m two linear integral equations for computing of $\rho_m(\eta, \zeta)$ and $\sigma_m(\eta, \zeta)$. Then, according to Eqs. (28), we express complete brightness coefficients.

Let us make an application of these equations. In the case of a medium with infinitely large optical thickness, we have only to find the functions $u_i{}^m$, because all functions $v_i{}^m$ are equal to zero.

Instead of Eq. (26), we then have

$$u_i{}^m(\eta, \zeta) = \frac{\lambda}{2} x_i \frac{(i-m)!}{(i+m)!} \sum_{j=m}^{n} \int_{-1}^{+1} \frac{\eta u_j{}^m(\eta, \zeta) - \eta' u_j{}^m(\eta', \zeta)}{\eta - \eta'}$$

$$\times P_i{}^m(\eta') P_j{}^m(\eta') \, d\eta' + \frac{\lambda}{4} c_{im} \frac{P_i{}^m(-\zeta)}{\eta + \zeta} \tag{32}$$

This can be rewritten as

$$u_i{}^m(\eta, \zeta) = \frac{\lambda}{2} x_i \frac{(i-m)!}{(i+m)!} \left[\int_{-1}^{+1} \frac{n \rho_m(\eta, \zeta) - \eta' \rho_m(\eta', \zeta)}{\eta - \eta'} P_i{}^m(\eta') \, d\eta' \right.$$

$$\left. - \sum_{j=m}^{n} u_j{}^m(\eta, \zeta) \int_{-1}^{+1} \frac{P_j{}^m(\eta) - P_j{}^m(\eta')}{\eta - \eta'} P_i{}^m(\eta') \, d\eta' \right]$$

$$+ \frac{\lambda}{4} c_{im} \frac{P_i{}^m(-\zeta)}{\eta + \zeta} \tag{33}$$

Now, for a given m we find $u_i{}^m$ from Eq. (33), insert the values of $u_i{}^m$ into Eq. (29a), and have as a result one integral equation for computing $\rho_m(\eta, \zeta)$. After this Eq. (28a) delivers the complete reflection coefficient.

For example, with an indicatrix of the form

$$x(\gamma) = 1 + x_1 \cos \gamma$$

we have

$$\rho(\eta, \zeta, \phi - \phi_0) = \rho_0(\eta, \zeta) + \rho_1(\eta, \zeta) \cos(\phi - \phi_0) \tag{34}$$

$$\rho_0(\eta, \zeta) = u_0{}^0(\eta, \zeta) + u_1{}^0(\eta, \zeta)\eta \tag{35}$$

$$\rho_1(\eta, \zeta) = u_1{}^1(\eta, \zeta)\sqrt{1 - \eta^2} \tag{36}$$

The functions $u_0{}^0(\eta, \zeta)$ and $u_1{}^0(\eta, \zeta)$ are found from the equations:

$$u_0{}^0(\eta, \zeta) = \frac{\lambda}{2} \int_{-1}^{+1} \frac{\eta u_0{}^0(\eta, \zeta) - \eta' u_0{}^0(\eta', \zeta)}{\eta - \eta'} \, d\eta'$$

$$+ \frac{\lambda}{2} \int_{-1}^{+1} \frac{\eta u_1{}^0(\eta, \zeta) - \eta' u_1{}^0(\eta', \zeta)}{\eta - \eta'} \eta' \, d\eta' + \frac{\lambda}{4} \frac{1}{\eta + \zeta} \tag{37}$$

$$u_1{}^0(\eta, \zeta) = \frac{\lambda}{2}x_1 \int_{-1}^{+1} \frac{\eta u_0{}^0(\eta, \zeta) - \eta' u_0{}^0(\eta', \zeta)}{\eta - \eta'}\eta' \, d\eta'$$

$$+ \frac{\lambda}{2}x_1 \int_{-1}^{+1} \frac{\eta u_1{}^0(\eta, \zeta) - \eta' u_1{}^0(\eta', \zeta)}{\eta - \eta'}\eta'^2 \, d\eta' - \frac{\lambda}{4}x_1 \frac{\zeta}{\eta + \zeta} \tag{38}$$

but the function $u_1{}^1(\eta, \zeta)$ is found from

$$u_1{}^1(\eta, \zeta) = \frac{\lambda}{4}x_1 \int_{-1}^{+1} \frac{\eta u_1{}^1(\eta, \zeta) - \eta' u_1{}^1(\eta', \zeta)}{\eta - \eta'}(1 - \eta'^2) \, d\eta'$$

$$+ \frac{\lambda}{4}x_1 \frac{\sqrt{1 - \zeta^2}}{\eta + \zeta} \tag{39}$$

Instead of Eqs. (37) and (38), we can write:

$$u_0{}^0(\eta, \zeta) = \frac{\lambda}{2} \int_{-1}^{+1} \frac{\eta \rho_0(\eta, \zeta) - \eta' \rho_0(\eta', \zeta)}{\eta - \eta'} \, d\eta' - \lambda \eta u_1{}^0(\eta, \zeta) + \frac{\lambda}{4}\frac{1}{\eta + \zeta} \tag{40}$$

$$u_1{}^0(\eta, \zeta) = \frac{\lambda}{2}x_1 \int_{-1}^{+1} \frac{\eta \rho_0(\eta, \zeta) - \eta' \rho_0(\eta', \zeta)}{\eta - \eta'}\eta' \, d\eta' - \frac{\lambda}{4}x_1 \frac{\zeta}{\eta + \zeta} \tag{41}$$

Inserting $u_0{}^0$ and $u_1{}^0$, which are found from Eqs. (40) and (41), into Eq. (35), we obtain

$$\rho_0(\eta, \zeta) = \frac{\lambda}{2} \int_{-1}^{+1} \frac{\eta \rho_0(\eta, \zeta) - \eta' \rho_0(\eta', \zeta)}{\eta - \eta'}[1 + (1 - \lambda) x_1 \eta \eta'] \, d\eta'$$

$$+ \frac{\lambda}{4}\frac{1 - (1 - \lambda) x_1 \eta \zeta}{\eta + \zeta} \tag{42}$$

Obviously, from Eqs. (36) and (39), it follows that

$$\rho_1(\eta, \zeta) = \frac{\lambda}{4}x_1 \int_{-1}^{+1} \frac{\eta \rho_1(\eta, \zeta)\sqrt{1 - \eta'^2} - \eta' \rho_1(\eta', \zeta)\sqrt{1 - \eta^2}}{\eta - \eta'}\sqrt{1 - \eta'^2} \, d\eta'$$

$$+ \frac{\lambda}{4}x_1 \frac{\sqrt{(1 - \eta^2)(1 - \zeta^2)}}{\eta + \zeta} \tag{43}$$

Thus, the problem of diffused reflection of light by a plane layer with infinitely large optical thickness and for the simplest form of the nonspherical indicatrix is reduced to linear integral equations, Eqs. (42) and (43).

We observe that for the case of the spherical indicatrix the coefficient of light reflection by a medium of infinitely large optical thickness is defined by

$$\rho(\eta, \zeta) = \frac{\lambda}{2} \int_{-1}^{+1} \frac{\eta \rho(\eta, \zeta) - \eta' \rho(\eta', \zeta)}{\eta - \eta'} \, d\eta' + \frac{\lambda}{4}\frac{1}{\eta + \zeta} \tag{44}$$

which is derived from Eq. (12) with $\tau_0 = \infty$ or from Eq. (42) with $x_1 = 0$. We remember that in Eq. (42) $\rho_0(\eta', \zeta)$ is equal to zero for $\eta' < 0$.

Comparing now Eqs. (42) and (44), we see that for $\lambda = 1$ they are identical. That means that for the case of pure scattering the reflection coefficient averaged over the azimuth and for the simplest non-spherical indicatrix coincides with the reflection coefficient for the spherical scattering indicatrix. This conclusion was reached earlier while analyzing other equations (see Ch. 3, Sec. 2).

2. The Integral Equations for the Auxiliary Functions

Linear integral equations obtained previously, and serving for computing brightness coefficients, permit us to derive also linear integral equations for auxiliary functions introduced by Ambartsumian.

Consider first the problem of diffused reflection by a medium with infinitely large optical thickness. In this case the brightness coefficient $\rho(\eta, \zeta)$ is given by Eq. (44), which can be rewritten as follows:

$$\rho(\eta, \zeta) a(\eta) = \frac{\lambda}{2} \int_0^1 \frac{\eta'}{\eta' - \eta} \rho(\eta', \zeta) \, d\eta' + \frac{\lambda}{4} \frac{1}{\eta + \zeta} \tag{45}$$

where

$$a(\eta) = 1 - \frac{\lambda}{2} \eta \lg \frac{1 + \eta}{1 - \eta} \tag{46}$$

Replacing now $\rho(\eta, \zeta)$ by a new unknown function $R(\eta, \zeta)$ which is defined by

$$\rho(\eta, \zeta) = \frac{\lambda}{4} \frac{R(\eta, \zeta)}{\eta + \zeta} \tag{47}$$

and putting Eq. (47) into Eq. (45), we obtain the following equation for computing $R(\eta, \zeta)$:

$$R(\eta, \zeta) a(\eta) - \frac{\lambda}{2} \eta \int_0^1 R(\eta', \zeta) \frac{d\eta'}{\eta' - \eta} = \frac{\lambda}{2} \zeta \int_0^1 R(\eta', \zeta) \frac{d\eta'}{\eta' + \zeta} + 1 \tag{48}$$

We see that the function $R(\eta, \zeta)$ may be found as a product of two functions: one depending only on η and another on ζ. Because $\rho(\eta, \zeta)$ is symmetrical, these functions should be similar. We therefore write:

$$R(\eta, \zeta) = \phi(\eta)\phi(\zeta) \tag{49}$$

Inserting Eq. (49) into Eq. (48), we have

$$\phi(\eta) a(\eta) - \frac{\lambda}{2} \eta \int_0^1 \frac{\phi(\eta')}{\eta' - \eta} \, d\eta' = \frac{\lambda}{2} \zeta \int_0^1 \frac{\phi(\eta')}{\eta' + \zeta} \, d\eta' + \frac{1}{\phi(\zeta)} \tag{50}$$

which is satisfied only with two conditions, namely:

$$\phi(\zeta) = 1 + \frac{\lambda}{2}\phi(\zeta)\zeta \int_0^1 \frac{\phi(\eta')}{\eta' + \zeta} \, d\eta' \tag{51}$$

and

$$\phi(\eta)a(\eta) - \frac{\lambda}{2}\eta \int_0^1 \frac{\phi(\eta')}{\eta' - \eta} \, d\eta' = 1 \tag{52}$$

Consequently, if Eq. (49) is a solution of Eq. (48), the function ϕ should satisfy both Eqs. (51) and (52).

It is easily shown that Eq. (52) follows from Eq. (51). In showing this, we multiply Eq. (51) by $1/(\zeta - \eta)$ and integrate it with respect to ζ in the interval from 0 to 1. After some small transformations, we find

$$\int_0^1 \frac{\phi(\zeta)}{\zeta - \eta} \, d\zeta = \int_0^1 \frac{d\zeta}{\zeta - \eta} + \frac{\lambda}{2}\eta \int_0^1 \frac{\phi(\eta')}{\eta + \eta'} \, d\eta' \int_0^1 \frac{\phi(\zeta)}{\zeta - \eta} \, d\zeta$$
$$+ \frac{\lambda}{2} \int_0^1 \frac{\phi(\eta')}{\eta + \eta'}\eta' \, d\eta' \int_0^1 \frac{\phi(\zeta)}{\eta' + \zeta} \, d\zeta \tag{53}$$

Multiplying Eq. (53) by $\phi(\eta)$ and recollecting Eq. (51), we obtain

$$-\phi(\eta)\lg\frac{1+\eta}{1-\eta} - \int_0^1 \frac{\phi(\zeta)}{\zeta - \eta} \, d\zeta + \phi(\eta)\int_0^1 \frac{\phi(\eta')}{\eta + \eta'} \, d\eta' = 0 \tag{54}$$

Multiplying Eq. (54) by $\lambda/2$ and again remembering Eq. (51), we derive Eq. (52).

We may, therefore, draw the following conclusion: the required function $\rho(\eta, \zeta)$ is given by Eqs. (47) and (49), but the function $\phi(\eta)$ by Eq. (51) or (52).

Equations (47), (49), and (51) were derived earlier (Ch. 3, Sec. 2). Now we have derived them by another method; at the same time we have obtained a new equation—linear integral Eq. (52)—which is satisfied by the function $\phi(\eta)$. It goes without saying that, with an assumption that the results of Chapter 3 are known, we might have limited ourselves to the derivation of Eq. (52) from Eq. (51).

Linear integral equations for auxiliary functions can be obtained also for an arbitrary scattering indicatrix. Consider the simplest case of nonspherical indicatrix $x(\gamma) = 1 + x_1 \cos \gamma$. The reflection coefficient is, in this case, represented by Eq. (34) and the quantities $\rho_0(\eta, \zeta)$ and $\rho_1(\eta, \zeta)$ are given by Eqs. (42) and (43).

On the other hand, the quantities ρ_0 and ρ_1 are, according to Section 2, Chapter 3, given by

$$\left.\begin{aligned}
\rho_0(\eta, \zeta) &= \frac{\lambda}{4} \frac{\phi_0{}^0(\eta)\phi_0{}^0(\zeta) - x_1\phi_1{}^0(\eta)\phi_1{}^0(\zeta)}{\eta + \zeta} \\[2ex]
\rho_1(\eta, \zeta) &= \frac{\lambda}{4}x_1 \frac{\phi_1{}^1(\eta)\phi_1{}^1(\zeta)}{\eta + \zeta}
\end{aligned}\right\} \qquad (55)$$

and the auxiliary functions $\phi_0{}^0(\eta)$ and $\phi_1{}^1(\eta)$ are determined by the system of functional equations, Eqs. (53) and (54), of the same chapter.

Proceeding in the same manner as in the case for the spherical scattering indicatrix, we find that the auxiliary functions $\phi_0{}^0$ and $\phi_1{}^1$ should satisfy not only functional equations but also the following linear integral equations:

$$\phi_0{}^0(\eta)\left[1 + \frac{\lambda}{2}\eta \int_{-1}^{+1} \frac{1 + (1-\lambda)x_1\eta\eta'}{\eta' - \eta} d\eta'\right]$$
$$= 1 + \frac{\lambda}{2}\eta \int_0^1 \frac{1 + (1-\lambda)x_1\eta\eta'}{\eta' - \eta}\phi_0{}^0(\eta') \, d\eta' \qquad (56)$$

$$\phi_1{}^0(\eta)\left[1 + \frac{\lambda}{2}\eta \int_{-1}^{+1} \frac{1 + (1-\lambda)x_1\eta\eta'}{\eta' - \eta} d\eta'\right]$$
$$= (1-\lambda)\eta + \frac{\lambda}{2}\eta \int_0^1 \frac{1 + (1-\lambda)x_1\eta\eta'}{\eta' - \eta}\phi_1{}^0(\eta') \, d\eta' \qquad (57)$$

$$\phi_1{}^1(\eta)\left[1 + \frac{\lambda}{4}x_1\eta \int_{-1}^{+1} \frac{1 - \eta'^2}{\eta' - \eta} d\eta'\right]$$
$$= \sqrt{1-\eta^2}\left[1 + \frac{\lambda}{4}x_1\eta \int_0^1 \frac{\sqrt{1-\eta'^2}}{\eta' - \eta}\phi_1{}^1(\eta') \, d\eta'\right] \qquad (58)$$

We may underline the advantages of these linear integral equations over the system of functional equations, Eqs. (53) and (54) of Chapter 3: (1) Each auxiliary function is defined by a separate equation; (2) as will be shown later, the solution of these equations is finite. These advantages remain valid even for the case of infinitely large optical thickness and for any form of scattering indicatrix.

For a medium of finite thickness τ_0 the reflection and transmission coefficients are determined by Eqs. (12) and (13) for the case of the spherical scattering indicatrix. On the other hand, as was demonstrated in Chapter 3, Section 4, these quantities are expressed by

$$\left.\begin{aligned}
\rho(\eta, \zeta) &= \frac{\lambda}{4} \frac{\phi(\eta)\phi(\zeta) - \psi(\eta)\psi(\zeta)}{\eta + \zeta} \\[2ex]
\sigma(\eta, \zeta) &= \frac{\lambda}{4} \frac{\phi(\zeta)\psi(\eta) - \psi(\zeta)\phi(\eta)}{\eta - \zeta}
\end{aligned}\right\} \qquad (59)$$

where the auxiliary functions $\phi(\eta)$ and $\psi(\eta)$ are found from the system of functional equations, Eqs. (79) and (80).

Inserting Eq. (59) into Eqs. (12) and (13), we see that the auxiliary functions ϕ and ψ should also satisfy the following system of linear integral equations:

$$\phi(\eta)a(\eta) = 1 + \frac{\lambda}{2}\eta \int_0^1 \frac{\phi(\eta')}{\eta' - \eta} d\eta' - \frac{\lambda}{2}e^{-\tau_0/\eta}\eta \int_0^1 \frac{\psi(\eta')}{\eta + \eta'} d\eta' \qquad (60)$$

$$\psi(\eta)a(\eta) = e^{-\tau_0/\eta} + \frac{\lambda}{2}\eta \int_0^1 \frac{\psi(\eta')}{\eta' - \eta} d\eta' - \frac{\lambda}{2}e^{-\tau_0/\eta}\eta \int_0^1 \frac{\phi(\eta')}{\eta + \eta'} d\eta' \qquad (61)$$

In this case, however, the linear integral equations do not have the advantage over the functional equations. The system of Eqs. (60) and (61) can be solved numerically. Recently, Busbridge[5] investigated these equations in detail and by means of another method.

3. The Solution of the Integral Equations

We have already seen that for a medium of infinitely large optical thickness the linear integral equations serving for determination of brightness coefficients have kernels of Cauchy type. This circumstance permits us to find accurate expressions for the brightness coefficient because the equations can be solved by means of Carleman's method.[6]

Assuming now an isotropic scattering of light in the medium, we know that the reflection coefficient $\rho(\eta, \zeta)$ is determined by Eq. (45). But for us it is convenient to analyze first not the reflection coefficient but the transmission coefficient; here we replace the transmission coefficient of radiation for a medium of infinitely large optical thickness by the asymptotic approximation of this coefficient for a medium of large optical thickness. Putting $\tau_0 = \infty$ in Eq. (13), we derive the following equation for finding the transmission coefficient in this case:

$$\sigma(\eta)a(\eta) = \frac{\lambda}{2} \int_0^1 \frac{\sigma(\eta')}{\eta' - \eta} \eta' \, d\eta' \qquad (62)$$

where $a(\eta)$ is represented by Eq. (46).

Equation (62) defines the transmission coefficient with an accuracy within a constant factor which depends on τ_0 and ζ; that is why we wrote not $\sigma(\eta, \zeta, \tau_0)$ but simply $\sigma(\eta)$, and why we conclude that this quantity $\sigma(\eta)$ represents only the relative angular distribution of diffusely transmitted radiation. The main point is that if we know

[5] Busbridge, *Astrophysical J.* **122**, No. 2 (1955).
[6] T. Carleman, Arkiv. för Mat., *Astr. och Fysik* **16**, No. 26 (1922).

$\sigma(\eta)$ we easily can find also the auxiliary function $\phi(\eta)$ which enters $\rho(\eta, \zeta)$.

As was shown above, the function $\phi(\eta)$ should satisfy Eq. (52). Using the relation

$$\frac{\lambda}{2} \int_0^1 \phi(\eta) \, d\eta = 1 - \sqrt{1-\lambda} \tag{63}$$

which follows from Eq. (51), we can rewrite Eq. (52):

$$\phi(\eta) a(\eta) = \sqrt{1-\lambda} + \frac{\lambda}{2} \int_0^1 \frac{\phi(\eta')}{\eta' - \eta} \eta' \, d\eta' \tag{64}$$

Comparing Eqs. (62) and (64), we see that the first one corresponds to an equation homogeneous with the second one. This means that the function $\phi(\eta)$ is determined from Eq. (64) only with the accuracy of an arbitrary constant. Therefore, we should bound the function $\phi(\eta)$ with some other conditions, for example, Eq. (63), in order to solve $\phi(\eta)$ completely.

It is easy to convince ourselves that if the function $\sigma(\eta)$ found from Eq. (62) is normalized by

$$\frac{\lambda}{2} \int_0^1 \sigma(\eta) \, d\eta = 1 \tag{65}$$

the function

$$\phi(\eta) = (1 - k\eta) \sigma(\eta) \tag{66}$$

where the constant k is defined by

$$\frac{\lambda}{2} k \int_0^1 \sigma(\eta)\eta \, d\eta = \sqrt{1-\lambda} \tag{67}$$

will satisfy both Eqs. (64) and (63).

After we have found the diffuse light transmission by a medium with infinitely large optical thickness, we can easily find also the diffuse light reflection by the same medium.

As we stated earlier, equations of the type of Eq. (62) are solved by the method of Carleman. The actual solution of Eq. (62) is

$$\sigma(\eta) = \frac{C}{1-\eta} \frac{e^{\omega(\eta)}}{\sqrt{a^2(\eta) + [(\lambda/2)\pi\eta]^2}} \tag{68}$$

where

$$\omega(\eta) = \frac{1}{\pi} \int_0^1 \text{arctg} \frac{(\lambda/2)\pi\eta'}{a(\eta')} \frac{d\eta'}{\eta' - \eta} \tag{69}$$

and C is an arbitrary constant.

Values of the function $\sigma(\eta)$ are given in Table 4.1 for different values of the parameter λ.

TABLE 4.1. TRANSMISSION COEFFICIENT $\sigma(\eta)$ FOR THE SPHERICAL INDICATRIX

λ / η	0.7	0.8	0.9	1.0	λ / η	0.7	0.8	0.9	1.0
0	1.00	1.00	1.00	1.00	0.6	2.68	2.54	2.37	2.19
0.1	1.21	1.23	1.24	1.25	0.7	3.28	2.98	2.67	2.37
0.2	1.42	1.43	1.44	1.45	0.8	4.14	3.55	3.01	2.55
0.3	1.64	1.65	1.65	1.64	0.9	5.58	4.34	3.41	2.73
0.4	1.91	1.90	1.87	1.83	1.0	8.38	5.51	3.90	2.91
0.5	2.25	2.19	2.11	2.01					

Let us consider the transmission coefficient only for the case of the spherical scattering indicatrix.

We know already that the transmission coefficient for infinitely large optical thickness does not depend on the azimuth; we make then $m = 0$ in Eqs. (28) and (29). Because we cannot determine a dependence of σ on τ_0 and ζ, we denote the transmission coefficient by $\sigma(\eta)$. Then we have

$$\sigma(\eta) = \sum_{i=0}^{n} v_i(\eta) P_i(\eta) \tag{70}$$

where $P_i(\eta)$ are Legendre polynomials. Putting $m=0$ and $\tau_0 = \infty$ into Eq. (27), we obtain the following equation for determining the functions $v_i(\eta)$:

$$v_i(\eta) = \frac{\lambda}{2} x_i \sum_{j=0}^{n} \int_{-1}^{+1} \frac{\eta v_j(\eta) - \eta' v_j(\eta')}{\eta - \eta'} P_j(\eta') P_i(\eta') \, d\eta' \tag{71}$$

Equation (71) can be rewritten

$$v_i(\eta) = \frac{\lambda}{2} x_i \int_{-1}^{+1} \frac{\eta \sigma(\eta) - \eta' \sigma(\eta')}{\eta - \eta'} P_i(\eta') \, d\eta' - \frac{\lambda}{2} x_i \eta \sum_{j=i+1}^{n} c_{ij}(\eta) v_j(\eta) \tag{72}$$

where we express $c_{ij}(\eta)$ by a polynomial

$$c_{ij}(\eta) = \int_{-1}^{+1} \frac{P_j(\eta) - P_j(\eta')}{\eta - \eta'} P_i(\eta') \, d\eta' \tag{73}$$

Regarding Eq. (72) as a system of linear algebraic equations of the argument $v_i(\eta)$, we have

$$v_i(\eta) = \frac{\lambda}{2} \sum_{j=i}^{n} x_j L_{ij}(\eta) \int_{-1}^{+1} \frac{\eta \sigma(\eta) - \eta' \sigma(\eta')}{\eta - \eta'} P_j(\eta') \, d\eta' \tag{74}$$

where $L_{ii}(\eta) = 1$, but

$$L_{ij}(\eta) = -\frac{\lambda}{2}x_i\eta \sum_{k=i}^{j-1} L_{ik}(\eta)c_{kj}(\eta) \qquad (j = i+1,...,n) \qquad (75)$$

Inserting Eq. (74) into Eq. (70), we derive

$$\sigma(\eta) = \frac{\lambda}{2} \int_{-1}^{+1} \frac{\eta\sigma(\eta) - \eta'\sigma(\eta')}{\eta - \eta'} A(\eta, \eta') \, d\eta' \qquad (76)$$

where

$$A(\eta, \eta') = \sum_{i=0}^{n} P_i(\eta) \sum_{j=i}^{n} x_j L_{ij}(\eta) P_j(\eta')$$

Interchanging now the order of summation and introducing

$$R_j(\eta) = \sum_{i=0}^{j} P_i(\eta) L_{ij}(\eta) \qquad (77)$$

we obtain

$$A(\eta, \eta') = \sum_{j=0}^{n} x_j R_j(\eta) P_j(\eta') \qquad (78)$$

Using Eq. (75) we can easily show that the function $R_j(\eta)$ satisfies the recurrent relation

$$R_j(\eta) = P_j(\eta) - \frac{\lambda}{2}\eta \sum_{k=0}^{j-1} x_k c_{kj}(\eta) R_k(\eta) \qquad (79)$$

Therefore, the transmission coefficient of radiation in a medium with infinitely large optical thickness is defined by Eq. (76), but the quantities $A(\eta, \eta')$ and $R_j(\eta)$ are defined by Eqs. (78) and (79) for any form of the scattering indicatrix.

In order to solve Eq. (76) by Carleman's method, we rewrite it as follows:

$$\sigma(\eta)a(\eta) = \frac{\lambda}{2} \int_{0}^{1} \frac{\eta'}{\eta' - \eta} A(\eta, \eta')\sigma(\eta') \, d\eta' + f(\eta) \qquad (80)$$

where

$$a(\eta) = 1 + \frac{\lambda}{2}\eta \int_{-1}^{+1} \frac{A(\eta, \eta')}{\eta' - \eta} \, d\eta' \qquad (81)$$

$$f(\eta) = \frac{\lambda}{2} \int_{0}^{1} \frac{A(\eta, \eta') - A(\eta', \eta')}{\eta' - \eta} \sigma(\eta')\eta' \, d\eta' \qquad (82)$$

The solution of Eq. (80) has the form

$$\sigma(\eta) = \frac{a(\eta)f(\eta)}{a^2(\eta) + \left[\frac{\lambda}{2}\pi\eta A(\eta,\eta)\right]^2} + \frac{e^{\omega(\eta)}}{\sqrt{a^2(\eta) + \left[\frac{\lambda}{2}\pi\eta A(\eta,\eta)\right]^2}}$$
$$\times \left\{\frac{\lambda}{2}\int_0^1 \frac{\eta' A(\eta',\eta')f(\eta')e^{-\omega(\eta')}}{\sqrt{a^2(\eta') + \left[\frac{\lambda}{2}\pi\eta' A(\eta',\eta')\right]^2}} \frac{d\eta'}{\eta'-\eta} + \frac{C}{1-\eta}\right\} \quad (83)$$

where

$$\omega(\eta) = \frac{1}{\pi}\int_0^1 \text{arctg}\frac{(\lambda/2)\pi\eta' A(\eta',\eta')}{a(\eta')} \frac{d\eta'}{\eta'-\eta} \quad (84)$$

and C is a constant. Coefficients of the polynomial $f(\eta)$ are found by substituting Eq. (83) into Eq. (82).

Values of $\sigma(\eta)$, for the scattering indicatrix $x(\gamma) = 1 + \cos\gamma$, for different values of the parameter λ, and computed with these formulas, are given in Table 4.2.

TABLE 4.2. TRANSMISSION COEFFICIENT $\sigma(\eta)$ FOR THE SCATTERING
INDICATRIX $x(\gamma) = 1+\cos\gamma$

η \ λ	0.7	0.8	0.9	1.0	η \ λ	0.7	0.8	0.9	1.0
0	1.00	1.00	1.00	1.00	0.6	2.87	2.62	2.39	2.19
0.1	1.24	1.24	1.25	1.25	0.7	3.46	3.04	2.68	2.37
0.2	1.48	1.47	1.46	1.45	0.8	4.24	3.54	2.99	2.55
0.3	1.74	1.71	1.67	1.64	0.9	5.35	4.18	3.34	2.73
0.4	2.05	1.97	1.90	1.83	1.0	7.06	5.01	3.74	2.91
0.5	2.42	2.27	2.14	2.01					

Our results can be applied to the problem of intensity of radiation diffusely transmitted by the clouds. If the optical thickness of the clouds is great, the relative distribution of brightness over the cloudy sky is given by Eq. (83) for any form of the scattering indicatrix and for any value of the parameter λ. In Tables 4.1 and 4.2 we give brightness at various points of the overcast sky as a ratio to the brightness at the horizon and for two simple scattering indicatrices with different values of the parameter λ. We observe that the ratio of the brightness at the zenith to that at the horizon is the greater the larger is the true absorption in the clouds.

The problem of diffuse radiation in a medium with large optical thickness arises also in the problem of radiative transfer in stellar photospheres. Radiation sources are located in the internal layers of the star or at a very great optical depth. The photosphere has neither sources nor reservoirs of energy. Therefore, we can assume that in such a case we have radiation diffusion without a true absorption. The scattering indicatrix is spherical in this case. Consequently, the distribution of integral brightness over the disc of a star is represented by Eq. (68) for $\lambda = 1$. Values of $\sigma(\eta)$ computed for this case are given in the last column of Table 4.1.

CHAPTER 5

THE SCATTERING OF POLARIZED LIGHT

In the previous chapters we have not taken into account polarization of radiation. Yet strictly speaking, we should have considered it, for in general the light becomes polarized as a result of scattering.

General intensity of scattered radiation can be greatly affected by polarization. Moreover—and this is even more important—it is of great interest to find the characteristics of the polarization of scattered radiation. The solution of this problem and successive comparisons of theory with observation provide us with additional possibilities to study physical properties of the scattering medium. In particular it is important for planetary atmospheres and also for the atmospheres of some stars which strikingly exhibit light scattering by free electrons.

In the present chapter we investigate this problem for the case of Rayleigh's law of scattering. First, we derive equations of radiative transfer and those of radiative equilibrium for light polarization. We use these equations to define the general radiation intensity more accurately than before, as well as quantities which characterize light polarization or the degree of light polarization and the position of the polarization plane. Next, we apply the deduced equations to a medium of infinitely large optical thickness and, by it, we determine the march of radiation in deep layers of the medium. Finally, we find intensities of diffusely reflected and diffusely transmitted radiation.

We analyze the problem using our own method.[1] Chandrasekhar analyzed the problem of the scattering of polarized light by means of another method and more thoroughly.[2]

1. THE BASIC EQUATIONS

In the case of polarized light we need to know only one quantity—the radiation intensity—in order to determine the radiation field. In this case the radiation field is characterized by three quantities; they may be arbitrary. We choose them so that all of them have dimensions of the intensity.

[1] V. V. Sobolev, On the Polarization of Scattered Light, *Ich. zap. LGU*, No. 16 (1949).

[2] S. Chandrasekhar, On the Radiative Equilibrium of a Stellar Atmosphere, *Astrophysical J.* **103**, 356 (1946); **104**, 110 (1946); **105**, 164 (1947); and others.

Consider in the plane perpendicular to the ray a rectangular co-ordinate system xOy. Denoting by I_x and I_y components of the radiation intensity along the axis Ox and Oy, by I_β the component of the radiation intensity in the direction of the angle β formed by the axis Ox, and by I_1 and I_2 the maximal and minimal values of I_β corresponding to the angles β_0 and $\beta_0 + \pi/2$, we have

$$I_x = I_1 \cos^2\beta_0 + I_2 \sin^2\beta_0 \tag{1}$$

$$I_y = I_1 \sin^2\beta_0 + I_2 \cos^2\beta_0 \tag{2}$$

$$I_\beta = I_1 \cos^2(\beta - \beta_0) + I_2 \sin^2(\beta - \beta_0) \tag{3}$$

Hence,

$$I_\beta = I_x \cos^2\beta + L \cos\beta \sin\beta + I_y \sin^2\beta, \tag{4}$$

$$L = (I_1 - I_2) \sin 2\beta_0 \tag{5}$$

Thus for any angle β, the quantity I_β is defined by three quantities I_x, I_y, and L. We shall now use these three quantities in the analysis of the radiation field.

It is convenient to introduce the following notation:

$$I_x + I_y = I, \qquad I_x - I_y = K \tag{6}$$

It is obvious that

$$I_1 + I_2 = I, \qquad I_1 - I_2 = \sqrt{K^2 + L^2} \tag{7}$$

In the adopted notations, the quantity I is a general intensity of radiation and the polarization p is

$$p = \frac{I_1 - I_2}{I_1 + I_2} = \frac{\sqrt{K^2 + L^2}}{I} \tag{8}$$

but the polarization plane is defined by Eq. (5). In the future we shall also use the quantities I, K, and L, instead of I_x, I_y, and L.

In order to write equations of radiative transfer for polarization, we introduce in our analysis the absorption and emission coefficients of radiation α and ϵ; also, as usual, we introduce the functions $B = \epsilon/\alpha$. Because the radiation per unit of volume is conditioned by the light scattering in the volume, it will be polarized, generally speaking. Denoting by B_β the component of B in the direction under the angle β formed with the axis Ox, we can, in analogy to Eq. (4), represent B_β in the form

$$B_\beta = B_x \cos^2\beta + D \cos\beta \sin\beta + B_y \sin^2\beta \tag{9}$$

In the future we shall use either the "troika" B_x, B_y, D, or the "troika"

B, C, D to characterize the emitting property of the volume unit and remember that

$$B = B_x + B_y, \qquad C = B_x - B_y \qquad (10)$$

It is apparent that the change of the quantities of I, K, L along the ray is defined by the following equations of transfer:

$$\frac{dI}{\alpha \, ds} = B - I, \qquad \frac{dK}{\alpha \, ds} = C - K, \qquad \frac{dL}{\alpha \, ds} = D - L \qquad (11)$$

which are a generalization of the usual equations of transfer for the case of light polarization.

In order now to write the equation of radiative equilibrium we must have the law of light scattering by elementary volume of the medium. Let us assume that the medium truly absorbs the light and that its scattering follows the law of Rayleigh. We denote the true absorption coefficient by κ, the scattering coefficient by σ, and, as before, write $\lambda = \sigma/\alpha = \sigma/(\kappa + \sigma)$.

As is known, the law of Rayleigh scattering is formulated as follows. Let $I_{\parallel}$ and $I_{\perp}$ be intensities of linearly polarized radiation with electric vectors corresponding to the parallel and perpendicular scattering planes. If the radiation falls on unit volume within the solid angle $d\omega$, the amount of energy scattered by this volume in the direction which forms the angle γ with the incident radiation per unit solid angle is equal to

$$\frac{3}{2}\sigma I_{\parallel} \cos^2\gamma \frac{d\omega}{4\pi} \quad \text{and} \quad \frac{3}{2}\sigma I_{\perp}\frac{d\omega}{4\pi} \qquad (12)$$

where we have assumed that the scattered radiation has the same direction of the electric vector as the incident radiation.

According to the law of Rayleigh we obtain the following equation of radiative equilibrium:

$$B_x \cos^2\beta + D \cos\beta \sin\beta + B_y \sin^2\beta$$

$$= \tfrac{3}{2}\lambda \int \{I_1[\cos(\psi - \beta_0)\cos\gamma\cos(\chi - \beta)$$

$$+ \sin(\psi - \beta_0)\sin(\chi - \beta)]^2 + I_2[\sin(\psi - \beta_0)\cos\gamma\cos(\chi - \beta)$$

$$- \cos(\psi - \beta_0)\sin(\chi - \beta)]^2\}\frac{d\omega}{4\pi} \qquad (13)$$

where ψ is the angle between the scattering plane and the axis Ox for the incident ray, and χ is that between the same plane and the same axis Ox for the scattered ray (Fig. 5.1).

Combining Eqs. (1), (2), and (5), we have, instead of Eq. (13),

$$B_x \cos^2\beta + D \cos\beta \sin\beta + B_y \sin^2\beta$$

$$= \tfrac{3}{2}\lambda \int \{[I_x \cos^2\psi + L \cos\psi \sin\psi + I_y \sin^2\psi] \cos^2\gamma \cos^2(\chi-\beta)$$

$$+ [I_x \sin^2\psi - L \cos\psi \sin\psi + I_y \cos^2\psi] \sin^2(\chi-\beta)$$

$$+ [(I_x - I_y) \sin 2\psi - L \cos 2\psi] \cos\gamma \cos(\chi-\beta)\sin(\chi-\beta)\}\frac{d\omega}{4\pi} \qquad (14)$$

Hence,

$$B_x = \tfrac{3}{2}\lambda \int \{[I_x \cos^2\psi + L \cos\psi \sin\psi + I_y \sin^2\psi] \cos^2\gamma \cos^2\chi$$

$$+ [I_x \sin^2\psi - L \cos\psi \sin\psi + I_y \cos^2\psi] \sin^2\chi$$

$$+ [(I_x - I_y) \sin 2\psi - L \cos 2\psi] \cos\gamma \cos\chi \sin\chi\}\frac{d\omega}{4\pi} \qquad (15)$$

$$B_y = \tfrac{3}{2}\lambda \int \{[I_x \cos^2\psi + L \cos\psi \sin\psi + I_y \sin^2\psi] \cos^2\gamma \sin^2\chi$$

$$+ [I_x \sin^2\psi - L \cos\psi \sin\psi + I_y \cos^2\psi] \cos^2\chi$$

$$- [(I_x - I_y) \sin 2\psi - L \cos 2\psi] \cos\gamma \cos\chi \sin\chi\}\frac{d\omega}{4\pi} \qquad (16)$$

$$D = \tfrac{3}{2}\lambda \int \{[I_x \cos^2\psi + L \cos\psi \sin\psi + I_y \sin^2\psi] \cos^2\gamma \sin 2\chi$$

$$- [I_x \sin^2\psi - L \cos\psi \sin\psi - I_y \cos^2\psi] \sin 2\chi$$

$$- [(I_x - I_y) \sin 2\psi - L \cos 2\psi] \cos\gamma \cos 2\chi\}\frac{d\omega}{4\pi} \qquad (17)$$

We denote the direction of the incident ray by the zenith distance θ' and the azimuth ϕ', and that of the scattered ray by the zenith distance θ and the azimuth ϕ, respectively (Fig. 5.1); in each case the Ox axis is directed perpendicularly at the polar axis.

From the properties of the spherical triangle formed by the polar axis, the incident ray and the scattered ray, we can derive expressions connecting the angles γ, ψ, and χ with the angles θ, θ', and $\phi-\phi'$. Having done so, instead of Eqs. (15), (16), and (17), we find

$$B_x = \frac{3\lambda}{8\pi} \int \{I_x \cos^2(\phi-\phi') + I_y \cos^2\theta' \sin^2(\phi-\phi')$$

$$- \tfrac{1}{2} L \cos\theta' \sin 2(\phi-\phi')\} \, d\omega \qquad (18)$$

$$B_y = \frac{3\lambda}{8\pi} \int \{I_x \cos^2\theta \sin^2(\phi-\phi')$$

$$+ I_y[\cos\theta \cos\theta' \cos(\phi-\phi') + \sin\theta \sin\theta']^2$$

$$+ L[\cos\theta \cos\theta' \cos(\phi-\phi') + \sin\theta \sin\theta'] \cos\theta \sin(\phi-\phi')\} \, d\omega \quad (19)$$

$$D = \frac{3\lambda}{8\pi} \int \{I_x \cos\theta \sin 2(\phi-\phi') - 2I_y[\cos\theta \cos\theta' \cos(\phi-\phi')$$

$$+ \sin\theta \sin\theta'] \cos\theta' \sin(\phi-\phi')$$

$$+ L[\sin\theta \sin\theta' \cos(\phi-\phi') + \cos\theta \cos\theta' \cos 2(\phi-\phi')]\} \, d\omega \quad (20)$$

This is the final form of the radiative equilibrium equation.

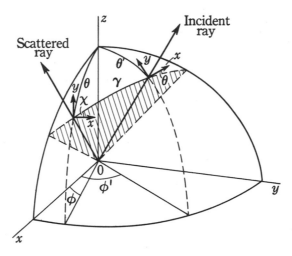

Fig. 5.1

We point out here that radiation scattering according to the law of Rayleigh is produced by molecules and free electrons. When the scattering of light is caused by molecules, the volume coefficient of scattering is equal to

$$\sigma = \frac{8\pi^3}{3} \frac{(n^2-1)^2}{\lambda^4 N} \quad (21)$$

where N is the number of molecules per 1 cm³, n is the refractive index of the medium, and λ is the wavelength of the radiation. Since the quantity $n-1$ is proportional to N, the scattering coefficient σ is also proportional to N, as it should be.

When the scattering is caused by free electrons, the same coefficient is equal to

$$\sigma = \frac{8\pi}{3}\left(\frac{e^2}{mc^2}\right)^2 \mathcal{N}_e \tag{22}$$

where $\mathcal{N}_e$ is the number of free electrons per 1 cm^3, c is the velocity of light, e is the charge of an electron, and m is its mass.

2. THE SCATTERING OF LIGHT IN THE EARTH'S ATMOSPHERE

The Earth's atmosphere. may be considered, to a first approximation, as a medium consisting of plane-parallel layers and illuminated by parallel rays. For a medium consisting of such layers all quantities which characterize the radiation field are functions of the optical depth τ, the angle θ formed by the ray and the normal to the layers and the azimuth ϕ. The equation of radiative transfer is then

$$\left.\begin{aligned}
\cos\theta\frac{dI_x(\tau,\theta,\phi)}{d\tau} &= B_x(\tau,\theta,\phi) - I_x(\tau,\theta,\phi) \\
\cos\theta\frac{dI_y(\tau,\theta,\phi)}{d\tau} &= B_y(\tau,\theta,\phi) - I_y(\tau,\theta,\phi) \\
\cos\theta\frac{dL(\tau,\theta,\phi)}{d\tau} &= D(\tau,\theta,\phi) - L(\tau,\theta,\phi)
\end{aligned}\right\} \tag{23}$$

It is usual, and is considered advisable, that the terms of radiative equilibrium equations which express the radiation coming directly from the sources should be separated. We assume that the medium is illuminated by unpolarized radiation which falls at an angle θ_0 with respect to the normal and which produces an illumination equal to πS perpendicular to the surface. For the unpolarized radiation, we have

$$I_x = I_y = \tfrac{1}{2}I, \qquad L = 0$$

Therefore, Eqs. (18), (19), and (20) provide the terms for the scattering of radiation coming directly from the light sources in the following form:

$$B_{1x} = \frac{3\lambda}{16}Se^{-\tau\sec\theta_0}(\cos^2\phi + \cos^2\theta_0\sin^2\phi) \tag{24}$$

$$B_{1y} = \frac{3\lambda}{16}Se^{-\tau\sec\theta_0}[\cos^2\theta\sin^2\phi$$
$$+ (\cos\theta\cos\theta_0\cos\phi + \sin\theta\sin\theta_0)^2] \tag{25}$$

$$D_1 = \frac{3\lambda}{16} S e^{-\tau \sec\theta_0} (\cos\theta \sin^2\theta_0 \sin 2\phi - \sin\theta \sin 2\theta_0 \sin\phi) \qquad (26)$$

In all these equations we have assumed that the azimuth of the incident rays is equal to zero.

These expressions for B_{1x}, B_{1y}, and D_1 we must introduce into the right-hand side of Eqs. (18), (19), and (20) in order to obtain the quantities of I_x, I_y, and L which will express the diffuse radiation only.

In the boundary conditions which should be added to the equations of radiative transfer and radiative equilibrium we should take into account the fact that there is no diffused radiation incident on the medium from outside.

By means of the expressions for B_{1x}, B_{1y}, and D_1 and the equations of radiative transfer, we can find intensities of diffusely transmitted and diffusely reflected radiation by taking into account scattering of the first order. For the intensities of diffusely transmitted radiation, we obtain

$$I_{1x}(\tau_0, \theta, \phi) = \tfrac{3}{4} S\sigma_1(\tau_0, \theta) \cos\theta_0 (\cos^2\phi + \cos^2\theta_0 \sin^2\phi) \qquad (27)$$

$$I_{1y}(\tau_0, \theta, \phi) = \tfrac{3}{4} S\sigma_1(\tau_0, \theta) \cos\theta_0 [\cos^2\theta \sin^2\phi$$
$$+ (\cos\theta \cos\theta_0 \cos\phi + \sin\theta \sin\theta_0)^2] \qquad (28)$$

$$L_1(\tau_0, \theta, \phi) = \tfrac{3}{4} S\sigma_1(\tau_0, \theta)(\cos\theta \sin^2\theta_0 \sin 2\phi$$
$$- \sin\theta \sin 2\theta_0 \sin\phi) \qquad (29)$$

where

$$\sigma_1 = \frac{\lambda}{4} \frac{e^{-\tau_0 \sec\theta_0} - e^{-\tau_0 \sec\theta}}{\cos\theta_0 - \cos\theta} \qquad (30)$$

and τ_0 is optical depth of the medium. Analogously, we can determine the quantities $I_1(0, \theta, \phi)$, $I(0, \theta, \phi)$, and $L_1(0, \theta, \phi)$.

By means of Eqs. (27), (28), and (29), we are able to determine quantities which characterize the sky illumination. As an example, we select points of the sky on the same vertical as the sun. Setting $\phi = 0$ and $\phi = \pi$ in Eqs. (27) to (29), we find

$$I_{1x} = \tfrac{3}{4} S\sigma_1 \cos\theta_0, \qquad I_{1y} = \tfrac{3}{4} S\sigma_1 \cos\theta_0 \cos^2(\theta \mp \theta_0), \qquad L_1 = 0 \quad (31)$$

It follows that the total radiation intensity is

$$I = \tfrac{3}{4} S\sigma_1 \cos\theta_0 [1 + \cos^2(\theta \mp \theta_0)] \qquad (32)$$

the degree of polarization is

$$p = \frac{1 - \cos^2(\theta \mp \theta_0)}{1 + \cos^2(\theta \mp \theta_0)} \qquad (33)$$

and the plane of polarization for all points on the sun vertical is the same; the preponderant oscillations occur perpendicular to the vertical plane. The largest degree of polarization $p = 1$ takes place at the angular distance of 90° from the sun.

We have obtained simple Eqs. (27) to (29) by taking into account scattering of the first order only. But if we consider scattering of higher order, in other words, if we solve the afore-mentioned equations of radiative transfer and radiative equilibrium, the picture of the distribution of radiative polarization will be more complicated in the vertical through the sun. The largest degree of polarization is then less than one. When the sun is low, there will be regions of negative polarization near it and opposite to it and, therefore, neutral points where the polarization changes sign. These results correspond, in general, with observation.

However, strictly speaking, we have to consider the following facts: (1) Light reflection by the Earth's surface; this we can solve simply by writing corresponding boundary conditions; (2) the atmosphere contains not only molecules but also large particles which do not scatter light in accordance with the law of Rayleigh; (3) optical anistropy of the molecules, which causes a depolarization of scattered light.

The foregoing equations of radiative transfer and radiative equilibrium may be solved by methods discussed in the preceding chapters. In particular, we can derive and solve linear integral equations for computing radiation intensities emerging from the medium. Later we shall show this for a medium of infinitely large optical thickness.

3. The Scattering of Light in Planetary Atmospheres

Consider the problem of diffused reflection of light by a medium of infinitely large optical thickness and with radiation scattering in accordance with the law of Rayleigh. This problem is interesting in the physics of planets with optically thick atmospheres. For simplicity's sake we imagine that the external radiation falls on the medium perpendicularly ($\theta_0 = 0$). In such a case the radiation field will possess an axial symmetry, that is, radiation intensities are independent of the azimuth ϕ. Further, it is obvious that for each ray the main fluctuations will occur either in the vertical plane passing through the ray or perpendicular to it. Thus we have $L = 0$ and $D = 0$.

We can obtain the equations of radiative equilibrium for this problem by integrating Eqs. (18) and (19) with respect to the azimuth ϕ' and by taking $\theta_0 = 0$ in Eqs. (24) and (25). As a result, we have

$$B_x(\tau, \theta) = \tfrac{3}{8}\lambda \int_0^\pi [I_x(\tau, \theta') + I_y(\tau, \theta') \cos^2\theta'] \sin\theta' \, d\theta' + \tfrac{3}{16}\lambda S e^{-\tau} \tag{34}$$

$$B_y(\tau, \theta) = \tfrac{3}{8}\lambda \int_0^\pi [I_x(\tau, \theta') \cos^2\theta$$

$$+ I_y(\tau, \theta')(\cos^2\theta \cos^2\theta' + 2\sin^2\theta \sin^2\theta')] \sin\theta' \, d\theta'$$

$$+ \tfrac{3}{16}\lambda \, Se^{-\tau} \cos^2\theta \tag{35}$$

We now express intensities I and K by intensities I_x and I_y with Eqs. (6) and quantities B and C by B_x and B_y with Eq. 10. Writing $\eta = \cos\theta$, $\eta' = \cos\theta'$, we obtain, instead of Eqs. (34) and (35),

$$B(\tau, \eta) = \frac{\lambda}{2} \int_{-1}^{+1} I(\tau, \eta')[1 + \tfrac{1}{2} P_2(\eta) P_2(\eta')] \, d\eta'$$

$$+ \tfrac{3}{8}\lambda P_2(\eta) \int_{-1}^{+1} K(\tau, \eta')(1 - \eta'^2) \, d\eta' + \tfrac{3}{16}\lambda \, Se^{-\tau}(1 + \eta^2) \tag{36}$$

$$C(\tau, \eta) = \tfrac{3}{8}\lambda(1 - \eta^2) \int_{-1}^{+1} I(\tau, \eta') P_2(\eta') \, d\eta'$$

$$+ \tfrac{9}{16}\lambda(1 - \eta^2) \int_{-1}^{+1} K(\tau, \eta')(1 - \eta'^2) \, d\eta' + \tfrac{3}{16}\lambda \, Se^{-\tau}(1 - \eta^2) \tag{37}$$

where $P_2(\eta)$ is the second polynomial of Legendre: $P_2(\eta) = \tfrac{3}{2}\eta^2 + \tfrac{1}{2}$.

The equation of radiative transfer for the same problem can be written as follows:

$$\left. \begin{array}{l} \eta \dfrac{dI(\tau, \eta)}{d\tau} = -B(\tau, \eta) + I(\tau, \eta) \\[2mm] \eta \dfrac{dK(\tau, \eta)}{d\tau} = -C(\tau, \eta) + K(\tau, \eta) \end{array} \right\} \tag{38}$$

For boundary conditions, we have

$$I(0, \eta) = 0, \qquad K(0, \eta) = 0 \quad \text{where} \quad \eta < 0. \tag{39}$$

We observe that η now denotes the cosine of the angle formed by the radiation and the outward normal.

Our problem in finding intensities of the emerging radiation, or the quantities:

$$I(\eta) = \int_0^\infty B(\tau, \eta) e^{-\tau/\eta} \frac{d\tau}{\eta}, \qquad K(\eta) = \int_0^\infty C(\tau, \eta) e^{-\tau/\eta} \frac{d\tau}{\eta} \tag{40}$$

In solving this problem we shall apply the method of the previous chapter and derive the linear integral equations which provide directly the quantities $I(\eta)$ and $K(\eta)$.

Introducing the following equations:

$$\bar{I}(\eta'', \eta) = \int_0^\infty B(\tau, \eta) e^{-\tau/\eta''} \frac{d\tau}{\eta''}$$

$$\bar{K}(\eta'', \eta) = \int_0^\infty C(\tau, \eta) e^{-\tau/\eta''} \frac{d\tau}{\eta''} \tag{41}$$

we see that

$$\bar{I}(\eta, \eta) = I(\eta), \qquad \bar{K}(\eta, \eta) = K(\eta) \tag{42}$$

The equation of radiative transfer provides

$$\left.\begin{array}{l} \displaystyle\int_0^\infty I(\tau, \eta') e^{-\tau/\eta''} \frac{d\tau}{\eta''} = \frac{\eta'' \bar{I}(\eta'', \eta') - \eta' \bar{I}(\eta', \eta')}{\eta'' - \eta'} \\[12pt] \displaystyle\int_0^\infty K(\tau, \eta') e^{-\tau/\eta''} \frac{d\tau}{\eta''} = \frac{\eta'' \bar{K}(\eta'', \eta') - \eta' \bar{K}(\eta', \eta')}{\eta'' - \eta'} \end{array}\right\} \tag{43}$$

Utilizing Eqs. (43), we find from Eqs. (36) and (37):

$$\bar{I}(\eta'', \eta) = \frac{\lambda}{2} \int_{-1}^{+1} \frac{\eta'' \bar{I}(\eta'', \eta') - \eta' \bar{I}(\eta', \eta')}{\eta'' - \eta'} [1 + \tfrac{1}{2} P_2(\eta) P_2(\eta')] \, d\eta'$$

$$+ \tfrac{3}{8} \lambda P_2(\eta) \int_{-1}^{+1} \frac{\eta'' \bar{K}(\eta'', \eta') - \eta' \bar{K}(\eta', \eta')}{\eta'' - \eta'} (1 - \eta'^2) \, d\eta'$$

$$+ \frac{\lambda}{4} S \frac{1 + \tfrac{1}{2} P_2(\eta)}{1 + \eta''} \tag{44}$$

$$\bar{K}(\eta'', \eta) = \tfrac{3}{8} \lambda (1 - \eta^2) \int_{-1}^{+1} \frac{\eta'' \bar{I}(\eta'', \eta') - \eta' \bar{I}(\eta', \eta')}{\eta'' - \eta'} P_2(\eta') \, d\eta'$$

$$+ \tfrac{9}{16} \lambda (1 - \eta^2) \int_{-1}^{+1} \frac{\eta'' \bar{K}(\eta'', \eta') - \eta' \bar{K}(\eta', \eta')}{\eta'' - \eta'} (1 - \eta'^2) \, d\eta'$$

$$+ \tfrac{3}{16} \lambda S \frac{1 - \eta^2}{1 + \eta''} \tag{45}$$

where now $\bar{I}(\eta', \eta') = 0$ and $\bar{K}(\eta', \eta') = 0$ for $\eta' < 0$.

From Eqs. (44) and (45), we find that the functions $\bar{I}(\eta'', \eta)$ and $\bar{K}(\eta'', \eta)$ have the form:

$$\bar{I}(\eta'', \eta) = u_0(\eta'') + u_2(\eta'') P_2(\eta), \qquad \bar{K}(\eta'', \eta) = \tfrac{3}{2} u_2(\eta'')(1 - \eta^2) \tag{46}$$

and therefore the required functions are

$$I(\eta) = u_0(\eta) + u_2(\eta) P_2(\eta), \qquad K(\eta) = \tfrac{3}{2} u_2(\eta)(1 - \eta^2) \tag{47}$$

Inserting Eq. (46) into Eqs. (44) and (45), we derive the following equations for determining of the auxiliary functions $u_0(\eta)$ and $u_2(\eta)$:

$$u_0(\eta) = \frac{\lambda}{2} \int_{-1}^{+1} \frac{\eta I(\eta) - \eta' I(\eta')}{\eta - \eta'} d\eta' - \tfrac{3}{2}\lambda\eta^2 u_2(\eta) + \frac{\lambda}{4}\frac{S}{1+\eta} \tag{48}$$

$$u_2(\eta) = \frac{\lambda}{4} \int_{-1}^{+1} \frac{\eta I(\eta) - \eta' I(\eta')}{\eta - \eta'} P_2(\eta') \, d\eta'$$

$$+ \tfrac{9}{16}\lambda \int_{-1}^{+1} \frac{\eta u_2(\eta) - \eta' u_2(\eta')}{\eta - \eta'}(1 - \eta'^2) \, d\eta' + \frac{\lambda}{8}\frac{S}{1+\eta} \tag{49}$$

If we had not taken into account the polarization of light, we should have obtained the following equation for determination of the general radiation intensity:

$$\left.\begin{array}{c} B(\tau, \eta) = \dfrac{\lambda}{2} \displaystyle\int_{-1}^{+1} I(\tau, \eta')[1 + \tfrac{1}{2}P_2(\eta) P_2(\eta')] \, d\eta' + \dfrac{3\lambda}{16} Se^{-\tau}(1 + \eta^2) \\[2ex] \eta\dfrac{dI(\tau, \eta)}{d\tau} = I(\tau, \eta) - B(\tau, \eta) \end{array}\right\} \tag{50}$$

From these equations we derive the already well-known Eq. (47) for the function $I(\eta)$, but for the auxiliary functions $u_0(\eta)$ and $u_2(\eta)$ we derive Eqs. (48) and (49) only without the second addend on the right-hand side of Eq. (49).

Computational results of the solution of the system of Eqs. (48) and (49) are given in Table 5.1 for $\lambda = 1$ and $S = 1$.   Table 5.1 gives

TABLE 5.1. DIFFUSE REFLECTION OF LIGHT

η	0	0.1	0.2	0.3	0.4	0.5	0.6	0.7	0.8	0.9	1.0
$I(\eta)$	0.60	0.70	0.77	0.83	0.88	0.93	0.98	1.02	1.07	1.11	1.15
$K(\eta)$	0.28	0.26	0.24	0.21	0.18	0.15	0.12	0.09	0.06	0.03	0
$p(\eta)$	0.45	0.37	0.31	0.25	0.20	0.16	0.12	0.09	0.06	0.03	0
$I'(\pi)$	0.65	0.75	0.82	0.87	0.91	0.95	0.98	1.01	1.04	1.07	1.10
$K_1(\eta)$	0.19	0.17	0.15	0.13	0.11	0.09	0.075	0.06	0.04	0.02	0

quantities $I(\eta)$ and $K(\eta)$ and also the degree of polarization $p(\eta) = K(\eta)/I(\eta)$. For comparison, we gave also the radiation intensity $I'(\eta)$ found without polarization of light. The last column contains the quantity:

$$K_1(\eta) = \tfrac{3}{16}(1 - \eta) \tag{51}$$

Comparing quantities $K_1(\eta)$ and $K(\eta)$, we conclude that the polarization of the reflected light is due basically to the scattering of the first order.

4. The Scattering of Light
in the Electron Atmosphere of a Star

As before, we assume that the medium scatters the light in accordance with the Rayleigh law and has a very large optical thickness. Let the radiation from the external light sources fall on the upper boundary of the medium. It is required to find intensities of the diffused radiation passing through the lower boundary.

As we have explained in Chapter 3, Section 6, the radiation from external light sources does not reach the lower layers of a medium with very large optical thickness. But the field of diffuse radiation possesses an axial symmetry in these layers for any direction of the external radiation incident on the medium.

The equations of radiative equilibrium in this case have the form

$$B(\tau, \eta) = \frac{\lambda}{2} \int_{-1}^{+1} I(\tau, \eta')[1 + \tfrac{1}{2}P_2(\eta)P_2(\eta')] \, d\eta'$$

$$+ \tfrac{3}{8}\lambda P_2(\eta) \int_{-1}^{+1} K(\tau, \eta')(1 - \eta'^2) \, d\eta' \tag{52}$$

$$C(\tau, \eta) = \tfrac{3}{8}\lambda(1 - \eta^2) \int_{-1}^{+1} I(\tau, \eta')P_2(\eta') \, d\eta'$$

$$+ \tfrac{9}{16}\lambda(1 - \eta^2) \int_{-1}^{+1} K(\tau, \eta')(1 - \eta'^2) \, d\eta' \tag{53}$$

They may be derived from Eqs. (36) and (37) by removing the free terms which correspond to the external radiation. The equations of radiative transfer are expressed in the form of Eq. (38).

Availing ourselves of the same method mentioned in the previous section, we see that these equations provide the following expressions for the required radiation intensities in a diffusely transmitting medium:

$$\left. \begin{aligned} I(\eta) &= v_0(\eta) + v_2(\eta) P_2(\eta) \\ K(\eta) &= \tfrac{3}{2} v_2(\eta)(1 - \eta^2) \end{aligned} \right\} \tag{54}$$

where the auxiliary functions v_0 and $v_2(\eta)$ are defined by the equations:

$$v_0(\eta) = \frac{\lambda}{2} \int_{-1}^{+1} \frac{\eta I(\eta) - \eta' I(\eta')}{\eta - \eta'} \, d\eta' - \tfrac{3}{2}\lambda\eta^2 v_2(\eta) \tag{55}$$

$$v_2(\eta) = \frac{\lambda}{4} \int_{-1}^{+1} \frac{\eta I(\eta) - \eta' I(\eta')}{\eta - \eta'} P_2(\eta') \, d\eta'$$

$$+ \tfrac{9}{16}\lambda \int_{-1}^{+1} \frac{\eta v_2(\eta) - \eta' v_2(\eta')}{\eta - \eta'}(1 - \eta'^2) \, d\eta' \tag{56}$$

We understand, of course, that here the quantities $I(\eta)$ and $K(\eta)$ are computed with accuracy limited only to an arbitrary factor.

If we had not taken into account the polarization of light, then we should also have obtained Eq. (54) for the radiation intensity $I'(\eta)$, but for the functions $v_0(\eta)$ and $v_2(\eta)$ we should have the system of Eqs. (55) and (56) without the last term in the second equation. We observe that the same result follows from Eqs. (70) and (72) of the previous chapter for the Rayleigh scattering indicatrix:

$$x(\gamma) = 1 + \tfrac{1}{2}P_2(\cos\gamma) \tag{57}$$

Computational results of the solution of Eqs. (55) and (56) are given in Table 5.2 which contains quantities $I(\eta)$, $K(\eta)$ and the degree of polarization $p(\eta)$ for the case of pure scattering ($\lambda = 1$). The quantity $I'(\eta)$ is not given because it differs little from $I(\eta)$.

TABLE 5.2. DIFFUSE TRANSMISSION OF LIGHT

η	0	0.1	0.2	0.3	0.4	0.5	0.6	0.7	0.8	0.9	1.0
$I(\eta)$	1.00	1.24	1.46	1.67	1.87	2.07	2.27	2.46	2.66	2.85	3.04
$10K(\eta)$	1.25	1.00	0.84	0.70	0.58	0.47	0.37	0.27	0.18	0.09	0
$p(\eta)\%$	12.5	8.0	5.8	4.2	3.1	2.3	1.6	1.1	0.7	0.3	0

Our results can now be employed in a study of atmospheres of hot stars. Computations show that the coefficient of light scattering by free electrons is much larger than the absorption coefficient in the atmospheres of spectral classes $B0$ and O, due to photoionization and free-free transitions. Because the light scattering by free electrons follows the law of Rayleigh, we have to use the foregoing equations for polarization of radiation in our analysis of radiative transfer in these atmospheres.

Table 5.2 shows that the law of limb darkening for a star with a pure electron atmosphere differs little from the law for an ordinary star, the ratio of brightness at the disk center to that at the edge being 3.04, instead of 2.91. But the presence of a large number of free electrons in a stellar atmosphere should be shown by the fact that the radiation coming from different parts of the disc will be polarized differently.

The maximal degree of polarization ($p = 12.5\%$) takes place for $\theta = 90°$ or at the limb of the star, and the radiation is polarized along the radius.

It is obvious that the radiation coming from the entire disk of a spherical star is nonpolarized. Therefore, the polarization effect of starlight caused by the radiation scattering by free electrons can be observed only in the case of eclipsing variables. This effect was theoretically predicted by Chandrasekhar and by the author, and later it was confirmed qualitatively by observations.[3] We cannot expect a quantitative confirmation because the theory is based on the assumption of a pure electron atmosphere which, in reality, does not occur. Interesting is the fact that during these observations, a new discovery was made: the light polarization of single stars. At the present time this phenomenon is intensively studied and several hypotheses have been proposed for its explanation.

5. The Radiation Field
in the Deep Layers of the Medium

Again we assume that the medium is of infinitely large optical thickness and it is required to find the radiation intensity in the deep layers of the medium. This problem was solved previously (Ch. 3, Sec. 6) without consideration of polarization. Again we assume the law of Rayleigh.

Because the radiation from external light sources is absent in the deep layers of the medium and the intensity of the diffused radiation is independent of the azimuth, the radiation field in these layers will be defined by the equations of radiative equilibrium, Eqs. (52) and (53), and by those of radiative transfer Eq. (38). In the latter equations we change the sign of η which corresponds to the counting of angles $\theta = \arccos \eta$ from the inward normal.

As in Chapter 3, Section 6, we are looking for the functions $B(\tau, \eta)$ and $C(\tau, \eta)$ in the form:

$$\left.\begin{array}{l} B(\tau, \eta) = b(\eta) e^{-k\tau} \\ C(\tau, \eta) = c(\eta) e^{-k\tau} \end{array}\right\} \tag{58}$$

Then the equation of radiative transfer provides

$$\left.\begin{array}{l} I(\tau, \eta) = \dfrac{b(\eta) e^{-k\tau}}{1 - k\eta} \\[2mm] K(\tau, \eta) = \dfrac{c(\eta) e^{-k\tau}}{1 - k\eta} \end{array}\right\} \tag{59}$$

[3] V. A. Dombrovskii, On the Polarization of the Radiation of Stars of Early Spectral Class, *DAN Arm SSR* **10**, No. 5 (1949).

Inserting Eqs. (58) and (59) into the equation of radiative equilibrium, we find

$$b(\eta) = b_0 + b_2 P_2(\eta), \qquad c(\eta) = \tfrac{3}{2} b_2 (1 - \eta^2) \qquad (60)$$

and for determination of the constants K and b_2/b_0, we obtain a system of equations:

$$\left. \begin{array}{l} b_0 = \dfrac{\lambda}{2} \displaystyle\int_{-1}^{+1} \dfrac{b_0 + b_2 P_2(\eta')}{1 - k\eta'} \, d\eta' \\[2ex] b_2 = \dfrac{\lambda}{4} \displaystyle\int_{-1}^{+1} \dfrac{b_0 + b_2 P_2(\eta')}{1 - k\eta'} P_2(\eta') \, d\eta' + \tfrac{9}{16}\lambda b_2 \displaystyle\int_{-1}^{+1} \dfrac{(1 - \eta'^2) \, d\eta'}{1 - k\eta'} \end{array} \right\} \quad (61)$$

Results of the solution of this system are given in Table 5.3 for four particular cases. Values of k were given, and those of λ and b_2/b_0 were computed; after this the functions $b(\eta)$ and $c(\eta)$ were found with Eq. (60) and for $b_0 = 1$.

TABLE 5.3. MARCH OF RADIATION IN DEEP LAYERS

η		0	0.1	0.2	0.3	0.4	0.5	0.6	0.7	0.8	0.9	1.0
$k = 0.6$	$b(\eta)$	0.96	0.96	0.96	0.97	0.98	0.99	1.00	1.02	1.04	1.06	1.09
$\lambda = 0.861$	$c(\eta)$	0.13	0.13	0.12	0.12	0.11	0.10	0.08	0.07	0.05	0.03	0
$\lambda' = 0.864$	$b'(\eta)$	0.98	0.98	0.98	0.99	0.99	1.00	1.00	1.01	1.02	1.02	1.03
$k = 0.7$	$b(\eta)$	0.94	0.94	0.95	0.96	0.97	0.99	1.01	1.03	1.06	1.09	1.12
$\lambda = 0.798$	$c(\eta)$	0.18	0.18	0.17	0.16	0.15	0.14	0.12	0.09	0.07	0.04	0
$\lambda' = 0.803$	$b'(\eta)$	0.97	0.97	0.98	0.98	0.99	0.99	1.00	1.01	1.02	1.04	1.05
$k = 0.8$	$b(\eta)$	0.92	0.92	0.93	0.94	0.96	0.98	1.01	1.04	1.08	1.12	1.17
$\lambda = 0.712$	$c(\eta)$	0.25	0.25	0.24	0.23	0.21	0.19	0.16	0.13	0.09	0.05	0
$\lambda' = 0.720$	$b'(\eta)$	0.96	0.96	0.97	0.97	0.98	0.99	1.00	1.02	1.04	1.06	1.08
$k = 0.9$	$b(\eta)$	0.88	0.89	0.90	0.92	0.94	0.97	1.01	1.06	1.11	1.17	1.23
$\lambda = 0.581$	$c(\eta)$	0.34	0.34	0.33	0.31	0.29	0.26	0.22	0.17	0.12	0.07	0
$\lambda' = 0.595$	$b'(\eta)$	0.94	0.94	0.95	0.96	0.97	0.98	1.00	1.03	1.06	1.09	1.12

For comparison we give in the same table values of the parameter λ and the function $b(\eta)$ computed for the scattering indicatrix of Rayleigh without taking account of polarization, and in accordance with the system of Eqs. (61) but without the last term on the right-hand side of these equations; these values are marked by λ' and $b'(\eta)$ similarly to λ and $b(\eta)$.

Table 5.3 shows that with increasing k or diminishing λ the degree of polarization of radiation $p(\eta) = c(\eta)/b(\eta)$ increases; in the case of pure scattering or for $\lambda = 1$, it is equal to zero. Without considering polarization the error of general intensity also increases with diminishing λ. This error is especially important in respect to the quantity k, which enters as a power in Eqs. (58) and (59).

CHAPTER 6

THE PROBABILITY OF QUANTUM EXIT
FROM THE MEDIUM

In the previous chapters we studied essentially the light scattering in a medium illuminated by parallel rays. However, there is an interest in problems of the luminescence of a medium with sources located within it. The most important astrophysical problem of this kind is found in the theory of stellar spectra. These problems can be solved by means of the methods prescribed earlier. But here we offer another method which is the easiest and which is based on a new conception— probability of quantum exit from a medium.[1]

Each quantum, absorbed at optical depth τ, has a definite probability of leaving the medium in a given direction either directly or after a series of scatterings. Obviously, this probability does not depend on the way in which the quantum enters the medium but depends only on the optical properties of the latter. Therefore, after having found the probability of quantum exit we can easily find intensities of the emergent radiation for any kind of radiation sources within the medium. For this we have only to multiply the amount of energy coming directly from the radiation sources and absorbed at a given depth by the probability of quantum exit at the same depth and then to integrate the product with respect to all depths.

The fact that, having found the probability of quantum exit, we can easily solve various problems of a luminous medium differing from each other in the location of radiation sources, gives this method considerable advantage over other methods. Moreover, as we shall see later, the probability of quantum exit coincides with the function $B(\tau, \zeta)$ accurately, within the last factor in the problem of light scattering in a medium illuminated by parallel rays. That is why we can use our earlier results about the function $B(\tau, \zeta)$ for investigating the probability of quantum exit.

In the present chapter we apply this method to a few of the simplest problems in the theory of radiative transfer, problems partially considered previously. In the next chapters we apply this method to more complicated problems which have not been considered before. In

[1] V. V. Sobolev, A New Method in the Theory of Light Scattering, *AJ* **28**, Bulletin 5 (1951).

this chapter, as well as in the following chapters, we assume $\lambda = \text{const.}$ The generalized case in which λ depends on τ is given in an article by the author.[2]

1. One-Dimensional Medium

Consider a one-dimensional medium with optical thickness τ_0 and isotropic scattering of light in the medium $(x = \frac{1}{2})$. As before, we denote by λ the probability of quantum lifetime during the elementary act of scattering.

We now introduce the conception of the probability of quantum exit. Let the quantum be absorbed at optical depth τ, and denote by $p(\tau)$ the probability of quantum exit at the boundary $\tau = 0$, directly from the depth τ as well as after some scattering in the medium.

Obviously, if the quantity $p(\tau)$ is known, we can easily find intensities of radiation leaving the medium for any kind of radiation sources causing its brightness.

Denoting by $f(\tau)\,d\tau$ the amount of energy coming directly from the radiation sources and absorbed in the interval of the optical depth from τ to $\tau + d\tau$, we find that the intensity of radiation emerging at the boundary $\tau = 0$ is equal to

$$I_2(0) = \int_0^{\tau_0} p(\tau) f(\tau)\,d\tau \tag{1}$$

Analogously, we find the intensity of radiation emerging at the boundary $\tau = \tau_0$ to be

$$I_1(\tau_0) = \int_0^{\tau_0} p(\tau_0 - \tau) f(\tau)\,d\tau \tag{2}$$

In order to find the function $p(\tau)$, we derive first a linear integral equation. The probability that the quantum, absorbed at the depth τ, leaves the medium without a scattering on its path is equal to $(\lambda/2)e^{-\tau}$. In order to find the probability of quantum exit after a series of scatterings we first have to multiply the probability of this quantum being absorbed in the depth interval, τ', $\tau' + d\tau'$, or the quantity $(\lambda/2)e^{-|\tau-\tau'|}\,d\tau$, by the probability of quantum exit at the depth τ', or by the quantity $p(\tau')$, and then integrate this product with respect to τ' over the interval from 0 to τ_0. Therefore, the required probability is equal to

$$\frac{\lambda}{2} \int_0^{\tau_0} p(\tau') e^{-|\tau-\tau'|}\,d\tau'$$

[2] *Dokl. Akad. Nauk* (1956).

In other words, the total probability is

$$p(\tau) = \frac{\lambda}{2}e^{-\tau} + \frac{\lambda}{2}\int_0^{\tau_0} p(\tau')e^{-|\tau-\tau'|}\,d\tau' \tag{3}$$

This equation defines the function $p(\tau)$.

Comparing this equation with Eq. (156) of Chapter 1, we see that the function $p(\tau)$ is equal to the function $B(\tau)$ for the problem of brightness of a medium illuminated by a radiation of unit intensity incident externally at the boundary $\tau = 0$. This circumstance permits us to write at once the solution of Eq. (3). Indeed, setting $I_0 = 1$ in Eqs. (157) and (158) of Chapter 1, we obtain

$$p(\tau) = \lambda\frac{(1+k)e^{k(\tau_0-\tau)} - (1-k)e^{-k(\tau_0-\tau)}}{(1+k)^2 e^{k\tau_0} - (1-k)^2 e^{-k\tau_0}} \tag{4}$$

where $k = \sqrt{1-\lambda}$ and

$$p(\tau) = \frac{1+\tau_0-\tau}{2+\tau_0} \tag{5}$$

where $\lambda = 1$.

We can also derive a functional equation for the quantity $p(\tau)$. For that we find the probability of the quantum exit at the optical depth $\tau+\Delta\tau$, or the quantity $p(\tau+\Delta\tau)$. Here we may neglect the square of the quantity $\Delta\tau$ by making it sufficiently small.

The quantum exit from the depth $\tau+\Delta\tau$ of the medium with thickness τ_0 may be considered as the quantum exit from the depth τ of the medium with thickness $\tau_0-\Delta\tau$ with its subsequent passing through the additional layer of thickness $\Delta\tau$; the probability of the exit only we denote by $p_1(\tau)$.

The probability of the quantum exit from the depth τ with the subsequent passing through the additional layer without an absorption is equal to $p_1(\tau)(1-\Delta\tau)$. The probability of the quantum exit from the depth τ with its subsequent absorption in the additional layer and with its leaving the medium after a series of scatterings is equal to $p_1(\tau)\,\Delta\tau p(0)$. Thus, we obtain

$$p(\tau+\Delta\tau) = p_1(\tau)(1-\Delta\tau) + p_1(\tau)\Delta\tau p(0) \tag{6}$$

For the quantity $p_1(\tau)$, we find easily

$$p_1(\tau) = p(\tau) - p(\tau_0-\tau)\Delta\tau p(\tau_0) \tag{7}$$

Inserting Eq. (7) into Eq. (6) and setting $\Delta\tau\to 0$, we derive the following equation for the function $p(\tau)$:

$$\frac{dp(\tau)}{d\tau} = -p(\tau) + p(\tau)p(0) - p(\tau_0-\tau)p(\tau_0) \tag{8}$$

The quantities $p(0)$ and $p(\tau_0)$ entering this equation can be expressed in the form

$$p(0) = \frac{\lambda}{2}(1+\rho), \qquad p(\tau_0) = \frac{\lambda}{2}(e^{-\tau_0}+\sigma) \qquad (9)$$

where

$$\rho = \int_0^{\tau_0} e^{-\tau}p(\tau)\,d\tau, \qquad \sigma = \int_0^{\tau_0} e^{-\tau}p(\tau_0-\tau)\,d\tau \qquad (10)$$

The quantity ρ is the probability of the diffuse reflection of the quantum by the medium, and the quantity σ is the probability of the diffuse transmission of the quantum by the medium. The quantities ρ and σ are connected with the coefficients r and q given in Section 1 of Chapter 2 by means of the relations: $r = \rho$; $q = \sigma + e^{-\tau_0}$. The difference between σ and q is that the former expresses diffuse radiation only and the latter, diffuse and direct.

We observe that ρ and σ are mutually connected in the form

$$2\rho = \frac{\lambda}{2}[(1+\rho)^2-(\sigma+e^{-\tau_0})^2] \qquad (11)$$

This relation we can obtain by multiplying Eq. (8) by $e^{-\tau}$ and by integrating with respect to τ in the interval from 0 to τ_0.

The solution of Eq. (8) has the form

$$p(\tau) = Ce^{-k\tau}+De^{k\tau} \qquad (12)$$

where the constants k, C, and D are connected by means of the relations

$$\left. \begin{array}{l} [1-p(0)-k]C+p(\tau_0)e^{k\tau_0}D = 0 \\ p(\tau_0)e^{-k\tau_0}C+[1-p(0)+k]D = 0 \end{array} \right\} \qquad (13)$$

Setting first $\tau = 0$ in Eq. (12) and then $\tau = \tau_0$, we find the expressions for C and D as follows

$$C = \frac{p(0)e^{k\tau_0}-p(\tau_0)}{e^{k\tau_0}-e^{-k\tau_0}}, \qquad D = \frac{p(\tau_0)-p(0)e^{-k\tau_0}}{e^{k\tau_0}-e^{-k\tau_0}} \qquad (14)$$

Inserting these quantities of C and D into the first relation of Eq. (13), we find

$$p^2(0)-p^2(\tau_0) = (1+k)[p(0)-p(\tau_0)e^{k\tau_0}] \qquad (15)$$

Further, regarding Eqs. (13) as equations for C and D, we obtain

$$k^2 = [p(0)-1]^2-p^2(\tau_0) \qquad (16)$$

Solving Eqs. (15) and (16) with respect to $p(0)$ and $p(\tau_0)$, we find

$$p(0) = (1 - k^2)\frac{(1 + k)e^{k\tau_0} - (1 - k)e^{-k\tau_0}}{(1 + k)^2 e^{k\tau_0} - (1 - k)^2 e^{-k\tau_0}} \tag{17}$$

$$p(\tau_0) = (1 - k^2)\frac{2k}{(1 + k)^2 e^{k\tau_0} - (1 - k)^2 e^{-k\tau_0}} \tag{18}$$

Inserting these quantities into Eq. (14) and then the values C and D in Eq. (12), we obtain the following formula for the required quantity $p(\tau)$:

$$p(\tau) = (1 - k^2)\frac{(1 + k)e^{k(\tau_0 - \tau)} - (1 - k)e^{-k(\tau_0 - \tau)}}{(1 + k)^2 e^{k\tau_0} - (1 - k)^2 e^{-k\tau_0}} \tag{19}$$

The parameter k entering this formula is connected with the parameter λ in a definite manner after we have inserted Eq. (9) into Eq. (16), namely:

$$k^2 = 1 - \lambda(1 + \rho) + \frac{\lambda^2}{4}(1 + \rho)^2 - \frac{\lambda^2}{4}(\sigma + e^{-\tau_0})^2 \tag{20}$$

or, remembering Eq. (11),

$$k^2 = 1 - \lambda \tag{21}$$

By placing Eq. (21) into Eq. (19), we derive a formula obtained earlier, Eq. (4).

For $\lambda = 1$ it is obvious that

$$p(\tau) - p(\tau_0 - \tau) = 1 \tag{22}$$

Using this, we obtain

$$\frac{dp(\tau)}{d\tau} = -p(\tau_0) \tag{23}$$

instead of Eq. (8), and hence

$$p(\tau) = p(0) - p(\tau_0)\tau \tag{24}$$

Setting $\tau = \tau_0$ in Eqs. (22) and (24), we find

$$p(0) = \frac{1 + \tau_0}{2 + \tau_0}, \qquad p(\tau_0) = \frac{1}{2 + \tau_0} \tag{25}$$

By placing Eq. (25) into Eq. (24), we again derive a formula obtained earlier, Eq. (5).

The expressions for the function $p(\tau)$ permit us to compute intensities of the emergent radiation for any kind of radiation sources. Equations (1) and (2), in which radiation sources are defined by the function $f(\tau)$, serve this very purpose.

If on the boundary $\tau = 0$ the radiation falls externally with an intensity I_0, then

$$f(\tau) = I_0 e^{-\tau} \tag{26}$$

Because

$$I_2(0) = I_0 \rho, \qquad I_1(\tau_0) = I_0 \sigma \tag{27}$$

we can in this case avail ourselves of Eq. (9) connecting ρ and σ with $p(0)$ and $p(\tau_0)$ and also of Eqs. (17) and (18) with the quantities $p(0)$ and $p(\tau_0)$, or Eqs. (25) with $\lambda = 1$, for computing the intensities $I_2(0)$ and $I_1(\tau_0)$.

But if the radiation sources are within the medium and if they radiate within an interval of depth from τ to $\tau + \Delta\tau$, an equal amount of energy in both directions $B_0(\tau)d\tau$, then we can say that in the given interval the absorbed energy $(2/\lambda)B_0(\tau)\,d\tau$ is scattered, or dispersed, with a probability of $\lambda/2$ in each direction. Therefore, we have

$$f(\tau) = \frac{2}{\lambda}B_0(\tau) \tag{28}$$

Placing Eq. 28 into Eqs. (1) and (2), we obtain

$$I_2(0) = \frac{2}{\lambda}\int_0^{\tau_0} B_0(\tau)p(\tau)\,d\tau, \qquad I_1(\tau_0) = \frac{2}{\lambda}\int_0^{\infty} B_0(\tau)p(\tau_0 - \tau)\,d\tau \tag{29}$$

Assuming now, for example, that B_0 is constant and λ is equal to 1, we find

$$I_2(0) = I_1(\tau_0) = B_0\tau_0 \tag{30}$$

having inserted Eq. (5) into Eqs. (29); this result we should have expected from physical considerations.

2. Medium of Infinitely Large Optical Thickness

Our results obtained in the previous section can conveniently be generalized for the case of a three-dimensional medium composed of plane parallel layers. First, we consider the luminscence of a medium with infinitely large optical thickness. For the sake of simplicity we assume here that the scattering indicatrix is spherical.

In such a case the function $B(\tau)$ is defined by the following integral equation:

$$B(\tau) = \frac{\lambda}{2}\int_0^{\infty} B(\tau')\mathrm{Ei}|\tau - \tau'|\,d\tau' + g(\tau) \tag{31}$$

where $g(\tau)d\tau$ is the amount of energy emitted by an elementary cylinder at the depth τ with a base of 1 cm² and optical thickness $d\tau$, per unit of solid angle per 1 sec (as the result of both the action of radiation sources in the medium and the scattering of radiation coming directly from the external sources).

If the medium is illuminated by plane parallel rays incident at the angle θ_0 to the normal, we have, instead of Eq. (31),

$$B(\tau, \theta_0) = \frac{\lambda}{2} \int_0^\infty B(\tau', \theta_0) \operatorname{Ei}|\tau - \tau'| \, d\tau' + \lambda \frac{S}{4} e^{-\tau \sec \theta_0} \tag{32}$$

where πS is brightness of the surface perpendicular to the incident rays with $\tau = 0$.

Intensities of radiation emergent from the medium at the angle θ to the normal are given by the function $B(\tau, \theta_0)$ in the form:

$$I(0, \theta, \theta_0) = \int_0^\infty B(\tau, \theta_0) e^{-\tau \sec \theta} \sec \theta \, d\tau \tag{33}$$

Now we solve our problem not with the aid of Eq. (31) but by another method, based as we said earlier, on the probability of quantum exit from the medium.

Let us denote by $p(\tau, \theta) d\omega$ the probability that the light quantum absorbed at optical depth τ emerges from the medium (generally speaking after a multiple scattering) at an angle θ to the normal and within the solid angle $d\omega$, and by $f(\tau) d\tau$ the amount of energy arriving directly from the radiation sources and absorbed by the elementary volume with the base of 1 cm^2 and with the optical thickness $d\tau$ at optical depth τ per 1 sec. Then, the fraction of the total amount of the energy absorbed by the given elementary volume, emerging at the angle θ to the normal and within the solid angle $d\omega$, will be

$$f(\tau) \, d\tau p(\tau, \theta) \, d\omega$$

Therefore the intensity of radiation leaving the medium at the angle θ to the normal will be

$$I(0, \theta) = \int_0^\infty p(\tau, \theta) f(\tau) \sec \theta \, d\tau \tag{34}$$

We observe that if the radiation sources are within the medium and if the amount of energy emitted by the elementary volume per unit of solid angle and 1 sec is equal to $B_0(\tau) d\tau$, then we can imagine that the amount of energy absorbed by this volume and per 1 sec is equal to $(4\pi/\lambda) B_0(\tau) d\tau$. In other words, the function $f(\tau)$ will be equal to

$$f(\tau) = \frac{4\pi}{\lambda} B_0(\tau) \tag{35}$$

We should emphasize that the probability of quantum exit depends only on the optical properties of the medium and not on the radiation sources. Consequently, we can compute the intensities of the emergent radiation for any kind of radiation sources by means of an integration of Eq. (34), after we have found the function $p(\tau, \theta)$.

We can derive an integral equation for determination of the function $p(\tau, \theta)$. In order to achieve it we recall that this function consists of two parts: the probability of quantum exit without a scattering on the path and the probability of quantum exit after a series of scatterings. Obviously, the first part is $(\lambda/4\pi)e^{-\tau \sec \theta}$. But the second part can be found from the following considerations.

The probability that the quantum, absorbed at the depth τ, is emitted at angles from θ' to $\theta' + d\theta'$ to the normal is

$$(\lambda/4\pi)2\pi \sin \theta' \, d\theta'$$

The probability that this quantum will be absorbed within the optical depths from τ' to $\tau' + d\tau'$ is

$$e^{-|\tau-\tau'|\sec\theta'} \sec \theta' \, d\tau'$$

Consequently, the probability that the quantum, absorbed at the depth τ, will be again absorbed between the depths τ' and $\tau' + d\tau'$ is

$$\frac{\lambda}{4\pi} \cdot 2\pi \, d\tau' \int_0^{\pi/2} e^{-|\tau-\tau'|\sec\theta'} \sec \theta' \sin \theta' \, d\theta'$$

Multiplying this expression by $p(\tau', \theta)$ and integrating with respect to τ' over the interval from 0 to ∞, we find the required probability of quantum exit after a series of scatterings:

$$\frac{\lambda}{2} \int_0^\infty p(\tau', \theta) \, d\tau' \int_0^{\pi/2} e^{-|\tau-\tau'|\sec\theta'} \sec \theta' \sin \theta' \, d\theta'$$

However, in accordance with Section 4 of Chapter 1, the interior integral of this expression is equal to $\mathrm{Ei}|\tau - \tau'|$. Consequently,

$$p(\tau, \theta) = \frac{\lambda}{4\pi}e^{-\tau\sec\theta} + \frac{\lambda}{2} \int_0^\infty p(\tau', \theta)\mathrm{Ei}|\tau - \tau'| \, d\tau' \tag{36}$$

This equation now defines the function $p(\tau, \theta)$. We should remark that Eqs. (36) and (34) can be derived not only from physical considerations, as we have done, but also by means of Eqs. (31) and (33), as has been done by Biberman.[3]

---

[3] L. M. Biberman, To the Theory of Light Scattering in Isotropic Media, *JETF* **23**, Bulletin 1(7) (1952).

Comparing Eq. (36) with Eq. (32), we see that

$$p(\tau, \theta) = \frac{B(\tau, \theta)}{\pi S} \tag{37}$$

in other words, the probability of quantum exit $p(\tau, \theta)$ is equal to the function $B(\tau, \theta)$ in the problem of light scattering in a medium illuminated by parallel rays and for $\pi S = 1$.

This conclusion is of great interest, because it means that all equations and formulas derived for the function $B(\tau, \theta)$ in this problem can be used for computing the probability of quantum exit from the medium $p(\tau, \theta)$.

As an example of an application of Eqs. (34) and (37), consider the problem of the brightness of a medium illuminated by parallel rays. In this case, we have for $f(\tau)$,

$$f(\tau) = \pi S e^{-\tau \sec \theta_0} \tag{38}$$

Inserting Eq. (38) into Eq. (34), we have

$$I(0, \theta, \theta_0) = \pi S \int_0^\infty p(\tau, \theta) e^{-\tau \sec \theta_0} \sec \theta \, d\tau \tag{39}$$

Comparing Eqs. (38) and (39) and using Eq. (37), we obtain

$$I(0, \theta, \theta_0) \cos \theta = I(0, \theta_0, \theta) \cos \theta_0 \tag{40}$$

We express now the intensity of the emergent radiation $I(0, \theta, \theta_0)$ in terms of the brightness coefficient $\rho(\theta, \theta_0)$ by means of the formula:

$$I(0, \theta, \theta_0) = S\rho(\theta, \theta_0) \cos \theta_0 \tag{41}$$

Then, instead of Eq. (40), we have

$$\rho(\theta, \theta_0) = \rho(\theta_0, \theta) \tag{42}$$

Thus, the brightness coefficient is a function symmetrical in respect to the angles of incidence and of reflection. We have obtained here a simple proof of an important theorem that we employed previously.

In finding the function $p(\tau, \theta)$ we could derive also a functional equation in addition to the integral equation, Eq. (36). To do so it is convenient to replace $\cos \theta$ by η and $p(\tau, \theta)$ by $p(\tau, \eta)$.

First we find the probability of quantum exit from the depth $\tau + \Delta\tau$, or $p(\tau + \Delta\tau, \eta)$. For that we imagine that the quantum emerges from the medium with optical depth τ and then passes through an additional layer with thickness $\Delta\tau$. Assuming that $\Delta\tau$ is small, we find

$$p(\tau + \Delta\tau, \eta) = p(\tau, \eta)\left(1 - \frac{\Delta\tau}{\eta}\right) + 2\pi \int_0^1 p(\tau, \eta') \frac{\Delta\tau}{\eta'} \, d\eta' p(0, \eta) \tag{43}$$

The first term on the right-hand side of this relation expresses the fact that the quantum may emerge from the depth τ and at the angle arccos η to the normal, and may pass through the additional layer without an absorption; the second term expresses the fact that the quantum may emerge from the same depth τ but in any direction, and may then be absorbed by the additional layer and scattered in the medium in the direction arccos η. Equation (43) provides

$$\frac{\partial p(\tau, \eta)}{\partial \tau} = -\frac{1}{\eta} p(\tau, \eta) + 2\pi p(0, \eta) \int_0^1 p(\tau, \eta') \frac{d\eta'}{\eta'} \tag{44}$$

The quantity $p(0, \eta)$ entering Eq. (44) consists of two probabilities: that of quantum exit from the additional layer directly and that of quantum scattering by the same layer toward the medium together with the diffuse quantum reflection by the medium. It is easy to obtain

$$p(0, \eta) = \frac{\lambda}{4\pi}[1 + 2\eta \int_0^1 \rho(\eta, \eta') \, d\eta'] \tag{45}$$

where $\rho(\eta, \eta')$ is the brightness coefficient introduced above, that is:

$$\rho(\eta, \eta')\eta' = \pi \int_0^\infty e^{-\tau/\eta'} p(\tau, \eta) \frac{d\tau}{\eta} \tag{46}$$

We note that Eq. (45) follows also from Eq. (36) with $\tau = 0$.

We observe that Eq. (44) for the function $p(\tau, \eta)$ coincides with Eq. (104) of Chapter 3 for the function $B(\tau, \eta)$ with $\pi S = 1$. We could anticipate this result from Eq. (37). However, the difference is that Eq. (104) solves only the problem of light scattering in a medium illuminated by parallel rays, whereas Eqs. (44) and (34) permit us to solve more complex problems of the luminescence of the medium.

Let us first find the quantity $p(\eta, \zeta)$ with the aid of Eq. (44). Multiplying Eq. (44) by $e^{-\tau/3} \, d\tau$ and integrating with respect to τ in the interval from 0 to ∞, we find

$$(\eta + \zeta)\rho(\eta, \zeta) = \pi p(0, \eta)[1 + 2\zeta \int_0^1 \rho(\eta', \zeta) \, d\eta'] \tag{47}$$

Substituting for $p(0, \eta)$, Eq. (45), and recollecting the above-mentioned symmetry of the function $\rho(\eta, \zeta)$, we find

$$\rho(\eta, \zeta) = \frac{\lambda}{4} \frac{\phi(\eta)\phi(\zeta)}{\eta + \zeta} \tag{48}$$

where we introduce a notation:

$$\phi(\eta) = 1 + 2\eta \int_0^1 \rho(\eta, \eta') \, d\eta' \tag{49}$$

This function is defined by the equation,

$$\phi(\eta) = 1 + \frac{\lambda}{2}\eta\phi(\eta) \int_0^1 \frac{\phi(\eta')}{\eta+\eta'} \, d\eta' \tag{50}$$

which we receive by substituting Eq. (49) into Eq. (48).

We remember here that Eqs. (48) and (50) were found in Chapter 3, Section 2.

Juxtaposition of Eqs. (45) and (49) provides

$$p(0, \eta) = \frac{\lambda}{4\pi}\phi(\eta) \tag{51}$$

Therefore the function $\phi(\eta)$ defines the probability of the emergence of the quantum which is absorbed by the layer at the boundary of the medium.

TABLE 6.1. VALUE OF $p(\tau, \eta)/p(0, \eta)$ FOR PURE SCATTERING

τ η	0	0.1	0.2	0.3	0.4	0.5	0.6	0.7	0.8	0.9	1.0	1.5	2.0	∞
0.1	1.00	0.53	0.33	0.25	0.21	0.20	0.19	0.18	0.18	0.18	0.18	0.17	0.17	0.17
0.2	1.00	0.81	0.65	0.55	0.48	0.44	0.41	0.39	0.38	0.37	0.36	0.35	0.35	0.35
0.3	1.00	0.94	0.85	0.78	0.72	0.67	0.64	0.61	0.59	0.57	0.56	0.53	0.52	0.52
0.4	1.00	1.01	0.97	0.93	0.89	0.86	0.83	0.81	0.79	0.77	0.76	0.72	0.71	0.69
0.5	1.00	1.05	1.05	1.04	1.02	1.01	0.999	0.97	0.96	0.95	0.94	0.90	0.88	0.87
0.6	1.00	1.09	1.11	1.12	1.13	1.12	1.12	1.11	1.11	1.10	1.10	1.07	1.06	1.04
0.7	1.00	1.11	1.16	1.19	1.21	1.22	1.23	1.23	1.23	1.24	1.24	1.23	1.23	1.21
0.8	1.00	1.13	1.19	1.24	1.27	1.30	1.32	1.33	1.34	1.35	1.36	1.38	1.39	1.39
0.9	1.00	1.14	1.22	1.28	1.32	1.36	1.39	1.42	1.44	1.45	1.47	1.51	1.54	1.56
1.0	1.00	1.15	1.24	1.31	1.37	1.42	1.45	1.49	1.52	1.54	1.56	1.64	1.68	1.73

Remembering Eq. (44) we can also find other properties of the function $p(\tau, \eta)$ analogous to those of the function $B(\tau, \eta)$ and found in Section 5 of Chapter 3. Indeed, introducing the notation

$$2\pi \int_0^1 p(\tau, \eta)\frac{d\eta}{\eta} = \Phi(\tau) \tag{52}$$

we obtain from Eq. (44) the equation,

$$p(\tau, \eta) = p(0, \eta)[e^{-\tau/\eta} + \int_0^\tau e^{-(\tau-\tau')/\eta}\Phi(\tau') \, d\tau'] \tag{53}$$

Then, placing Eq. (53) into Eq. (52), we find

$$\Phi(\tau) = K(\tau) + \int_0^\tau K(\tau-\tau')\Phi(\tau') \, d\tau' \tag{54}$$

where

$$K(\tau) = \frac{\lambda}{2} \int_0^1 e^{-\tau/\eta}\phi(\eta)\frac{d\eta}{\eta} \tag{55}$$

Thus we see that, having found the function Φ from Eq. (54), we can find the probability of quantum exit $p(\tau, \eta)$ by means of Eq. (53).

The values of the function $p(\tau, \eta)$ are given in Table 6.1 for the case of pure scattering.

From Eq. (44) we can also derive the asymptotic expression for the function $p(\tau, \eta)$ at greater optical depths. Indeed, as in Chapter 3, Section 5, we find that for large values of τ,

$$p(\tau, \eta) = A\frac{\phi(\eta)\eta}{1 - k\eta}e^{-k\tau} \tag{56}$$

where the constants k and A are defined by:

$$\frac{\lambda}{2k}\lg\frac{1+k}{1-k} = 1 \tag{57}$$

$$2\pi A \int_0^1 \frac{\phi(\eta)\eta\, d\eta}{(1-k\eta)^2} = 1 \tag{58}$$

For pure scattering, we have $\lambda = 1$ and $k = 0$. Therefore, we can write, instead of Eq. (56),

$$p(\tau, \eta) = \frac{\phi(\eta)\eta}{2\pi \int_0^1 \phi(\eta)\eta\, d\eta} \tag{59}$$

We observe that if the radiation sources are situated in the thin layer with the thickness $\Delta\tau$ at the optical depth τ, the intensity of the emergent radiation will, in accordance with Eqs. (34) and (35), be equal to

$$I(0, \eta) = \frac{4\pi}{\lambda}B_0 p(\tau, \eta)\frac{\Delta\tau}{\eta} \tag{60}$$

If the radiative layer is at a great optical depth, we find, substituting Eq. (60) for Eq. (56),

$$I(0, \eta) = \frac{4\pi}{\lambda}B_0 A\frac{\phi(\eta)}{1 - k\eta}e^{-k\tau} \tag{61}$$

For pure scattering this formula gives

$$I(0, \eta) = 2B_0\Delta\tau\frac{\phi(\eta)}{\int_0^1 \phi(\eta)\eta\, d\eta} \tag{62}$$

Thus we found that for this case the intensity of the emergent radiation is proportional to the function $\phi(\eta)$.

We now can apply Eq. (62), in particular, to stellar atmospheres. In the stars the radiation sources are at great depths in the stars' interiors and the method of transport of the integrated radiation in the photosphere may be regarded as pure scattering. Therefore, Eq. (62) provides us the integrated brightness over the star disk.

As stated previously, having found the function $p(\tau, \eta)$ with the aid of Eq. (34), we can find the intensity of the emergent radiation for any kind of radiation sources. In some cases, however, we can compute the integral Eq. (34) without the function $p(\tau, \eta)$ but only using Eq. (44) directly. Such a case occurs when $f(\tau)$ appears to be a polynomial or an exponential function of τ. We investigate the intensities for these cases in the next section.

3. INTERNAL RADIATION SOURCES

Consider the internal radiation sources with

$$B_0(\tau) = b_0 + b_1\tau + b_2\tau^2 + \dots \tag{63}$$

In this case Eqs. (34) and (35) provide the intensity of the emergent radiation in the following form:

$$I(0, \eta) = \frac{4\pi}{\lambda}\left[b_0 \int_0^\infty p(\tau, \eta)\frac{d\tau}{\eta} + b_1 \int_0^\infty p(\tau, \eta)\tau\frac{d\tau}{\eta} + \dots \right] \tag{64}$$

Thus, we have to compute the quantities

$$A_n(\eta) = \int_0^\infty p(\tau, \eta)\tau^n\frac{d\tau}{\eta} \tag{65}$$

before we find the radiation intensity $I(0, \eta)$, which is obtained by means of the following expression:

$$I(0, \eta) = \frac{4\pi}{\lambda}[b_0 A_0(\eta) + b_1 A_1(\eta) + b_2 A_2(\eta) + \dots] \tag{66}$$

To find the quantities $A_n(\eta)$ themselves, we can use Eq. (44) directly. Remembering Eq. (51), we can rewrite Eq. (44) in the form

$$\frac{\partial p(\tau, \eta)}{\partial \tau} = -\frac{1}{\eta}p(\tau, \eta) + \frac{\lambda}{2}\phi(\eta)\int_0^1 p(\tau, \eta')\frac{d\eta'}{\eta'} \tag{67}$$

Multiplying Eq. (67) by τ^n and integrating with respect to τ in the interval from 0 to ∞, we find (with $n \geqslant 1$)

$$-n\eta A_{n-1}(\eta) = -A_n(\eta) + \frac{\lambda}{2}\phi(\eta)\int_0^1 A_n(\eta')\, d\eta' \tag{68}$$

We integrate Eq. (68) with respect to η in the interval from 0 to ∞ and find its integral in the form:

$$n \int_0^1 A_{n-1}(\eta)\eta \, d\eta = \left[1 - \frac{\lambda}{2} \int_0^1 \phi(\eta) \, d\eta\right] \int_0^1 A_n(\eta) \, d\eta \qquad (69)$$

But from Eq. (50) follows:

$$1 - \frac{\lambda}{2} \int_0^1 \phi(\eta) \, d\eta = \sqrt{1-\lambda} \qquad (70)$$

(see Section 3, Chapter 3). Hence,

$$\int_0^1 A_n(\eta) \, d\eta = \frac{n}{\sqrt{1-\lambda}} \int_0^1 A_{n-1}(\eta)\eta \, d\eta \qquad (71)$$

Inserting Eq. (71) into Eq. (68) we, finally obtain

$$A_n(\eta) = n\eta \, A_{n-1}(\eta) + \frac{\lambda}{2} \frac{n}{\sqrt{1-\lambda}} \phi(\eta) \int_0^1 A_{n-1}(\eta)\eta \, d\eta \qquad (72)$$

We have thus derived the recurrent formula for the determination of the required quantity $A_n(\eta)$.

Now we find the quantity $A_0(\eta)$. Integrating Eq. (67) with respect to τ, in the interval from 0 to ∞, and recollecting Eq. (51), we have

$$-\frac{\lambda}{4\pi}\phi(\eta) = -A_0(\eta) + \frac{\lambda}{2}\phi(\eta) \int_0^1 A_0(\eta') \, d\eta' \qquad (73)$$

Hence,

$$\int_0^1 A_0(\eta) \, d\eta = \frac{\lambda}{4\pi\sqrt{1-\lambda}} \int_0^1 \phi(\eta) \, d\eta \qquad (74)$$

Placing Eq. (74) into Eq. (73) and again using Eq. (70), we find

$$A_0(\eta) = \frac{\lambda}{4\pi} \frac{\phi(\eta)}{\sqrt{1-\lambda}} \qquad (75)$$

With known $A_0(\eta)$, we can find all the quantities $A_1(\eta)$, $A_2(\eta)$, etc., using Eq. (72). Setting in it $n = 1$ and inserting in it Eq. (75), we obtain

$$A_1(\eta) = \frac{\lambda}{4\pi}\phi(\eta)\left[\frac{\eta}{\sqrt{1-\lambda}} + \frac{\lambda}{2}\frac{\alpha_1}{1-\lambda}\right] \qquad (76)$$

where

$$\alpha_n = \int_0^1 \phi(\eta)\eta^n \, d\eta \qquad (77)$$

Analogously, we find

$$A_2(\eta) = \frac{\lambda}{4\pi} \phi(\eta) \left[2\frac{\eta^2}{\sqrt{1-\lambda}} + \lambda\frac{\alpha_1\eta}{1-\lambda} + \frac{\lambda^2\alpha_1^2}{2(1-\lambda)^{3/2}} + \frac{\lambda\alpha_2}{1-\lambda} \right] \quad (78)$$

We note that if the radiation sources are distributed uniformly in the medium ($B_0 = $ const), the intensity of the emergent radiation is, according to Eqs. (66) and (75), equal to

$$I(0,\eta) = B_0\frac{\phi(\eta)}{\sqrt{1-\lambda}} \quad (79)$$

If $B_0(\tau) = b_0 + b_1$, it follows from Eqs. (66), (75), and (76) that

$$I(0,\eta) = \frac{\phi(\eta)}{\sqrt{1-\lambda}}\left[b_0 + b_1\left(\eta + \frac{\lambda}{2}\frac{\alpha_1}{\sqrt{1-\lambda}}\right) \right] \quad (80)$$

It is of course understood that this problem of the luminescence of the medium with an infinitely large optical thickness and with the radiation sources specified by Eq. (63) is meaningful only if $\lambda < 1$. If, however, λ is equal to 1, the entire energy produced within the medium leaves it and therefore the intensities of the emergent radiation become infinitely large in this case.

As stated previously, the intensities of the emergent radiation can be easily found not only in the case when the function $f(\tau)$ is a polynomial but also when $f(\tau)$ is an exponential function. Assuming that

$$f(\tau) = \frac{4\pi}{\lambda}B_0 e^{-m\tau} \quad (81)$$

where B_0 and m are constants, we have

$$I(0,\eta) = \frac{4\pi}{\lambda}B_0 \int_0^\infty p(\tau,\eta)e^{-m\tau}\frac{d\tau}{\eta} \quad (82)$$

As previously, from Eq. (67), we obtain

$$I(0,\eta) = \frac{B_0}{1 - \frac{\lambda}{2}\displaystyle\int_0^1 \frac{\phi(\eta')}{1+m\eta'}d\eta'}\frac{\phi(\eta)}{1+m\eta} \quad (83)$$

If $m = (1/\zeta) \geqslant 1$, from Eq. (83) and in conjunction with Eq. (50) it follows that,

$$I(0,\eta) = B_0\frac{\phi(\eta)\phi(\zeta)}{\eta+\zeta}\zeta$$

which normally agrees with Eqs. (41) and (48) for $B_0 = (\lambda/4)S$. Setting $m = 0$ in Eq. (83) we obtain Eq. (79).

Equation (83) is correct even when $f(\tau)$ increases exponentially with an increase of τ, or when $m < 0$. But in this case we must have: $-m < k$, where k is defined by Eq. (57). For $-m \geqslant k$, Eq. (82) delivers infinitely large values of the intensity of the emergent radiation because the probability of quantum exit, according to Eq. (56) and for large τ, is proportional to $e^{-k\tau}$.

4. Contours of Absorption Lines in Stellar Spectra

As an example for applying the aforementioned results, we shall solve the important astrophysical problem of the contours of absorption lines in stellar spectra. First, we assume that the radiation scattering in a spectral line occurs without a change in frequency. This assumption is common in the theory of absorption line formation; only recently has the redistributon of radiation over the frequency within the line begun to be taken into consideration, and we shall discuss this in Chapter 8.

We have formulated exactly our problem in Section 8 of Chapter 1. There we obtained the function $B_\nu(\tau_\nu)$ in the form of the following integral equation:

$$B_\nu(\tau_\nu) = \frac{\lambda_\nu}{2} \int_0^\infty B_\nu(\tau_\nu) \mathrm{Ei}|\tau_\nu - \tau_\nu'| \, d\tau_\nu' + (1 - \lambda_\nu) B_\nu^*(T) \qquad (84)$$

where $\lambda_\nu = \sigma_\nu/(\kappa + \sigma_\nu)$, $d\tau_\nu = -(\kappa + \sigma_\nu)dr$, σ_ν is the absorption coefficient of the line, κ is the absorption coefficient of the continuum, and $B_\nu^*(T)$ is the Planck intensity for the temperature T. Our task is to find the intensity of the emergent radiation $I_\nu(0, \eta)$.

Here, however, we shall not use Eq. (84) but solve the problem by means of the probability of quantum exit from the medium. In our case the amount of energy emitted by an elementary volume with a cross-section 1 cm^2 and the optical thickness $d\tau_\nu$ per unit of solid angle and in 1 sec is equal to $(1 - \lambda_\nu)B_\nu^*(T)d\tau_\nu$. Therefore, for the function $f_\nu(\tau_\nu)$, we obtain

$$f_\nu(\tau_\nu) = \frac{4\pi}{\lambda_\nu}(1 - \lambda_\nu)B_\nu^*(T) \qquad (85)$$

Substituting Eq. (85) into Eq. (34), we find

$$I_\nu(0, \eta) = 4\pi \frac{1 - \lambda_\nu}{\lambda_\nu} \int_0^\infty B_\nu^*(T) p_\nu(\tau_\nu, \eta) \frac{d\tau_\nu}{\eta} \qquad (86)$$

where $p_\nu(\tau_\nu, \eta)$ is the probability of quantum exit in the frequency ν, at the optical depth τ_ν and at the angle arccos η to the normal within unit solid angle.

The function $B^*_\nu(T)$ can be expanded in the following series:

$$B_\nu^*(T) = B_\nu^*(T_0)(1 + \beta_1\tau + \beta_2\tau^2 + \ldots) \tag{87}$$

where T_0 is the surface temperature, and τ is the optical depth in the continuum. Usually one employs only the first two terms of Eq. (87), but we should be aware that such an approximation may not be sufficiently accurate.

We should now put Eq. (87) into Eq. (86), but first replace τ by τ_ν in the same expression. Because $\tau = (1 - \lambda_\nu)\,\tau_\nu$, we have

$$B_\nu^*(T) = B_\nu^*(T_0)[1 + \beta_1(1-\lambda_\nu)\tau_\nu + \beta_2(1-\lambda_\nu)^2\tau_\nu^2 + \ldots] \tag{88}$$

Inserting now Eq. (88) into Eq. (86), we find

$$I_\nu(0,\eta) = 4\pi\frac{1-\lambda_\nu}{\lambda_\nu}B_\nu^*(T_0)[A_{\nu 0}(\eta) + \beta_1(1-\lambda_\nu)\,A_{\nu 1}(\eta)$$

$$+ \beta_2(1-\lambda_\nu)^2 A_{\nu 2}(\eta) + \ldots] \tag{89}$$

where the quantities $A_{\nu n}(\eta)$ are defined by Eq. (65) and ν expresses their dependence on the frequency by means of λ_ν.

The quantities $A_{\nu n}$ were already found in the previous section and therefore we can consider the intensity of the emergent radiation within the spectral line known for any number of terms in Eq. (87).

The intensity within a line $I_\nu(0, \eta)$ is usually expressed in terms of the intensities of the continuum near the line, in other words, one finds the quantity

$$r_\nu(\eta) = \frac{I_\nu(0,\eta)}{I(0,\eta)} \tag{90}$$

We can obtain the intensity of the continuum $I(0, \eta)$ from the formula for $I_\nu(0, \eta)$ with $\lambda_\nu = 0$. For the case of an isothermal atmosphere, or for $B_\nu^*(T) = B_\nu^*(T_0)$, Eqs. (89) and (75) give

$$r_\nu(\eta) = \phi_\nu(\eta)\sqrt{1-\lambda_\nu} \tag{91}$$

Limiting ourselves to the two first terms in Eq. (87), we find

$$r_\nu(\eta) = \frac{\phi_\nu(\eta)\sqrt{1-\lambda_\nu}}{1+\beta_1\eta}\left\{1 + \beta_1\sqrt{1-\bar{\lambda}_\nu}\left(\eta\sqrt{1-\lambda_\nu} + \frac{\lambda_\nu}{2}\alpha_{\nu 1}\right)\right\} \tag{92}$$

But, taking into account the three first terms in Eq. (87) and utilizing Eqs. (89), (75), (76) and (78), we have

$$r_\nu(\eta) = \frac{\phi_\nu(\eta)\sqrt{1-\lambda_\nu}}{1+\beta_1\eta+2\beta_2\eta^2}\Bigg\{1+\beta_1\sqrt{1-\lambda_\nu}\Big(\eta\sqrt{1-\lambda_\nu}+\frac{\lambda_\nu}{2}\alpha_{\nu1}\Big)$$

$$+\beta_2(1-\lambda_\nu)\bigg[2\eta^2(1-\lambda_\nu)+\eta\lambda_\nu\sqrt{1-\lambda_\nu}\alpha_{\nu1}$$

$$+\frac{\lambda_\nu^2}{2}\alpha_{\nu1}{}^2+\lambda_\nu\sqrt{1-\lambda_\nu}\alpha_{\nu2}\bigg]\Bigg\} \tag{93}$$

Analogously, we can find the expressions for $r_\nu(\eta)$ for any number of terms in Eq. (87).

The formulas given above permit us to compute the intensity in the center of a line and at a given distance from the center of the star disk, or the quantity $r_{\nu_0}(\eta)$. For strong lines the ratio σ_{ν_0}/χ is very large and for this reason the quantity λ_{ν_0} is very close to unity. Therefore, for these lines Eq. (93) provides

$$r_{\nu0} \approx \frac{\phi_{\nu_0}(\eta)\sqrt{1-\lambda_{\nu_0}}}{1+\beta_1\eta+2\beta_2\eta^2} \tag{94}$$

Remembering the physical meaning of the quantity λ_ν, we can rewrite Eq. (49) as follows:

$$r_{\nu0} \approx \frac{\phi_{\nu_0}(\eta)}{1+\beta_1\eta+2\beta_2\eta^2}\sqrt{\frac{\chi}{\chi+\sigma_{\nu_0}}} \tag{95}$$

It is also of interest to investigate the behavior of the outer parts of the absorption line at the center and at the limb of the star disk. In these parts the quantity λ_ν is small and, consequently, the quantity $r_\nu(\eta)$ approaches unity. Therefore we can use the quantity

$$C(\eta) = \lim_{\lambda_\nu\to0}\frac{1-r_\nu(\eta)}{\lambda_\nu} \tag{96}$$

for analyzing the behavior of the outer parts of the line. Substituting Eq. (93) into Eq. (96) and recollecting that, for small λ_ν,

$$\phi_\nu(\eta) = 1+\frac{\lambda_\nu}{2}\eta\lg\frac{1+\eta}{\eta} \tag{97}$$

we find

$$C(\eta) = \frac{3}{2}-\frac{\eta}{2}\lg\frac{1-\eta}{\eta}-\frac{1}{1+\beta_1\eta+2\beta_2\eta^2}\bigg[1+\frac{\beta_1}{4}+\beta_2\Big(\frac{1}{3}+\frac{\eta}{4}-2\eta^2\Big)\bigg] \tag{98}$$

The quantity $r_\nu(\eta)$ expresses the contour of an absorption line at an angular distance arccos η from the star center. In order to find the line contour in the spectrum of the whole star we have to compute the quantity

$$r_\nu = \frac{\int_0^1 r_\nu(\eta) I(0, \eta)\eta \, d\eta}{\int_0^1 I(0, \eta)\eta \, d\eta} \tag{99}$$

Using Eq. (93) and

$$I(0, \eta) = B_\nu^*(T_0)(1 + \beta_1\eta + 2\beta_2\eta^2) \tag{100}$$

we obtain

$$r_\nu = \frac{2\sqrt{1-\lambda_\nu}}{1 + \frac{2}{3}\beta_1 + \beta_2}\left\{\alpha_{\nu 1} + \beta_1\sqrt{1-\lambda_\nu}\left(\alpha_{\nu 2}\sqrt{1-\lambda_\nu} + \frac{\lambda_\nu}{2}\alpha_{\nu 1}^2\right)\right.$$

$$+ \beta_2(1-\lambda_\nu)\left[2\alpha_\nu^3(1-\lambda_\nu) + \alpha_{\nu 2}\alpha_{\nu 1}\lambda_\nu\sqrt{1-\lambda_\nu}\right.$$

$$\left.\left. + \frac{\lambda_\nu^2}{2}\alpha_{\nu 1}^3 + \lambda_\nu\sqrt{1-\lambda_\nu}\alpha_{\nu 2}^2\right]\right\} \tag{101}$$

The numerical values of the quantities α_n which are moments of the function $\phi(\eta)$ are given in Table 6.2.

TABLE 6.2. MOMENTS OF THE FUNCTION $\phi(\eta)$

λ	α_0	α_1	α_2	α_3	α_4
0	1.000	0.500	0.333	0.250	0.200
0.1	1.026	0.516	0.344	0.258	0.207
0.2	1.056	0.533	0.357	0.268	0.215
0.3	1.089	0.553	0.371	0.279	0.224
0.4	1.127	0.576	0.387	0.292	0.234
0.5	1.172	0.603	0.407	0.307	0.247
0.6	1.225	0.637	0.431	0.326	0.262
0.7	1.292	0.679	0.461	0.350	0.282
0.8	1.382	0.736	0.503	0.382	0.309
0.85	1.442	0.774	0.532	0.405	0.327
0.90	1.519	0.825	0.569	0.435	0.352
0.925	1.570	0.859	0.594	0.455	0.368
0.950	1.635	0.902	0.627	0.480	0.390
0.975	1.727	0.964	0.674	0.518	0.422
1.000	2.000	1.155	0.820	0.637	0.522

5. LINE CONTOURS WITH ALLOWANCE FOR FLUORESCENCE

In Chapter 5 we analyzed the contours of absorption lines for the simple case when all quanta absorbed in a spectral line are emitted in the same line. However, there are other more complicated processes which are possible during radiative transfer in stellar atmospheres. The most important ones are the two mutually opposed processes: One consists of an ionization of the atom at the *lower* state with a subsequent recombination at the *higher* one with an *emission* of the quantum in the line; and the other, of an ionization of the atom at the *higher* state with a subsequent recombination at the *lower* one with an *absorption* of the quantum in the line. The first process increases the number of quanta in the line; the second one diminishes it.

An equation of radiative transfer corresponding to these processes of fluorescence was derived by Strömgren.[4]

$$\cos\theta\frac{dI_\nu}{dr} = -(\sigma_\nu+\kappa)I_\nu+(1-\epsilon)\sigma_\nu\int I_\nu\frac{d\omega}{4\pi}+(\kappa+Q\epsilon\sigma_\nu)B_\nu^*(T) \qquad (102)$$

where ϵ is the fraction of the transitions from the second state into the ionized one, which diminish the number of quanta in the line; $Q\epsilon\sigma_\nu B_\nu^*(T)$ is the coefficient of the true radiation in the line caused by the ionization at the lower state and the recombination at the upper one; Q is a certain constant.

Equation (102) can be rewritten as follows:

$$\cos\theta\frac{dI_\nu}{d\tau_\nu} = I_\nu-\lambda_\nu\int I_\nu\frac{d\omega}{4\pi}-(1-\lambda_\nu^0+Q\epsilon\lambda_\nu^0)B_\nu^*(T) \qquad (103)$$

where

$$\lambda_\nu = (1-\epsilon)\frac{\sigma_\nu}{\kappa+\sigma_\nu}, \qquad \lambda_\nu^0 = \frac{\sigma_\nu}{\kappa+\sigma_\nu} \qquad (104)$$

We remind the reader that in the previous chapter the quantity λ_ν^0, or the value of λ_ν for $\epsilon = 0$, was denoted simply by λ_ν.

In order to find the intensity of the emergent radiation we again use the probability of quantum exit. Since in this case

$$f_\nu(\tau_\nu) = \frac{4\pi}{\lambda_\nu}(1-\lambda_\nu^0+Q\epsilon\lambda_\nu^0)B_\nu^*(T) \qquad (105)$$

we have

$$I_\nu(0,\eta) = \frac{4\pi}{\lambda_\nu}(1-\lambda_\nu^0+Q\epsilon\lambda_\nu^0)\int_0^\infty B_\nu^*(T)p_\nu(\tau_\nu,\eta)\frac{d\tau_\nu}{\eta} \qquad (106)$$

As before, we express the function $B_\nu^*(T)$ in the form of Eq. (87), and transform τ to τ_ν by means of the relation $\tau = (1-\lambda_\nu^0)\tau_\nu$. Then, instead of Eq. (87), we have

$$B_\nu^*(T) = B_\nu^*(T_0)[1+\beta_1(1-\lambda_\nu^0)\tau_\nu+\beta_2(1-\lambda_\nu^0)^2\tau_\nu^2+ \ ...] \qquad (107)$$

[4] B. Strömgren, The Influence of Electron Capture on the Contours of Fraunhofer Lines, *Zs. f. Ap.* **10**, 237 (1935).

Inserting Eq. (107) into Eq. (106), we obtain

$$I_\nu(0, \eta) = (1 - \lambda_\nu{}^0 + Q \epsilon \lambda_\nu{}^0) B_\nu^*(T_0) \frac{\phi_\nu(\eta)}{\sqrt{1 - \lambda_\nu}}$$

$$\times \left\{ 1 + \beta_1(1 - \lambda_\nu{}^0)\left(\eta + \frac{\lambda_\nu}{2} \frac{\alpha_{\nu 1}}{\sqrt{1 - \lambda_\nu}} \right) \right.$$

$$\left. + \beta_2(1 - \lambda_\nu{}^0)^2 \left[2\eta^2 + \eta \frac{\lambda_\nu \alpha_{\nu 1}}{\sqrt{1 - \lambda_\nu}} + \frac{\lambda_\nu{}^2}{2} \frac{\alpha_{\nu 1}{}^2}{1 - \lambda_\nu} + \frac{\lambda_\nu \alpha_{\nu 2}}{\sqrt{1 - \lambda_\nu}} \right] \right\} \quad (108)$$

where we have used the quantities $A_n(\eta)$ found in Section 3.

Recollecting now Eq. (90), we derive

$$r_\nu(\eta) = \frac{1 - \lambda_\nu{}^0 + Q \epsilon \lambda_\nu{}^0}{1 + \beta_1 \eta + 2\beta_2 \eta^2} \cdot \frac{\phi_\nu(\eta)}{\sqrt{1 - \lambda_\nu}}$$

$$\times \left\{ 1 + \beta_1(1 - \lambda_\nu{}^0)\left(\eta + \frac{\lambda_\nu}{2} \frac{\alpha_{\nu 1}}{\sqrt{1 - \lambda_\nu}} \right) \right.$$

$$\left. + \beta_2(1 - \lambda_\nu{}^{40})^2 \left[2\eta^2 + \eta \frac{\lambda_\nu \alpha_{\nu 1}}{\sqrt{1 - \lambda_\nu}} + \frac{\lambda_\nu{}^2}{2} \frac{\alpha_{\nu 1}{}^2}{1 - \lambda_\nu} + \frac{\lambda_\nu \alpha_{\nu 2}}{\sqrt{1 - \lambda_\nu}} \right] \right\} \quad (109)$$

This is the formula for the determination of the absorption line contours with allowance for fluorescence.

Let us consider some consequences of Eq. (109).

The central intensity of a strong line, because in that case the quantity $\lambda_\nu{}^0$ approaches unity, is equal to

$$r_{\nu 0} \approx \frac{\phi_{\nu 0}(\eta)}{1 + \beta_1 \eta + 2\beta_2 \eta^2} Q \sqrt{\epsilon} \quad (110)$$

The quantity $C(\eta)$ defining the outer parts of the line is

$$C(\eta) = \tfrac{3}{2} - (Q - \tfrac{1}{2})\epsilon - \frac{1 - \epsilon}{2} \eta \lg \frac{1 + \eta}{\eta}$$

$$- \frac{1}{1 + \beta_1 \eta + 2\beta_2 \eta^2} \left[1 - 2\beta_2 \eta^2 + (1 - \epsilon)\left(\frac{\beta_1}{4} + \frac{\beta_2}{2}\eta + \frac{\beta_2}{3} \right) \right] \quad (111)$$

On account of the smallness of the quantity ϵ the values of $C(\eta)$ in this equation are hardly different from those obtained by means of Eq. (98).

Finally, we compute the line contours in the spectrum of the whole star by inserting Eqs. (100) and (109) into Eq. (99):

$$r_\nu = \frac{2}{\sqrt{1-\lambda_\nu}} \frac{1-\lambda_\nu{}^0 + Q\epsilon\lambda_\nu{}^0}{1+\frac{2}{3}\beta_1+\beta_2}$$

$$\times \left\{ \alpha_{\nu 1}+\beta_1(1-\lambda_\nu{}^0)\left(\alpha_{\nu 2}+\frac{\lambda_\nu}{2}\frac{\alpha_{\nu 1}{}^2}{\sqrt{1-\lambda_\nu}}\right) +\beta_2(1-\lambda_\nu{}^0)^2 \right.$$

$$\left. \times \left[2\alpha_{\nu 3}+\lambda_\nu\frac{\alpha_{\nu 1}\alpha_{\nu 2}}{\sqrt{1-\lambda_\nu}}+\frac{\lambda_\nu{}^2}{2}\frac{\alpha_{\nu 1}{}^3}{1-\lambda_\nu}+\lambda_\nu\frac{\alpha_{\nu 1}\alpha_{\nu 2}}{\sqrt{1-\lambda_\nu}}\right]\right\} \qquad (112)$$

While deriving Eqs. (109) and (112), we have taken into consideration three first terms in the series of the function $B_\nu{}^*(T)$ in the power of τ. Analogous formulas were obtained by Chandrasekhar,[5] who took into consideration the two first terms in the aforementioned expansion.

We should observe that the function $B_\nu{}^*(T)$ is sometimes presented not in the form of an expansion in powers of τ but as follows:

$$B_\nu{}^*(T) = B_\nu{}^*(T_0)[\beta_0+\beta_1\tau+(1-\beta_0)e^{-m\tau}]$$

where β_0, β_1, and m are constants especially chosen. To find the quantities $r_\nu(\eta)$ does not present any difficulties in this case either. In order to take into account the presence of the exponential term, in this expression for $B_\nu{}^*$ we have to use Eq. (83).

6. Medium with Finite Optical Thickness

Let us now apply the method of this chapter to the problem of the luminescence of a medium with finite optical thickness τ_0. As previously, we assume that there is an isotropic scattering of the light in the medium.

Letting $p(\tau, \eta)d\omega$ be the probability of the emergence of the quantum absorbed at the optical depth τ at the angle arccos η to the normal within the solid angle $d\omega$, we can write, for the intensities of radiation emergent from the medium at the boundaries $\tau = 0$ and $\tau = \tau_0$, as follows:

$$I(0, \eta) = \int_0^{\tau_0} p(\tau, \eta)f(\tau)\frac{d\tau}{\eta} \qquad (113a)$$

$$I(\tau_0, \eta) = \int_0^{\tau_0} p(\tau_0-\tau, \eta)f(\tau)\frac{d\tau}{\eta} \qquad (113b)$$

[5] S. Chandrasekhar, On the Radiative Equilibrium of a Stellar Atmosphere, XX, *Astrophysical J.* **106**, 145 (1947).

where $f(\tau)d\tau$ is the amount of energy coming directly from the radiation sources and absorbed by the elementary volume with cross section 1 cm², and optical thickness $d\tau$ per 1 sec.

To find the function $p(\tau, \eta)$ we can, as in the case $\tau_0 = \infty$, derive a linear integral equation of the following kind:

$$p(\tau, \eta) = \frac{\lambda}{4\pi}e^{-\tau/\eta} + \frac{\lambda}{2}\int_0^{\tau_0} p(\tau', \eta)\mathrm{Ei}|\tau - \tau'|\, d\tau' \qquad (114)$$

Comparing Eq. (114) with the integral equation, defining the function $B(\tau, \zeta)$ in the problem of the luminescence of a medium illuminated by parallel rays, which is

$$B(\tau, \zeta) = \frac{\lambda}{4}Se^{-\tau/\zeta} + \frac{\lambda}{2}\int_0^{\tau_0} B(\tau', \zeta)\mathrm{Ei}|\tau - \tau'|\, d\tau' \qquad (115)$$

we conclude that the function $p(\tau, \eta)$ is equal to the function $B(\tau, \eta)$ for $\pi S = 1$.

Applying Eqs. (113) to the problem of the luminescence of a medium illuminated by parallel rays, or setting in them $f(\tau) = \pi Se^{-\tau/\zeta}$, and replacing the radiation intensities by the brightness coefficients by means of the following relations:

$$\left.\begin{array}{l} I(0, \eta, \zeta) = Sp(\eta, \zeta)\zeta \\ I(\tau_0, \eta, \zeta) = S\sigma(\eta, \zeta)\zeta \end{array}\right\} \qquad (116)$$

we find

$$\left.\begin{array}{l} p(\eta, \zeta)\zeta = \pi\displaystyle\int_0^{\tau_0} e^{-\tau/\zeta}p(\tau, \eta)\frac{d\tau}{\eta} \\[3mm] \sigma(\eta, \zeta)\zeta = \pi\displaystyle\int_0^{\tau_0} e^{-\tau/\eta}p(\tau_0 - \tau, \eta)\frac{d\tau}{\eta} \end{array}\right\} \qquad (117)$$

Comparing these formulas with those which express the quantities ρ and σ by the function $B(\tau, \zeta)$ in the forms:

$$\left.\begin{array}{l} Sp(\eta, \zeta)\zeta = \displaystyle\int_0^{\tau_0} B(\tau, \zeta)e^{-\tau/\eta}\frac{d\tau}{\eta} \\[3mm] S\sigma(\eta, \zeta)\zeta = \displaystyle\int_0^{\tau_0} B(\tau, \zeta)\zeta e^{-(\tau_0-\tau)/\eta}\frac{d\tau}{\eta} \end{array}\right\} \qquad (118)$$

and recollecting that $p(\tau, \eta) = B(\tau, \eta)/\pi S$, we conclude:

$$\rho(\eta, \zeta) = \rho(\zeta, \eta), \qquad \sigma(\eta, \zeta) = \sigma(\zeta, \eta) \qquad (119)$$

or, there is a symmetry of the brightness coefficients relative to the angles of the incident and reflection (of transmission).

In addition to Eqs. (113) for defining the function $p(\tau, \eta)$ we can also derive a functional equation. For this, as in Section 1, we find the probability of quantum exit at optical depth $\tau + \Delta\tau$, or the quantity $p(\tau + \Delta\tau, \eta)$.

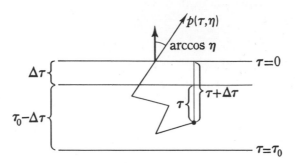

Fig. 6.1

We divide the medium with the optical thickness τ_0 in two parts, one of optical thickness $\tau_0 - \Delta\tau$ and another of small optical thickness $\Delta\tau$ (Fig. 6.1). Letting $p_1(\tau, \eta)$ be the probability of quantum exit at optical depth τ from the medium with optical thickness $\tau_0 - \Delta\tau$, we find the quantity $p(\tau + \Delta\tau, \eta)$ as follows:

$$p(\tau + \Delta\tau, \eta) = p_1(\tau, \eta)\left(1 - \frac{\Delta\tau}{\eta}\right) + 2\pi \int_0^1 p_1(\tau, \eta') \frac{\Delta\tau}{\eta'} \, d\eta' p(0, \eta) \quad (120)$$

On the other hand, the quantity $p_1(\tau, \eta)$ is

$$p_1(\tau, \eta) = p(\tau, \eta) - 2\pi \int_0^1 p(\tau_0 - \tau, \eta') \frac{\Delta\tau}{\eta'} \, d\eta' p(\tau_0, \eta) \quad (121)$$

Inserting Eq. (121) into Eq. (120) and setting $\Delta\tau \to 0$, we find

$$\frac{\partial p(\tau, \eta)}{\partial \tau} = -\frac{1}{\eta} p(\tau, \eta) + 2\pi p(0, \eta) \int_0^1 p(\tau, \eta') \frac{d\eta'}{\eta'}$$

$$- 2\pi p(\tau_0, \eta) \int_0^1 p(\tau_0 - \tau, \eta') \frac{d\eta'}{\eta'} \quad (122)$$

This equation is a general form of Eq. (44) derived for the case $\tau_0 = \infty$.

In computing the quantities $p(0, \eta)$ and $p(\tau_0, \eta)$ in Eq. (122), we should remember that the quantum absorbed by the boundary layer can emerge from the medium either directly from the layer or as the result of the diffuse reflection (or transmission) of the radiation by the medium. Therefore, we obtain

$$\left. \begin{array}{l} p(0,\eta) \; - \; \dfrac{\lambda}{4\pi}\left[1+2\eta\displaystyle\int_0^1 \rho(\eta,\eta')\,d\eta'\right] \\[4mm] p(\tau_0,\eta) \; = \; \dfrac{\lambda}{4\pi}\left[e^{-\tau_0/\eta}+2\eta\displaystyle\int_0^1 \sigma(\eta,\eta')\,d\eta'\right] \end{array}\right\} \tag{123}$$

where $\rho(\eta,\zeta)$ and $\sigma(\eta,\zeta)$ are the brightness coefficients defined by Eq. (117).

Let us now find these quantities ρ and σ with the aid of Eq. (122). Multiplying Eq. (122) first by $e^{-\tau/\zeta}\,d\tau$, then by $e^{-(\tau_0-\tau)/\zeta}\,dt$, and integrating with respect to τ in the interval from 0 to τ_0, we have

$$(\eta+\zeta)\rho(\eta,\zeta) \; = \; \pi p(0,\eta)[1+2\zeta\int_0^1 \rho(\eta',\zeta)\,d\eta']$$

$$-\pi p(\tau_0,\eta)[e^{-\tau_0/\zeta}+2\zeta\int_0^1 \sigma(\eta',\zeta)\,d\eta'] \tag{124}$$

$$(\zeta-\eta)\sigma(\eta,\zeta) \; = \; \pi p(0,\eta)[e^{-\tau_0/\zeta}+2\zeta\int_0^1 \sigma(\eta',\zeta)\,d\eta']$$

$$-\pi p(\tau_0,\eta)[1+2\zeta\int_0^1 \rho(\eta',\zeta)\,d\eta'] \tag{125}$$

Using Eqs. (123) and recollecting the symmetry of the functions ρ and σ, proved above, we find

$$\left. \begin{array}{l} \rho(\eta,\zeta) \; = \; \dfrac{\lambda}{4}\dfrac{\phi(\eta)\phi(\zeta)-\psi(\eta)\psi(\zeta)}{\eta+\zeta} \\[4mm] \sigma(\eta,\zeta) \; = \; \dfrac{1}{4}\dfrac{\phi(\eta)\psi(\zeta)-\phi(\zeta)\psi(\eta)}{\zeta-\eta} \end{array}\right\} \tag{126}$$

where

$$\phi(\eta) \; = \; 1+2\eta\int_0^1 \rho(\eta,\eta')\,d\eta', \qquad \psi(\eta) \; = \; e^{-\tau_0/\eta}+2\eta\int_0^1 \sigma(\eta,\eta')\,d\eta' \tag{127}$$

A substitution of Eqs. (126) in Eqs. (127) gives the following equations for the functions $\phi(\eta)$ and $\psi(\eta)$:

$$\left. \begin{array}{l} \phi(\eta) \; = \; 1+\dfrac{\lambda}{2}\eta\displaystyle\int_0^1 \dfrac{\phi(\eta)\phi(\eta')-\psi(\eta)\psi(\eta')}{\eta+\eta'}\,d\eta' \\[4mm] \psi(\eta) \; = \; e^{-\tau_0/\eta}+\dfrac{\lambda}{2}\eta\displaystyle\int_0^1 \dfrac{\phi(\eta)\psi(\eta')-\phi(\eta')\psi(\eta)}{\eta'-\eta}\,d\eta' \end{array}\right\} \tag{128}$$

From Eqs. (123) and (127) follow

$$\left.\begin{array}{l} p(0, \eta) \ = \ \dfrac{\lambda}{4\pi}\phi(\eta) \\[3mm] p(\tau_0, \eta) \ = \ \dfrac{\lambda}{4\pi}\psi(\eta) \end{array}\right\} \tag{129}$$

These formulas define the physical meaning of the functions ϕ and ψ.

The Eqs. (126) and (128) for the quantities ρ and σ, and ϕ and ψ, respectively, were derived earlier (Chapter 3, Section 4). However, now we can also solve other problems of the luminescence of the medium under consideration by means of Eqs. (113) and (122). Some of these problems we shall discuss in the following section.

At the present time let us consider the solution of Eqs. (128) for a case of pure scattering. The point is that in this case the general solution of Eqs. (128) includes an arbitrary constant C. Indeed, if the functions $\phi_*(\eta)$ and $\psi_*(\eta)$ represent a solution of the system of Eqs. (128), the functions

$$\left.\begin{array}{l} \phi(\eta) \ = \ \phi_*(\eta) + C\eta[\phi_*(\eta) + \psi_*(\eta)\,] \\[2mm] \psi(\eta) \ = \ \psi_*(\eta) - C\eta[\phi_*(\eta) + \psi_*(\eta)\,] \end{array}\right\} \tag{130}$$

will also be a solution of this system. In Eqs. (130), C is a constant.

In order to determine the constant C we can use the so-called K-integral which was mentioned in Chapter 3, Section 4. But we can find the constant C by means of another method based on the physical meaning of the functions $\phi(\eta)$ and $\psi(\eta)$ expressed in Eqs. (129).

For a case of pure scattering, the equation,

$$2\pi \int_0^1 p(\tau, \eta)\ d\eta + 2\pi \int_0^1 p(\tau_0 - \tau, \eta)\ d\eta \ = \ 1 \tag{131}$$

should be correct, which means that all quanta absorbed at any optical depth τ should leave the medium.

Setting $\tau = 0$ in Eq. (131) and using Eqs. (129) for $\lambda = 1$, we find

$$\tfrac{1}{2} \int_0^1 \phi(\eta)\ d\eta + \tfrac{1}{2} \int_0^1 \psi(\eta)\ d\eta \ = \ 1 \tag{132}$$

Here, however, this relation cannot serve for the determination of the constant C because, by substituting Eqs. (130) into Eq. (132), we exclude the constant C. This is because Eq. (132) is a consequence of Eqs. (128) with $\lambda = 1$.

But we can derive from Eq. (131), and also by means of Eq. (122), other formulas of the functions $\phi(\eta)$ and $\psi(\eta)$ which are not implicit in Eqs. (128).

Integrating Eq. (131) with respect to τ in the interval from 0 to τ_0, we have

$$4\pi \int_0^1 d\eta \int_0^{\tau_0} p(\tau, \eta) \, d\tau = \tau_0 \qquad (133)$$

Further, integrating Eq. (122) likewise, we obtain

$$\int_0^{\tau_0} p(\tau, \eta) \frac{d\tau}{\eta} = [p(0, \eta) - p(\tau_0, \eta)] \left[1 + 2\pi \int_0^1 d\eta' \int_0^{\tau_0} p(\tau, \eta') \frac{d\tau}{\eta'} \right] \qquad (134)$$

But the integral on the right-hand side of Eq. (134) can easily be found by integrating the same Eq. (134) with respect to η in the interval from 0 to 1. As the result, we obtain

$$\int_0^{\tau_0} p(\tau, \eta) \frac{d\tau}{\eta} = \frac{\lambda}{4\pi} \frac{\phi(\eta) - \psi(\eta)}{1 - \frac{\lambda}{2} \int_0^1 [\phi(\eta) - \psi(\eta)] \, d\eta} \qquad (135)$$

while paying attention to Eqs. (129).

Equation (135) is correct for any value of λ. Inserting the value of the integral Eq. (135) for $\lambda = 1$ into Eq. (133), we find

$$\alpha_1 - \beta_1 = \tau_0[1 - \tfrac{1}{2}(\alpha_0 - \beta_0)] \qquad (136)$$

where the following notations were employed:

$$\alpha_n = \int_0^1 \phi(\eta) \eta^n \, d\eta, \qquad \beta_n = \int_0^1 \psi(\eta) \eta^n \, d\eta \qquad (137)$$

Equation (136) can indeed serve for the determination of the constant C in the case of pure scattering. If we put Eqs. (130) into Eq. (136), we obtain

$$C = \frac{\tau_0[1 - \tfrac{1}{2}(\alpha_0{}^* - \beta_0{}^*)] - \alpha_1{}^* + \beta_1{}^*}{2(\alpha_2{}^* + \beta_2{}^*) + \tau_0(\alpha_1{}^* + \beta_1{}^*)} \qquad (138)$$

where $\alpha_n{}^*$ and $\beta_n{}^*$ are moments of the functions $\phi^*(\eta)$ and $\psi^*(\eta)$.

In the future we assume that the functions $\phi(\eta)$ and $\psi(\eta)$, found from Eq. (128) with $\lambda = 1$, satisfy Eq. (136), that is, they have the physical meaning which is required by Eqs. (129).

In an article[6] the author has shown that by this method of quantum exit we can easily derive Eqs. (102) and (103) of Chapter 3 for the functions $\phi(\eta)$ and $\psi(\eta)$ and also some new equations. In the same article, he gave the asymptotic formulas for $\phi(\eta)$ and $\psi(\eta)$ for large values of τ_0.

[6] V. V. Sobolev, *Russian Astronomical J.* (in press).

7. Luminescence of a Medium
for Various Radiation Sources

The knowledge of the function $p(\tau, \eta)$, together with Eqs. (113), permits us to compute the intensities of the emergent radiation with any kind of radiation sources. However, sometimes we can compute the intensities $I(0, \eta)$ and $I(\tau_0, \eta)$ from Eqs. (113) without previous knowledge of this function by the direct use of Eq. (122) and by taking into account Eq. (129). Now we give some examples of such computations.

1. The radiation sources are within the medium; the function $B_0(\tau)$ is expressed by a series expanded in powers of τ, that is, it has the form of Eq. (63). In this case the function $f(\tau)$ according to Eq. (35) becomes

$$f(\tau) = \frac{4\pi}{\lambda}(b_0 + b_1\tau + b_2\tau^2 + \ldots) \tag{139}$$

Inserting Eq. (139) into Eqs. (113), we obtain

$$I(0, \eta) = \frac{4\pi}{\lambda}[b_0 A_0(\eta) + b_1 A_1(\eta) + b_2 A_2(\eta) + \ldots] \tag{140}$$

$$I(\tau_0, \eta) = \frac{4\pi}{\lambda}[b_0 D_0(\eta) + b_1 D_1(\eta) + b_2 D_2(\eta) + \ldots] \tag{141}$$

where we have introduced the following notations:

$$A_n(\eta) = \int_0^{\tau_0} p(\tau, \eta)\tau^n \frac{d\tau}{\eta}, \qquad D_0(\eta) = \int_0^{\tau_0} p(\tau_0 - \tau, \eta)\tau^n \frac{d\tau}{\eta} \tag{142}$$

In solving Eqs. (142) we first rewrite Eq. (122) in the form:

$$\frac{\partial p(\tau, \eta)}{\partial \tau} = -\frac{1}{\eta}p(\tau, \eta)$$

$$+ \frac{\lambda}{2}\phi(\eta)\int_0^1 p(\tau, \eta')\frac{d\eta'}{\eta'} - \frac{\lambda}{2}\phi(\eta)\int_0^1 p(\tau_0 - \tau, \eta')\frac{d\eta'}{\eta'} \tag{143}$$

Then we multiply Eq. (143) by τ^n and integrate with respect to τ in the interval from 0 to τ_0 and, for $n \geqslant 1$, we find

$$p(\tau_0, \eta)\tau_0{}^n - n\eta A_{n-1}(\eta)$$

$$= -A_n(\eta) + \frac{\lambda}{2}\phi(\eta)\int_0^1 A_n(\eta')\, d\eta' - \frac{\lambda}{2}\psi(\eta)\int_0^1 D_n(\eta')\, d\eta' \tag{144}$$

Obviously,

$$D_n(\eta) = \tau_0{}^n A_0(\eta) - C_n{}^1\tau_0{}^{n-1}A_1(\eta) + \ldots + (-1)^n A_n(\eta) \tag{145}$$

where $C_n{}^k$ are binomial coefficients. Therefore, instead of Eq. (144), we have

$$A_n(\eta) = -\frac{\lambda}{4\pi}\psi(\eta)\tau_0{}^n + n\eta A_{n-1}(\eta)$$

$$+ \frac{\lambda}{2}\phi(\eta)a_n - \frac{\lambda}{2}\psi(\eta)[\tau_0{}^n a_0 - C_n{}^1\tau_0{}^{n-1}a_1 + \dots + (-1)^n a_n] \quad (146)$$

where

$$a_n = \int_0^1 A_n(\eta)\,d\eta \quad (147)$$

Finally, integrating Eq. (146) with respect to η in the interval from 0 to 1, we obtain

$$\left[1 - \frac{\lambda}{2}\alpha_0 + (-1)^n\frac{\lambda}{2}\beta_0\right]a_n = -\frac{\lambda}{4\pi}\beta_0\tau_0{}^n$$

$$+ n\int_0^1 \eta A_{n-1}(\eta)\,d\eta - \frac{\lambda}{2}\beta_0[\tau_0{}^n a_0 - C_n{}^1\tau_0{}^{n-1}a_1$$

$$+ \dots + (-1)^{n-1}C_n{}^1\tau_0 a_{n-1}] \quad (148)$$

If we set the values a_n, given by this relation, in Eq. (146), we receive the recurrent formula for determination of the quantities $A_n(\eta)$. The quantity $A_0(\eta)$ was found earlier by means of Eq. (135).

Having found the quantities $A_n(\eta)$ in accordance with Eq. (145), we can also find the quantities $D_n(\eta)$.

Let us apply these formulas to some particular cases. Assuming first the case of the uniform distribution of radiation sources in the medium, we use Eqs. (140), (141), and (135) and, for $B_0 = $ const, we find

$$I(0,\eta) = I(\tau_0,\eta) = \frac{4\pi}{\lambda}B_0 A_0(\eta) \quad (149)$$

where

$$A_0(\eta) = \frac{\lambda}{4\pi}\frac{\phi(\eta) - \psi(\eta)}{1 - (\lambda/2)\alpha_0 - \beta_0)} \quad (150)$$

For $\tau_0 = \infty$ and from Eq. (149) follows Eq. (79).

Next, we consider the case $B_0(\tau) = b_1\tau$. With $n = 1$, Eqs. (146) and (148) become

$$A_1(\eta) = -\frac{\lambda}{4\pi}\psi(\eta)\tau_0 + \eta A_0(\eta) + \frac{\lambda}{2}[\phi(\eta) + \psi(\eta)]a_1 - \frac{\lambda}{2}\psi(\eta)\tau_0 a_0 \quad (151)$$

$$\left(1 - \frac{\lambda}{2}\alpha_0 - \frac{\lambda}{2}\beta_0\right)a_1 = -\frac{\lambda}{4\pi}\beta_0\tau_0 + \int_0^1 \eta A_0(\eta)\,d\eta - \frac{\lambda}{2}B_0\tau_0 a_0 \quad (152)$$

Using Eq. (150), we find that the constant a_0 is equal to

$$a_0 = \frac{\lambda}{4\pi} \frac{\alpha_0 - \beta_0}{1 - (\lambda/2)\alpha_0 + (\lambda/2)\beta_0} \tag{153}$$

To find the constant a_1 we have to substitute Eq. (150) into Eq. (152). Hence,

$$\left(1 - \frac{\lambda}{2}\alpha_0 - \frac{\lambda}{2}\beta_0\right)a_1 = \frac{\lambda}{4\pi} \frac{\alpha_1 - \beta_1 - \beta_0\tau_0}{1 - (\lambda/2)\alpha_0 + (\lambda/2)\beta_0} \tag{154}$$

But from Eqs. (128) it follows that

$$\left(1 - \frac{\lambda}{2}\alpha_0 - \frac{\lambda}{2}\beta_0\right)\left(1 - \frac{\lambda}{2}\alpha_0 + \frac{\lambda}{2}\beta_0\right) = 1 - \lambda \tag{155}$$

(see Chapter 3, Section 4). Therefore, Eq. (154) gives

$$a_1 = \frac{\lambda}{4\pi} \frac{\alpha_1 - \beta_1 - \beta_0\tau_0}{1 - \lambda} \tag{156}$$

Substituting Eqs. (150), (153), and (156) into (155), we find the required quantity $A_1(\eta)$:

$$A_1(\eta) = \frac{\lambda}{4\pi}\left\{\eta\frac{\phi(\eta) - \psi(\eta)}{1 - (\lambda/2)\alpha_0 + (\lambda/2)\beta_0} - \tau_0\frac{\psi(\eta)}{1 - (\lambda/2)\alpha_0 + (\lambda/2)\beta_0}\right.$$
$$\left. + \frac{\lambda}{2}\frac{\alpha_1 - \beta_1 - \beta_0\tau_0}{1 - \lambda}[\phi(\eta) + \psi(\eta)]\right\} \tag{157}$$

The intensities of the emergent radiation in this case will be

$$I(0, \eta) = \frac{4\pi}{\lambda}b_1 A_1(\eta), \qquad I(\tau_0, \eta) = \frac{4\pi}{\lambda}b_1[\tau_0 A_0(\eta) - A_1(\eta)] \tag{158}$$

Let us consider one more application: $B_0(\tau) = b_2\tau^2$. For this particular distribution of sources, we have

$$I(0, \eta) = \frac{4\pi}{\lambda}b_2 A_2(\eta), \qquad I(\tau_0, \eta) = \frac{4\pi}{\lambda}b_2 D_2(\eta) \tag{159}$$

where, following Eq. (145),

$$D_2(\eta) = \tau_0^2 A_0(\eta) - 2\tau_0 A_1(\eta) + A_2(\eta) \tag{160}$$

To determine the quantity $A_2(\eta)$, we have to put $n = 2$ into Eqs. (146) and (148). The result is

$$A_2(\eta) = -\frac{\lambda}{4\pi}\psi(\eta)\tau_0^2 + 2\eta A_1(\eta) + \frac{\lambda}{2}[\phi(\eta) - \psi(\eta)]a_2$$
$$- \frac{\lambda}{2}\psi(\eta)(\tau_0^2 a_0 - 2\tau_0 a_1) \tag{161}$$

$$\left(1 - \frac{\lambda}{2}\alpha_0 + \frac{\lambda}{2}\beta_0\right)a_2$$

$$= -\frac{\lambda}{4\pi}\beta_0\tau_0{}^2 + 2\int_0^1 \eta A_1(\eta)\, d\eta - \frac{\lambda}{2}\beta_0(\tau_0{}^2 a_0 - 2\tau_0 a_1) \qquad (162)$$

Inserting now the quantities $A_1(\eta)$ and a_0, found earlier, we obtain

$$\left(1 - \frac{\lambda}{2}\alpha_0 + \frac{\lambda}{2}\beta_0\right)a_2$$

$$= \frac{\lambda}{4\pi}\frac{2(\alpha_2 - \beta_2) - 2\tau_0\beta_1 - \tau_0{}^2\beta_0}{1 - (\lambda/2)a_0 + (\lambda/2)\beta_0} + \lambda(\alpha_1 + \beta_1 + \tau_0\beta_0)a_1 \qquad (163)$$

If we insert a_2 of Eq. (163) into Eq. (161), we arrive at the expression for the quantity $A_2(\eta)$.

We draw attention to the fact that for $\lambda = 1$ the derived expressions for $A_1(\eta)$ and $A_2(\eta)$ become undetermined due to the indeterminateness of the constant a_1. To find this constant, we apply the same method developed at the end of the foregoing section for the determination of the constant C, that is, we shall use Eq. (131).

Multiplying Eq. (131) by τ^n and integrating with respect to τ in the interval from 0 to τ_0, we find

$$2\pi \int_0^1 A_n(\eta)\eta\, d\eta + 2\pi \int_0^1 D_n(\eta)\eta\, d\eta = \frac{\tau_0{}^{n+1}}{n+1} \qquad (164)$$

Putting $n = 1$ and remembering Eqs. (145) and (150), we obtain the relation

$$\alpha_1 - \beta_1 - \beta_0\tau_0 = 0 \qquad (165)$$

which follows also from Eq. (156) for a_1 and with $\lambda = 1$. Assuming $n = 2$ in Eq. (164) and utilizing Eq. (160), we have now

$$\int_0^1 A_2(\eta)\eta\, d\eta + \frac{\tau_0{}^2}{2}\int_0^1 A_0(\eta)\eta\, d\eta - \tau_0\int_0^1 A_1(\eta)\, d\eta = \frac{\tau_0{}^3}{12\pi} \qquad (166)$$

Finally inserting in Eq. (166) the expressions of $A_0(\eta)$, $A_1(\eta)$, and $A_2(\eta)$ found above, we obtain

$$a_1 = \frac{1}{4\pi}\frac{(\tau_0{}^3/3)\beta_0 + \tau_0{}^2\beta_1 + 2\tau_0\beta_2 - 2(\alpha_3 - \beta_3)}{\beta_0[\alpha_2 + \beta_2 + (\tau_0/2)(\alpha_1 + \beta_1)]} \qquad (167)$$

In the case of pure scattering, this value of a_1 should be inserted in the formula of $A_1(\eta)$ and $A_2(\eta)$.

Analogously, we can eliminate the indeterminateness caused by $\lambda = 1$ in expressions for any other quantities $A_n(\eta)$.

We point out that Horak and Lundquist[7] have published three articles on the problem of the luminescence of a medium with finite optical thickness and the case of the function $B_0(\tau)$ being a polynomial, using a more involved method.

2. Previously we assumed that radiation sources located in the medium radiate an equal amount of energy in all directions. However, the function $p(\tau, \eta)$ permits us to solve also the problems with non-isotropic emission of energy.

We denote by $B_0(\tau, \eta)d\omega$ the amount of energy emitted by the radiation sources found at the optical depth τ in the elementary volume with the cross section 1 cm^2 and the optical thickness $d\tau$, at the angle arccos η to the normal within the solid angle $d\omega$ per 1 sec. Obviously we cannot here define the function $f(\tau)$ by means of Eq. (35); in other words, we cannot assume that the energy emitted by the elementary volume is the energy scattered by the same volume because the radiation scattering was supposed to be isotropic. Therefore, we compute the function $f(\tau)$ in accordance with its formal definition: we find the amount of energy coming directly from the radiation sources and being absorbed at a given place in the medium.

It is easy to obtain

$$f(\tau) = 2\pi \int_0^1 d\eta' \int_0^\tau e^{-(\tau-\tau')/\eta'} B_0(\tau', \eta') \frac{d\tau'}{\eta'}$$

$$+ 2\pi \int_0^1 d\eta' \int_\tau^{\tau_0} e^{-(\tau'-\tau)/\eta'} B_0(\tau', -\eta') \frac{d\tau'}{\eta'} \qquad (168)$$

Inserting this expression for $f(\tau)$ into Eq. (113) we find the intensities of the diffuse radiation emergent from the medium. To find total intensities we have to add to them the intensities of the radiation due to the radiation sources directly. As the result, we obtain the total intensity $I(0, \eta)$ of the emergent radiation in the following expression:

$$I(0, \eta) = 2\pi \int_0^{\tau_0} p(\tau, \eta) \frac{d\tau}{\eta} \int_0^1 d\eta' \left[\int_0^\tau e^{-(\tau-\tau')/\eta'} B_0(\tau', \eta') \frac{d\tau'}{\eta'} \right.$$

$$+ \left. \int_\tau^{\tau_0} e^{-(\tau'-\tau)/\eta'} B_0(\tau', -\eta') \frac{d\tau'}{\eta'} \right] + \int_0^{\tau_0} B_0(\tau, -\eta) e^{-\tau/\eta} \frac{d\tau}{\eta} \qquad (169)$$

and a similar expression for $I(\tau_0, \eta)$.

Equations (169) and (143) permit us to compute the quantities $I(0, \eta)$ and $I(\tau_0, \eta)$ in many special cases of the dependence of B_0

[7] H. G. Horak, Ch. A. Lundquist, The Transfer of Radiation by an Emitting Atmosphere, *Astrophysical J.* **116**, 477 (1952); **119**, 542 (1954); **121**, 175 (1955).

on τ and η. We limit ourselves, however, by the case when the radiation sources are uniformly distributed in the medium, that is, when $B_0(\tau, \eta) = B_0(\eta)$.

In this case Eq. (169) becomes

$$I(0, \eta) = 2\pi \int_0^1 B_0(\eta') \, d\eta' \int_0^{\tau_0} (1 - e^{-\tau/\eta'}) p(\tau, \eta) \frac{d\tau}{\eta}$$

$$+ 2\pi \int_0^1 B_0(-\eta') \, d\eta' \int_0^{\tau_0} (1 - e^{-(\tau_0 - \tau)/\eta'} p(\tau, \eta) \frac{d\tau}{\eta}$$

$$+ B_0(-\eta)(1 - e^{-\tau_0/\eta}) \tag{170}$$

Using Eqs. (117) and (135), instead of Eq. (170), we find

$$I(0, \eta) = \frac{\lambda}{2} \frac{\phi(\eta) - \psi(\eta)}{1 - (\lambda/2)(\alpha_0 - \beta_0)} \int_0^1 [B_0(\eta') + B_0(-\eta')] \, d\eta'$$

$$- 2 \int_0^1 B_0(\eta')\rho(\eta, \eta')\eta' \, d\eta' - 2 \int_0^1 B_0(-\eta')\sigma(\eta, \eta')\eta' \, d\eta'$$

$$+ B_0(-\eta)(1 - e^{-\tau_0/\eta}) \tag{171}$$

Thus we have found that in this case the intensities of the emergent radiation are very simply expressed by the functions $\phi(\eta)$ and $\psi(\eta)$ introduced above.

It is easy to be convinced that for $B_0(\eta) = B_0 = $ const, Eq. (171) becomes Eq. (149). For that we have to avail ourselves only of Eqs. (126) and (128) which define the functions $\phi(\eta)$ and $\psi(\eta)$.

If the quantity B_0 depends not only on τ and η but also on the azimuth, $B_0(\tau, \eta)$ will mean the quantity B_0 averaged over the azimuth in all the terms of the above-derived formulas that determine the intensity of the diffuse radiation.

3. Now we assume that there is an external radiation whose intensity depends on the zenith distance and azumith. Denoting by $I_0(\zeta)$ the intensity of such a radiation averaged over the azimuth, we find that the function $f(\tau)$ will then be

$$f(\tau) = 2\pi \int_0^1 e^{-\tau/\zeta} I_0(\zeta) \, d\zeta \tag{172}$$

Inserting Eq. (172) into Eq. (113a), we obtain

$$I(0, \eta) = 2\pi \int_0^1 I_0(\zeta) \, d\zeta \int_0^{\tau_0} p(\tau, \eta) e^{-\tau/\zeta} \frac{d\tau}{\eta} \tag{173}$$

Or, recollecting Eqs. (117),

$$I(0, \eta) = 2 \int_0^1 I_0(\zeta)\rho(\eta, \zeta)\zeta \, d\zeta \tag{174}$$

Similarly, we find the expression for the intensity of the radiation emergent from the other boundary of the medium.

$$I(\tau_0, \eta) = 2 \int_0^1 I_0(\zeta) \sigma(\eta, \zeta) \zeta \, d\zeta \tag{175}$$

It goes without saying that Eqs. (174) and (175) could have been derived directly from Eqs. (116).

In the case when the medium is illuminated by isotropic radiation ($I_0 = $ const), Eqs. (174) and (175) with aid of Eqs. (126) and (128) become

$$I(0, \eta) = I_0\left[1 - \left(1 - \frac{\lambda}{2}\alpha_0\right)\phi(\eta) - \frac{\lambda}{2}\beta_0\psi(\eta)\right] \tag{176}$$

$$I(\tau_0, \eta) = I_0\left[\left(1 - \frac{\lambda}{2}\alpha_0\right)\psi(\eta) + \frac{\lambda}{2}\beta_0\phi(\eta) - e^{-\tau_0/\eta}\right] \tag{177}$$

We shall not again apply Eq. (122) to the solution of other problems about the luminescence of a medium. We merely draw attention to the fact that the solutions obtained in the previous section can easily be generalized for the case when the medium is bounded by the surface reflecting the radiation. This generalization will be made in the next chapter.

8. Point Source of Light

When we have formulated problems of the luminescence of the medium consisting of the plane parallel layers, we have made an assumption, always implicit, that the radiation sources at different points are similar at the same depth. But there are cases when these radiation sources are different. The simplest example is the case of the point source of radiation located either within or outside the medium.

Although this problem of the point source of radiation is extremely important, it has scarcely been investigated in the past. Some particular problems connected with the point sources of radiation were discussed by Ambartsumian[8] and by the author.[9]

The problems with the point sources of radiation are much more involved than those considered earlier. This is because the quantities I and B depend in such cases not only on the depth but also on other

[8] V. A. Ambartsumian, Point Source of Light in a Turbid Medium, *Bull. Erev. astr. obser.*, No. 6 (1945).

[9] V. V. Sobolev, Point Source of Light Between Parallel Planes, *DAN SSSR* **42**, 176 (1944).

coordinates. For example, these quantities become functions of the depth and the distance from the normal to the boundary of the medium in the case of the point source of light. If we try to solve such problems approximately by the aid of the averaging of radiation intensities over the angles, we shall derive not the usual differential equations found earlier, but partial differential equations for defining the function B.

However, with the aid of the above-introduced function $p(\tau, \eta)$, we can gather some information about the luminescence of the medium even in the case of the different radiation sources at different points and at the same depth.

The function $p(\tau, \eta)$ defines the probability of quantum exit from the medium at an angle arccos η to the normal (within the unity of the solid angle) after the quantum was absorbed at the optical depth τ. At the same time it is not important how the quantum appeared at the given depth. Therefore, we can always find **the total amount of energy** emergent in the required direction after we have multiplied the amount of energy coming from the radiation sources and absorbed at the depth between τ and $\tau + d\tau$ by the function $p(\tau, \eta)$ and after we have integrated with respect to all depths. On the other hand, we cannot, generally speaking, determine the number of quanta passing the boundary of the medium at a given place; in other words, we cannot determine the radiation intensity by the aid of the function $p(\tau, \eta)$. This can be done only in the previously discussed case of the uniform distribution of the radiation sources at the same depth. In this simplest case we know that the same number of quanta passes through the unit of surface and at any place of the boundary.

Assuming now that the distribution of the radiation source is arbitrary and denoting by $F(\tau)d\tau$ the amount of energy arriving directly from the radiation sources and absorbed by the whole medium between the optical depths τ and $\tau + d\tau$ per 1 sec., we find that the total amount of energy emitted by the medium at an angle arccos η to the normal per unit of solid angle and time, and at the boundary $\tau = 0$ will be equal to

$$E(0, \eta) = \int_0^{\tau_0} p(\tau, \eta) F(\tau) \, d\tau \qquad (178)$$

Analogously, we derive the amount of energy emitted by the medium at the boundary $\tau = \tau_0$:

$$E(\tau_0, \eta) = \int_0^{\tau_0} p(\tau_0 - \tau, \eta) F(\tau) \, d\tau \qquad (179)$$

We apply now Eqs. (178) and (179) to the problem of the point source of light with the intensity L emitted equally in all directions.

We first assume that the point source is above the medium (Fig. 6.2). Then the amount of energy falling on the medium at an angle arccos ζ to the normal within the solid angle $2\pi\, d\zeta$ is equal to $(2\pi\, d\zeta/4\pi)L$. The fraction of this amount absorbed between the depths τ and $\tau+d\tau$ is equal to

$$\frac{L}{2}\, d\zeta e^{-\tau/\zeta}\frac{d\tau}{\zeta}$$

Therefore, the total energy absorbed by the medium between the depths τ and $\tau+d\tau$ will be

$$\frac{L}{2}\, d\tau \int_0^1 e^{-\tau/\zeta}\frac{d\zeta}{\zeta}$$

or

$$F(\tau) = \frac{L}{2}\mathrm{Ei}\,\tau \tag{180}$$

Inserting Eq. (180) into Eqs. (178) and (179), we find

$$\left.\begin{aligned}
E(0,\eta) &= \frac{L}{2}\int_0^{\tau_0} p(\tau,\eta)\mathrm{Ei}\tau\, d\tau \\[2mm]
E(\tau_0,\eta) &= \frac{L}{2}\int_0^{\tau_0} p(\tau_0-\tau,\eta)\mathrm{Ei}\,\tau\, d\tau
\end{aligned}\right\} \tag{181}$$

These integrals we can compute with the aid of the integral Eq. (114), defining the function $p(\tau,\eta)$ setting first $\tau=0$ and then $\tau=\tau_0$. We have

$$\left.\begin{aligned}
p(0,\eta) &= \frac{\lambda}{2}\int_0^{\tau_0}\mathrm{Ei}\,\tau\, p(\tau,\eta)\, d\tau +\frac{\lambda}{4\pi} \\[2mm]
p(\tau_0,\eta) &= \frac{\lambda}{2}\int_0^{\tau_0}\mathrm{Ei}(\tau_0-\tau)p(\tau,\eta)\, d\tau +\frac{\lambda}{4\pi}e^{-\tau_0/\eta}
\end{aligned}\right\} \tag{182}$$

Hence,

$$\left.\begin{aligned}
E(0,\eta) &= \frac{L}{\lambda}\left[p(0,\eta)-\frac{\lambda}{4\pi}\right] \\[2mm]
E(\tau_0,\eta) &= \frac{L}{\lambda}\left[p(\tau_0,\eta)-\frac{\lambda}{4\pi}e^{-\tau_0/\eta}\right]
\end{aligned}\right\} \tag{183}$$

But the quantities $p(0,\eta)$ and $p(\tau_0,\eta)$ can be expressed by the functions $\phi(\eta)$ and $\psi(\eta)$ by means of Eqs. (129) and so, finally, we obtain

$$E(0,\eta) = \frac{L}{4\pi}[\phi(\eta)-1], \qquad E(\tau_0,\eta) = \frac{L}{4\pi}[\psi(\eta)-e^{-\tau_0/\eta}] \tag{184}$$

We observe that the quantities $E(0, \eta)$ and $E(\tau_0, \eta)$ do not depend on the height of the light source above the medium.

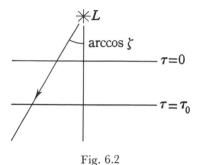

Fig. 6.2

Now we assume that the point source is within the medium at the optical depth τ. It is easy to show that in this case

$$F(\tau') \;=\; \frac{L}{2}\mathrm{Ei}|\tau - \tau'| \tag{185}$$

Substituting Eq. (185) into Eqs. (178) and (179) and recollecting Eq. (114), we find

$$
\left.
\begin{aligned}
E(0, \eta) &= \frac{L}{\lambda}\left[p(\tau, \eta) - \frac{\lambda}{4\pi}e^{-\tau/\eta}\right]\\[2mm]
E(\tau_0, \eta) &= \frac{L}{\lambda}\left[p(\tau_0 - \tau, \eta) - \frac{\lambda}{4\pi}e^{-(\tau_0-\tau)/\eta}\right]
\end{aligned}
\right\} \tag{186}
$$

It goes without saying that the Eqs. (186) define only the energy emergent from the medium after the scattering and not directly from the sources. If we had remembered the physical meaning of the quantity $p(\tau, \eta)$ we could have written these equations at once.

Equations (184) and (186) can be applied to the problem of the amount of energy scattered by a nebula illuminated by a star, or stars, in different directions. Such an application was made by Kaplan[10] who discussed the luminescence of the dust nebulae. The optical thickness was assumed infinitely large and the star to be outside the nebula. He used also the formula for the quantity $E(0, \eta)$ derived for the simplest nonspherical indicatrix:

$$x(\gamma) \;=\; 1 + x_1 \cos\gamma$$

in addition to the first formula of Eqs. (184).

[10] S. A. Kaplan, Light Reflection by Dust Nebulae, *Russian Astronomical J.* **29**, Bulletin 3 (1952).

We may remark that Kaplan and Klimishin[11] considered the problem of the luminescence of a spherico-symmetrical nebula with a star within it. Because the thickness of the nebula was assumed small as compared with its radius, it could be assumed that the nebula consisted of the plane-parallel layers and the illumination was the same at each place of the same depth. Therefore not only was the total energy emitted by the nebula found, but also the intensity of radiation emergent from the nebula.

Let us emphasize that it is impossible to find the intensity of the emergent radiation in a general case with the aid of the function $p(\tau, \eta)$, that is, with a nonuniform distribution of radiation sources at one and the same depth. In order to solve this problem completely we must find the probability of the quantum exit in the given direction and **at a definite place;** or, more precisely, at a definite distance from the perpendicular passing through the elementary volume in which the quantum was absorbed. However, we shall not discuss this problem.

9. THE STATISTICAL MEANING OF THE RADIATIVE TRANSFER PROBLEM

Having solved some concrete problems with the aid of the function $p(\tau, \eta)$, we should like to express our general ideas concerning the radiative transfer.

All quantities which characterize the elementary act of scattering have a simple probabilistic meaning. The absorption coefficient α is defined so that the quantity αds represents the probability of the quantum absorption on the path ds. The ratio of the absorption coefficient to the sum of the scattering coefficient and the true absorption, denoted by us as λ, is the probability of the quantum "lifetime" during the elementary act of scattering. The quantity $x(\gamma)\ (d\omega/4\pi)$, where $x(\gamma)$ is the scattering indicatrix, represents the probability of the quantum scattering at an angle γ to the incident radiation within the solid angle $d\omega$.

The problem of radiative transfer (more precisely—multiple scattering) may also be considered only as a probabilistic problem. We have already seen that the introduction of the probability of quantum exit from the medium in the theory of radiative transfer permits us to find easily the radiation field outside the medium. If we generalize this method fittingly, we can find also the radiation field within the medium.

The point is that, inasmuch as the quantities used previously in the theory of radiative transfer can be interpreted in terms of the probability

[11] S. A. Kaplan and I. A. Klimishin, Light Scattering in Spherical Nebulae, *Circ. Astr. obser. Lwow Inst.*, No. 27 (1953).

we do not need to introduce new quantities in our future analysis. This permits us to give a statistical rendition of radiative transfer and also to obtain several new interrelationships.

As an example, consider the radiative transfer in the medium with an infinitely large optical thickness and consisting of the plane-parallel layers with the spheric scattering indicatrix. The function $B(\tau)$ is defined in such a case as

$$B(\tau) = \frac{\lambda}{2} \int_0^\infty B(\tau') \mathrm{Ei}|\tau - \tau'| \, d\tau' + g(\tau) \tag{187}$$

where $g(\tau)d\tau$ is the amount of energy emitted by the elementary volume with the cross section 1 cm² and the optical thickness $d\tau$ per unit solid angle and time, as the result of the direct effect of the radiation sources. Formally, we can write the solution of Eq. (187) as

$$B(\tau) = g(\tau) + \int_0^\infty \Gamma(\tau, \tau')g(\tau') \, d\tau' \tag{188}$$

where $\Gamma(\tau, \tau')$ is the resolvent.

It is known that this quantity can be given in the form of a series:

$$\Gamma(\tau, \tau') \, d\tau' = \frac{\lambda}{2}\mathrm{Ei}|\tau - \tau'| \, d\tau'$$

$$+ \frac{\lambda^2}{4} \, d\tau' \int_0^\infty \mathrm{Ei}|\tau - \tau''|\mathrm{Ei}|\tau'' - \tau'| \, d\tau'' + \ldots \tag{189}$$

It is obvious that the first term of this expansion represents the probability that the quantum emitted at the depth τ will be re-emitted between the depths τ' and $\tau' + d\tau'$ after having suffered *one* scattering. The second term gives analogously the probability that the quantum has suffered *two* scatterings, etc. Consequently, the quantity $\Gamma(\tau, \tau')d\tau'$ is the probability that the quantum emitted at the depth τ is re-emitted between the depths τ' and $\tau' + d\tau'$ after any number of scatterings in the medium.

At the same time the function $g(\tau)d\tau$ can be rendered as the relative probability of the quantum origin between the depths τ and $\tau + d\tau$, and the quantity $B(\tau)d\tau$ as the relative probability that the quantum will be re-emitted between the depths τ and $\tau + d\tau$ after multiple scattering in the medium where the quantum originated with a given distribution of the radiation sources, that is, with a given function of distribution probabilities for the origin of the quanta. In other words, the solution of the problem of radiative transfer consists in finding these probabilities for one quantum with a given initial distribution of probabilities.

This interpretation of the quantities $g(\tau)$, $B(\tau)$, and $\Gamma(\tau, \tau')$ can be employed for the solution of several problems of the radiative transfer. We give some examples.

1. From the above discussion about the resolvent it follows that the quantity $(\lambda/4\pi)\,\Gamma(\tau, \tau')d\tau'$ represents the probability that the quantum absorbed at the depth τ will be emitted after several scatterings in the medium between the depths τ' and $\tau' + d\tau'$ per unit solid angle. Therefore, by multiplying this quantity by $e^{-(\tau'/\eta)}$ and integrating with respect to τ' in the interval from 0 to ∞, we should obtain the probability of the quantum exit from the medium under the angle arccos η to the normal and absorbed at the depth τ. If we add to the integral so obtained, the quantity $(\lambda/4\pi)e^{-(\tau/\eta)}$ which represents the probability of the quantum exit directly at the depth τ, we shall derive the function $p(\tau, \eta)$ previously known to us. In other words we shall have

$$p(\tau, \eta) = \frac{\lambda}{4\pi}e^{-\tau/\eta} + \frac{\lambda}{4\pi}\int_0^\infty \Gamma(\tau, \tau')e^{-\tau'/\eta}\,d\tau' \qquad (190)$$

Comparing Eq. (190) with Eq. (188) for $g(\tau) = (\lambda/4\pi)e^{-(\tau/\eta)}$, we see that in this case $B(\tau, \eta)$ is equal $p(\tau, \eta)$; in other words, the function $B(\tau, \eta)$ is equal to the probability of quantum exit from the medium in the problem of its luminescence while being illuminated by parallel rays. This conclusion was reached in Section 2 with the aid of another method.

2. Let us form the equation for finding the resolvent $\Gamma(\tau, \tau')$. For that, let us imagine that a small layer of optical thickness $\Delta\tau$ is added to the given medium. Recollecting the probabilistic rendition of the resolvent we obtain

$$\Gamma(\tau + \Delta\tau, \tau' + \Delta\tau) = \Gamma(\tau, \tau') + \Gamma(\tau, 0)\Delta\tau\Gamma(0, \tau') \qquad (191)$$

Hence,

$$\frac{\partial\Gamma}{\partial\tau} + \frac{\partial\Gamma}{\partial\tau'} = \Gamma(\tau, 0)\Gamma(0, \tau') \qquad (192)$$

Equation (192) gives, with $\tau' > \tau$,

$$\Gamma(\tau, \tau') = \Gamma(0, \tau' - \tau) + \int_0^\tau \Gamma(x, 0)\Gamma(0, x + \tau' - \tau)\,dx \qquad (193)$$

Thus, the function of two variables $\Gamma(\tau, \tau')$ is expressed by the function of one variable $\Gamma(\tau, 0)$ due to the symmetry of the resolvent: $\Gamma(0, \tau) = \Gamma(\tau, 0)$.

Apropos of the function $\Gamma(\tau, 0)$, we observe that it is equal to

$$\Gamma(\tau, 0) = 2\pi \int_0^1 p(\tau, \eta)\frac{d\eta}{\eta} \qquad (194)$$

Remembering Eq. (52), we obtain

$$\Gamma(\tau, 0) = \Phi(\tau) \tag{195}$$

where $\Phi(\tau)$ is the function defined by Eq. (54).

Thus the search for the resolvent is reduced to the solution of the known equation of Volterra. Having solved this equation, we find the resolvent with the aid of Eq. (193) and the function $B(\tau)$ with the aid of the Eq. (188). At the same time we determine the radiation field within the medium as well as outside it for any kind of radiation sources.

Analogously, we could give a statistical rendition of the fundamental quantities and interrelationships in radiative transfer for more complicated instances, for example, for a medium of any form, for a nonspherical scattering indicatrix, etc.

CHAPTER 7

LUMINESCENCE OF A MEDIUM LIMITED BY
REFLECTING SURFACE

In this chapter we shall consider some problems of luminescence of a medium with a boundary which reflects radiation. The most important example of such media is the planetary atmosphere limited below by the planetary surface. Another example is a gas or a liquid in a vessel.

In considering these problems we should remember especially that the light quantum may first be reflected from the surface, then scattered in its direction, reflected again, and so on. This process results in diffuse radiation falling on the medium from the boundary. The intensity of this radiation is not yet known. In computing the luminescence of the medium in such cases we should write down the corresponding boundary conditions for the reflecting properties of the surface; this is what makes the present problem differ from problems previously discussed. We are well aware that previously we did not consider the external diffuse radiation; see Eqs. (52) in Chapter 1.

In Section 1 of the present chapter the problem of the luminescence of a medium in contact with the reflecting surface will be reduced to an integral equation of the function $B(\tau)$.

Later we again introduce the probability of quantum exit from the medium; moreover we shall be able to express it by the probability of quantum exit from a medium without a reflecting surface. This permits us to write expressions for the intensities of radiation emergent from the given medium by means of the well-known functions $\phi(\eta)$ and $\psi(\eta)$.

Finally, we shall apply the results to planetary atmospheres and to the sea.

1. Integral Equation for $B(\tau)$

Consider the light scattering in a medium with optical thickness τ_0, the spherical scattering indicatrix, and with a probability of quantum lifetime λ. In contrast to the previous problems, we assume here that the medium has a reflecting surface below it.

For the precise formulation of this problem we should know the reflecting properties of the surface. Let us denote by $y(\theta_1, \theta_0)(d\omega/2\pi)$

170

the probability that the light quantum incident on the surface at the angle θ_0 to the normal will be reflected from it at the angle θ_1 to the normal within the elementary solid angle $d\omega$. Then if radiation of intensity I_0 falls on the reflecting surface at the angle θ_0 to the normal, the intensity I_1 of the radiation reflected by the surface at the angle θ_1 to the normal will be defined as

$$I_1 \cos \theta_1 = \frac{y(\theta_1, \theta_0)}{2\pi} I_0 \cos \theta_0 \tag{1}$$

Now, admitting that the luminescence of the medium is caused by the internal as well as external sources of radiation incident on the upper boundary of the medium ($\tau = 0$) in the form of parallel rays at the angle θ_0 to the normal, we can write the equations of radiative transfer and radiative equilibrium as follows:

$$\left. \begin{array}{l} \cos \theta \dfrac{dI}{d\tau} = -I + B \\[2ex] B = \dfrac{\lambda}{4\pi} \displaystyle\int I \, d\omega + B_0 + \dfrac{\lambda}{4} S e^{-\tau \sec \theta_0} \end{array} \right\} \tag{2}$$

where $B_0(\tau)$ is the ratio of the coefficient of the true radiation which is conditioned directly by the internal radiation sources to the absorption coefficient, and πS is the illumination of the area perpendicular to the external radiation at the upper boundary of the medium (see Chapter 1, Section 4).

For the boundary condition at the upper limit of the medium we have, as before,

$$I(0, \theta) = 0 \qquad \left(\theta < \frac{\pi}{2} \right) \tag{3}$$

To write the boundary condition at the lower limit we should recollect that the boundary in contact with the medium is illuminated by the radiation coming from the medium as well as by the external radiation which passes through the medium. Denoting by $\bar{I}(\theta_1)$ the intensity of the radiation reflected by the surface at the angle θ_1 to the normal and using Eq. (1) we obtain,

$$\bar{I}(\theta_1) \cos \theta_1 = \int_0^{\pi/2} y(\theta_1, \theta) I(\tau_0, \theta) \cos \theta \sin \theta \, d\theta$$

$$+ \frac{S}{2} e^{-\tau_0 \sec \theta_0} y(\theta_1, \theta_0) \cos \theta_0 \tag{4}$$

Therefore the boundary condition for $\tau = \tau_0$ has the form:

$$I(\tau_0, \theta) = \bar{I}(\pi - \theta) \qquad \left(\theta > \frac{\pi}{2}\right) \tag{5}$$

From Eqs. (2) and the boundary conditions of Eqs. (3) and (5), we can derive the following integral equation for the determination of the function $B(\tau)$:

$$B(\tau) = \frac{\lambda}{2} \int_0^{\tau_0} \mathrm{Ei}|\tau - \tau'| B(\tau') \, d\tau' + B_0(\tau) + \frac{\lambda}{4} S e^{-\tau \sec \theta_0}$$

$$+ \frac{\lambda}{2} \int_0^{\pi/2} \bar{I}(\theta) e^{-(\tau_0 - \tau)\sec \theta} \sin \theta \, d\theta \tag{6}$$

Here the quantity $\bar{I}(\theta)$ is defined by Eq. (4), but the quantity $I(\tau_0, \theta)$ entering in this equation is expressed by the required function $B(\tau)$ with the aid of the formula:

$$I(\tau_0, \theta) = \int_0^{\tau_0} B(\tau) e^{-(\tau_0 - \tau)\sec \theta} \sec \theta \, d\tau \tag{7}$$

The function $y(\theta_1, \theta_0)$ which defines the reflecting property of the surface may be very different. But in practice it is often assumed that the reflected radiation is isotropic. Therefore the case of isotropic reflection deserves special consideration.

Because in this case the intensity of the reflected radiation does not depend on the direction, we obtain, in accordance with Eq. (1),

$$y(\theta_1, \theta_0) = 2A(\theta_0)\cos \theta_1 \tag{8}$$

and the formula itself becomes

$$I_1 = \frac{A(\theta_0)}{\pi} I_0 \cos \theta_0 \tag{9}$$

It is easy to see that the quantity $A(\theta_0)$ is the albedo of the surface, or the ratio of the total energy reflected by the surface to the incident energy.

Generally speaking, the albedo of the surface depends on the angle of incidence of the radiation, but we assume that $A = \mathrm{const.}$ In this case we have, instead of Eq. (4),

$$\bar{I} = 2A \int_0^{\pi/2} I(\tau_0, \tau)\cos \theta \sin \theta \, d\theta + A S e^{-\tau_0 \sec \theta_0} \cos \theta_0 \tag{10}$$

Inserting Eq. (7) into Eq. (10), we find

$$\bar{I} = 2A \int_0^{\tau_0} B(\tau) \mathrm{Ei}_2(\tau_0 - \tau) \, d\tau + A S e^{-\tau_0 \sec \theta_0} \cos \theta_0 \tag{11}$$

where

$$\text{Ei}_2 x = \int_1^\infty e^{-xz} \frac{dz}{z^2} \tag{12}$$

Therefore the integral equation for the function $B(\tau)$ becomes

$$B(\tau) = \frac{\lambda}{2} \int_0^{\tau_0} \text{Ei}|\tau - \tau'| B(\tau')\ d\tau' + B_0(\tau) + \frac{\lambda}{4} S e^{-\tau \sec \theta_0}$$

$$+ \frac{\lambda}{2} \text{Ei}_2(\tau_0 - \tau)[2A \int_0^{\tau_0} B(\tau') \text{Ei}_2(\tau_0 - \tau')\ d\tau'$$

$$+ A e^{-\tau_0 \sec \theta_0} \text{cc s } \theta_0] \tag{13}$$

Equation (13), as well as the generalized Eq. (6), may be solved by the methods described in Chapter 2.

For $B_0 = 0$, the present equations define the function $B(\tau)$ in the problem of the scattered radiation in a medium illuminated by parallel rays and with a reflecting surface. In particular we arrive at the same problem in investigating planetary atmospheres.

Kusnetsov[1] discussed Eq. (13) in detail for $B = 0$ with the purpose of making an application to the atmosphere of the Earth. He[2] also studied more general integral equations which express some other forms of the dependence of the reflecting properties on the angles of incidence and reflection.

2. Probability of Quantum Exit from the Medium

The above-formulated problem of the luminescence of a medium limited by a reflecting surface can easily be solved by means of the probability of quantum exit from the medium.

As in Section 1 we assume that the medium is limited from below by the reflecting surface. Then, instead of one function $p(\tau, \eta)$ which was used in the case without a reflecting surface, we should consider two quantities: the probability of the quantum exit through the upper boundary, and the probability of the quantum reaching the lower boundary.

We denote by $p_1(\tau, \eta)(d\omega/4\pi)$ and $p_2(\tau_0 - \tau, \eta)(d\omega/4\pi)$ the respective probabilities that the quantum absorbed at optical depth τ either leaves the medium at its upper boundary or reaches the lower boundary

[1] E. S. Kuznetsov, Light Scattering in a Medium in Contact with a Reflecting Wall of a Given Albedo, *Izv. AN SSSR, series geogr.-geophys.*, No. 5 (1942).

[2] E. S. Kuznetsov, On the Computation of the Diffusely Reflected Light by the Earth Surface in the Problem of Light Scattering in the Atmosphere, *Izv. AN SSSR, series. geogr.-geophys.* **8**, No. 1 (1945).

at an angle arccos η to the normal within the solid angle $d\omega$. Then if, we denote by $f(\tau)\,d\tau$ the amount of energy emitted by the radiation sources and absorbed by the elementary cylinder with cross section 1 cm² and optical thickness $d\tau$ in one second, we find that the intensities of the radiation emerging from the medium at the boundary $\tau = 0$ and falling on the boundary $\tau = \tau_0$ will be, respectively:

$$I(0, \eta) = \int_0^{\tau_0} f(\tau) p_1(\tau, \eta) \frac{d\tau}{\eta} \tag{14a}$$

$$I(\tau_0, \eta) = \int_0^{\tau_0} f(\tau) p_2(\tau_0 - \tau, \eta) \frac{d\tau}{\eta} \tag{14b}$$

We now form the equations for the quantities $p_1(\tau, \eta)$ and $p_2(\tau, \eta)$, assuming that the function $p(\tau, \eta)$ is known.

The probability of quantum exit from the given medium consists of two parts: the probabilities of quantum exit without and with reflection. Thus we obtain

$$p_1(\tau, \eta) = p(\tau, \eta)$$
$$+ 2\pi \int_0^1 p(\tau_0 - \tau, \eta')\, d\eta' \int_0^1 y(\eta'', \eta')\, d\eta'' \int_0^{\tau_0} e^{-(\tau_0 - \tau')/\eta''} p_1(\tau', \eta) \frac{d\tau'}{\eta''} \tag{15}$$

where $y(\eta'', \eta')(d\omega/2\pi)$ is the probability that the quantum falling on the surface at the angle arccos η' to the normal will be reflected by it at the angle arccos η'' to the normal within the solid angle $d\omega$. Analogously we find

$$p_2(\tau_0 - \tau, \eta) = p(\tau_0 - \tau, \eta)$$
$$+ 2\pi \int_0^1 p(\tau_0 - \tau, \eta')\, d\eta' \int_0^1 y(\eta'', \eta')\, d\eta''$$
$$\times \int_0^{\tau_0} e^{-(\tau_0 - \tau')/\eta''} p_2(\tau_0 - \tau', \eta) \frac{d\tau'}{\eta''} \tag{16}$$

We now introduce the following notations:

$$\pi \int_0^{\tau_0} e^{-(\tau_0 - \tau)/\zeta} p_1(\tau, \eta) \frac{d\tau}{\eta} = \sigma_*(\eta, \zeta)\zeta$$

$$\pi \int_0^{\tau_0} e^{-(\tau_0 - \tau)/\zeta} p_2(\tau_0 - \tau, \eta) \frac{d\tau}{\eta} = \rho_*(\eta, \zeta)\zeta \tag{17}$$

The quantities $\sigma_*(\eta, \zeta)$ and $\rho_*(\eta, \zeta)$ represent the brightness coefficients of the medium illuminated from below by parallel rays making an angle arccos ζ to the normal.

Using Eq. (17), we obtain, instead of Eqs. (15) and (16),

$$p_1(\tau, \eta) = p(\tau, \eta)$$

$$+ 2\eta \int_0^1 p(\tau_0 - \tau, \eta') \, d\eta' \int_0^1 y(\eta'', \eta') \sigma_*(\eta, \eta'') \, d\eta'' \qquad (18)$$

$$p_2(\tau_0 - \tau, \eta) = p(\tau_0 - \tau, \eta)$$

$$+ 2\eta \int_0^1 p(\tau_0 - \tau, \eta') \, d\eta' \int_0^1 y(\eta'', \eta') \rho_*(\eta, \eta'') \, d\eta'' \qquad (19)$$

In order to find the functions $p_1(\tau, \eta)$ and $p_2(\tau, \eta)$ we should first find the quantities $\sigma_*(\eta, \zeta)$ and $\rho_*(\eta, \zeta)$. This we can do by using Esq. (18) and (19). Multiplying these equations by $\pi e^{-(\tau_0 - \tau)/\zeta} \, d\tau/\eta$ and integrating with respect to τ over the interval from 0 to τ_0, we find

$$\sigma_*(\eta, \zeta) = \sigma(\eta, \zeta) + 2 \int_0^1 \rho(\eta', \zeta) \eta' \, d\eta' \int_0^1 y(\eta'', \eta') \sigma_*(\eta, \eta'') \, d\eta'' \qquad (20)$$

$$\rho_*(\eta, \zeta) = \rho(\eta, \zeta) + 2 \int_0^1 \rho(\eta', \zeta) \eta' \, d\eta' \int_0^1 y(\eta'', \eta') \rho_*(\eta, \eta'') \, d\eta'' \qquad (21)$$

where $\sigma(\eta, \zeta)$ and $\rho(\eta, \zeta)$ are the brightness coefficients of the medium without a reflecting surface, or

$$\left. \begin{array}{l} \sigma(\eta, \zeta)\zeta = \pi \displaystyle\int_0^{\tau_0} e^{-\tau/\zeta} p(\tau_0 - \tau, \eta) \frac{d\tau}{\eta} \\[2ex] \rho(\eta, \zeta)\zeta = \pi \displaystyle\int_0^{\tau_0} e^{-\tau/\zeta} p(\tau, \eta) \frac{d\tau}{\eta} \end{array} \right\} \qquad (22)$$

When the function $y(\eta'', \eta')$ has the form

$$y(\eta'', \eta') = \sum u_i(\eta'') v_i(\eta') \qquad (23)$$

Eqs. (20) and (21) can be solved without any difficulty. It is easy to see that in this case the determination of the functions $\sigma_*(\eta, \zeta)$ and $\rho_*(\eta, \zeta)$ are reduced to a knowledge of the quantities

$$\int_0^1 \sigma_*(\eta, \zeta) u_i(\zeta) \, d\zeta, \qquad \int_0^1 \rho_*(\eta, \zeta) u_i(\zeta) \, d\zeta$$

found from the system of linear algebraic equations.

Let us consider the case, important in practice, when the surface reflects radiation isotropically, or when the function $y(\eta'', \eta')$ is defined by Eq. (8). For the sake of simplicity we assume that the albedo of the surface, A, does not depend on the angular direction of the incident radiation.

In this case, Eqs. (18) and (19) become

$$p_1(\tau, \eta) = p(\tau, \eta) + 4A\eta \int_0^1 p(\tau_0 - \tau, \eta')\, d\eta' \int_0^1 \sigma_*(\eta, \eta'')\eta''\, d\eta'' \quad (24)$$

$$p_2(\tau_0 - \tau, \eta) = p(\tau_0 - \tau, \eta)$$

$$+ 4A\eta \int_0^1 p(\tau_0 - \tau, \eta')\, d\eta' \int_0^1 \rho_*(\eta, \eta'')\eta''\, d\eta'' \quad (25)$$

and instead of Eqs. (20) and (21) we have

$$\sigma_*(\eta, \zeta) = \sigma(\eta, \zeta) + 4A \int_0^1 \rho(\eta', \zeta)\eta'\, d\eta' \int_0^1 \sigma_*(\eta, \eta'')\eta''\, d\eta'' \quad (26)$$

$$\rho_*(\eta, \zeta) = \rho(\eta, \zeta) + 4A \int_0^1 \rho(\eta', \zeta)\eta'\, d\eta' \int_0^1 \rho_*(\eta, \eta'')\eta''\, d\eta'' \quad (27)$$

Hence,

$$\left.\begin{aligned}
\int_0^1 \sigma_*(\eta, \eta'')\eta''\, d\eta'' &= \frac{\displaystyle\int_0^1 \sigma(\eta, \eta'')\eta''\, d\eta''}{1 - AC} \\[2em]
\int_0^1 \rho_*(\eta, \eta'')\eta''\, d\eta'' &= \frac{\displaystyle\int_0^1 \rho(\eta, \eta'')\eta''\, d\eta''}{1 - AC}
\end{aligned}\right\} \quad (28)$$

where we have introduced the notation,

$$C = 4 \int_0^1 \zeta\, d\zeta \int_0^1 \rho(\eta, \zeta)\eta\, d\eta \quad (29)$$

Inserting Eqs. (28) into Eqs. (24) and (25), we obtain

$$p_1(\tau, \eta) = p(\tau, \eta)$$

$$+ \frac{4A}{1 - AC}\eta \int_0^1 p(\tau_0 - \tau, \eta)\, d\eta'' \int_0^1 \sigma(\eta, \eta'')\eta''\, d\eta'' \quad (30)$$

$$p_2(\tau_0 - \tau, \eta) = p(\tau_0 - \tau, \eta)$$

$$+ \frac{4A}{1 - AC}\eta \int_0^1 p(\tau_0 - \tau, \eta')\, d\eta' \int_0^1 \rho(\eta, \eta'')\eta''\, d\eta'' \quad (31)$$

Thus we have obtained the formulas for expressing the quantities $p_1(\tau, \eta)$ and $p_2(\tau_0 - \tau, \eta)$ in terms of $p(\tau, \eta)$.

Equations (14), (30), and (31) enable us to solve various problems of the luminescence of a medium limited by a reflecting surface. Some examples of these problems are given in the next sections.

3. LUMINESCENCE OF A PLANETARY ATMOSPHERE

We have previously formulated (Chapter 1, Section 6) the problem of the luminescence of a planetary atmosphere and have discussed it thoroughly in Chapters 3 and 4. But there we did not take into account the radiation reflected from the surface of the planet. We shall now do this and shall assume, for the sake of simplicity, that the reflected radiation is isotropic and that the albedo of the surface is equal to A.

Assuming that the sun's rays fall on the atmosphere at an angle arccos ζ to the normal and produce an illumination πS of the small area of the upper boundary perpendicular to the rays, let us find the intensities of the emergent radiation, supposing at first that the scattering indicatrix is spherical.

In order to use Eqs. (14), we must find the quantity $f(\tau)\,d\tau$, or the amount of energy arriving from the sun at the given elementary volume without scattering in the atmosphere, and absorbed by this volume. Since in this case the sun's rays reach each volume directly as well as after reflection by the surface of the planet, we have

$$f(\tau) = \pi S e^{-\tau/\zeta} + 2\pi A\, S e^{-\tau_0/\zeta\zeta} \int_0^1 e^{-(\tau_0-\tau)/\eta''}\, d\eta'' \tag{32}$$

Setting Eq. (32) in Eqs. (14b) and recalling Eqs. (31) and (22), we obtain

$$I(\tau_0, \eta, \zeta) = S\sigma(\eta, \zeta)\zeta$$

$$+\frac{A S\zeta}{1 - AC}2 \int_0^1 \rho(\eta, \eta'')\eta''\, d\eta''\left[e^{-\tau_0/\zeta} + 2\int_0^1 \sigma(\eta', \zeta)\eta'\, d\eta'\right] \tag{33}$$

With the following new notations

$$e^{-\tau_0/\eta} + 2\int_0^1 \sigma(\eta', \zeta)\eta'\, d\eta' = \mu(\zeta); \qquad 2\int_0^1 \rho(\eta, \eta'')\eta''\, d\eta'' = \nu(\eta) \tag{34}$$

Equation (33) becomes

$$I(\tau_0, \eta, \zeta) = \left[\sigma(\eta, \zeta) + \frac{A}{1 - AC}\nu(\eta)\mu(\zeta)\right] S\zeta \tag{35}$$

Now, setting Eq. (32) in Eq. (14a) we find the intensity of the radiation that is diffusely reflected by the surface of the planet without the radiation coming directly from it. The total intensity of the radiation emerging from the upper boundary of the planetary atmosphere will then be determined by the formula,

$$I(0, \eta, \zeta) = \int_0^{\tau_0} f(\tau)p_1(\tau, \eta)\frac{d\tau}{\eta} + Ae^{-\tau_0/\eta}\left[2\int_0^1 I(\tau_0, \eta', \zeta)\eta'\, d\tau' + Se^{-\tau_0/\zeta\zeta}\right] \tag{36}$$

Inserting Eqs. (32) and (35) into Eq. (36), we find

$$
I(0, \eta, \zeta) = \pi S \int_0^{\tau_0} e^{-\tau/\zeta} p_1(\tau, \eta) \frac{d\tau}{\eta}
$$

$$
+ 2\pi A S e^{-\tau_0/\zeta\zeta} \int_0^1 d\eta'' \int_0^{\tau_0} e^{-(\tau_0-\tau)/\eta''} p_1(\tau, \eta) \frac{d\tau}{\eta}
$$

$$
+ \frac{A S}{1 - A C} e^{-\tau_0/\eta} \mu(\zeta) \zeta \tag{37}
$$

or, using Eqs. (30) and (22),

$$
I(0, \eta, \zeta) = \left[\rho(\eta, \zeta) + \frac{A}{1 - A C} \mu(\eta) \mu(\zeta) \right] S \zeta \tag{38}
$$

Equations (35) and (38) are the required ones. They express explicitly the intensities of the radiation emerging from the atmosphere with $A \neq 0$ by means of the brightness coefficients of the atmosphere $\rho(\eta, \zeta)$ and $\sigma(\eta, \zeta)$ with $A = 0$.

These coefficients were expressed earlier in terms of the auxiliary functions $\phi(\eta)$ and $\psi(\eta)$; therefore it is reasonable to express the quantities $\mu(\eta)$ and $\nu(\eta)$ also in terms of the same functions. Remembering Eqs. (126) and (128) of the previous chapter, we obtain

$$
\mu(\zeta) = \left(1 - \frac{\lambda}{2}\alpha_0 \right) \psi(\zeta) + \frac{\lambda}{2}\beta_0 \phi(\zeta) \tag{39}
$$

$$
\nu(\zeta) = 1 - \left(1 - \frac{\lambda}{2}\alpha_0 \right) \phi(\zeta) - \frac{\lambda}{2}\beta_0 \psi(\zeta) \tag{40}
$$

where α_0 and β_0 are zero moments of the functions $\phi(\eta)$ and $\psi(\eta)$.

It is obvious that the quantities $\mu(\zeta)$ and $\nu(\zeta)$ have a simple physical meaning. The first is the ratio of the brightness at the surface of the planet to the brightness at the upper boundary of the atmosphere, and the second is the ratio of the illumination of the upper boundary of the atmosphere from below to its illumination from above (for $A = 0$).

We have derived Eqs. (35) and (38) for the spherical scattering indicatrix only. However, this apparent limitation does not jeopardize the general value of the formulas derived. It is easy to show that for isotropic reflection of radiation these formulas are valid for any form of the scattering indicatrix when the quantities $\mu(\zeta)$ and $\nu(\zeta)$ have the afore-mentioned physical meanings.

Equations (35) and (38) were found earlier by the author[3] and by

[3] V. V. Sobolev, On Brightness Coefficients on a Plain Layer in a Turbid Medium, *DAN SSSR* **61**, No. 5 (1948).

van de Hulst[4] in a different manner. Even earlier the author obtained formulas of the same kind as Eqs. (35) and (38) for any scattering indicatrix (see Chapter 10).

4. Internal Radiation Sources

In the previous section we solved the problem of the luminescence of a medium in contact with a reflecting surface and illuminated from above by parallel rays, and in Section 2 we derived the brightness coefficients $\sigma_*(\eta, \zeta)$ and $\rho_*(\eta, \zeta)$ of a medium illuminated by parallel rays from below. We now find the intensities of the radiation emergent from a medium with internal radiation sources.

We assume that the energy emitted by the sources is isotropic, and denote this energy by $B_0(\tau)$. Because we assume that the radiation scattering is also isotropic, we can consider the energy emitted by an elementary volume as the energy scattered by the same volume, that is,

$$B_0(\tau) = \frac{\lambda}{4\pi} f(\tau)$$

Thus, instead of Eqs. (14), we have in this case

$$\left.\begin{array}{l} I(0,\eta) = \dfrac{4\pi}{\lambda} \displaystyle\int_0^{\tau_0} B_0(\tau) p_1(\tau, \eta) \dfrac{d\tau}{\eta} \\[4mm] I(\tau_0,\eta) = \dfrac{4\pi}{\lambda} \displaystyle\int_0^{\tau_0} B_0(\tau) p_2(\tau_0 - \tau, \eta) \dfrac{d\tau}{\eta} \end{array}\right\} \quad (41)$$

Equations (30) and (31), defining the quantities $p_1(\tau, \eta)$ and $p_2(\tau, \eta)$, can be rewritten as follows by means of Eqs. (34):

$$p_1(\tau, \eta) = p(\tau, \eta) + \frac{2A}{1 - AC}\eta[\mu(\eta) - e^{-\tau_0/\eta}]\int_0^{\tau_0} p(\tau_0 - \tau, \eta')\, d\eta' \quad (42)$$

$$p_2(\tau_0 - \tau, \eta) = p(\tau_0 - \tau, \eta) + \frac{2A}{1 - AC}\eta\nu(\eta)\int_0^{\tau_0} p(\tau_0 - \tau, \eta')\, d\eta' \quad (43)$$

Inserting Eqs. (42) and (43) into Eqs. (41), we obtain

$$I(0, \eta) = I_0(0, \eta) + \frac{2A}{1 - AC}[\mu(\eta) - e^{-\tau_0/\eta}]\int_0^1 I_0(\tau_0, \eta')\eta'\, d\eta' \quad (44)$$

$$I(\tau_0, \eta) = I_0(\tau_0, \eta) + \frac{2A}{1 - AC}\nu(\eta)\int_0^1 I_0(\tau_0, \eta')\eta'\, d\eta' \quad (45)$$

[4] H. van de Hulst, Scattering in a Planetary Atmosphere, *Astrophysical J.* **107**, 220 (1948).

where $I_0(0, \eta)$ and $I_0(\tau_0, \eta)$ are the intensities of the radiation emergent from the given medium in the absence of a reflecting surface.

Equation (44) gives the intensity of radiation emergent from the upper boundary of the medium without the radiation coming directly from the boundary.

To obtain the total radiation intensity at the boundary it is necessary to add the term

$$Ae^{-\tau_0/\eta} \, 2 \int_0^1 I(\tau_0, \eta')\eta' \, d\eta'$$

to the right-hand side of Eq. (44). Using Eqs. (45) we find that this term is equal to

$$\frac{2A}{1 - AC}e^{-\tau_0/\eta} \int_0^1 I_0(\tau_0, \eta')\eta' \, d\eta'$$

Hence the total radiation intensity at the boundary $\tau = 0$ is

$$I(0, \eta) \; = \; I_0(0, \eta) + \frac{2A}{1 - AC}\mu(\eta) \int_0^1 I_0(\tau_0, \eta')\eta' \, d\eta' \qquad (46)$$

Equations (45) and (46) express the radiation intensities at the boundaries of the medium with $A \neq 0$ by means of the radiation intensities at the same boundaries, but with $A = 0$.

In Chapter 6, Section 7, we determined the intensities of the radiation emergent from a medium without a reflecting surface, and for the case where the function $B_0(\tau)$ represents a series expanded in powers of τ. Now, using Eqs. (45) and (46) we can find the intensities of the radiation emergent from a medium with the same radiation sources and with a reflecting surface.

For example, we take the case of radiation sources distributed uniformly in the medium, or $B_0 = \text{const.}$ Recalling the quantities $I_0(0, \eta)$ and $I_0(\tau, \eta)$ given by Eq. (149) of Chapter 6 which in this case are equal to one another, and inserting them in Eqs. (45) and (46), we obtain

$$I(\tau_0, \eta) \; = \; \frac{B_0}{1 - (\lambda/2)(\alpha_0 - \beta_0)}\left[\phi(\eta) - \psi(\eta) + \frac{2A}{1 - AC}(\alpha_1 - \beta_1)\nu(\eta)\right] \qquad (47)$$

$$I(0, \eta) \; = \; \frac{B_0}{1 - (\lambda/2)(\alpha_1 - \beta_0)}\left[\phi(\eta) - \psi(\eta) + \frac{2A}{1 - AC}(\alpha_1 - \beta_1)\mu(\eta)\right] \qquad (48)$$

For $\lambda = 1$ or in the absence of true absorption, these formulas can be somewhat simplified. Recollecting that in this case the relations

$\alpha_0 + \beta_0 = 2$, $\alpha_1 - \beta_1 = \beta_0 \tau_0$, derived in Chapter 6, Section 6, are valid, we have, instead of the foregoing expressions,

$$I(\tau_0, \eta) = B_0 \frac{\phi(\eta) - \psi(\eta)}{\beta_0} + B_0 \frac{A}{1 - AC} \tau_0 \{2 - \beta_0 [\phi(\eta) + \psi(\eta)]\} \qquad (49)$$

$$I(0, \eta) = B_0 \frac{\phi(\eta) - \psi(\eta)}{\beta_0} + B_0 \frac{A}{1 - AC} \tau_0 \beta_0 [\phi(\eta) + \psi(\eta)] \qquad (50)$$

5. Specular Reflection of Light

In addition to the case just considered there is a practical phenomenon of great interest when the surface reflects not isotropically but like a mirror. An example of a medium limited by a mirror-like surface is furnished by the atmosphere above a quiet sea. Here we neglect the diffuse radiation emergent from the sea.

In the case of specular reflection from a surface, the light quanta incident on the surface at an angle arccos ζ to the normal are reflected from the surface at the same angle to the normal and, moreover, the incident ray, the normal, and the reflected ray are in the same plane. Generally speaking, not all the quanta incident on the surface are reflected, but only a fraction which we shall denote by $r(\zeta)$. The remainder, $1 - r(\zeta)$, goes through the surface. This part of the radiation does not interest us here. The function $r(\zeta)$, which characterizes the optical properties of the surface, will be assumed to be known.

As before, we assume that the reflecting surface is in contact with the medium from below, $\tau = \tau_0$. We can derive the equations defining the probabilities of quantum exit by utilizing the general Eqs. (18) and (19) and by inserting in them:

$$y(\eta'', \eta') = \delta(\eta'' - \eta') r(\eta') \qquad (51)$$

where δ is the Dirac function. As a result, we find

$$p_1(\tau, \eta) = p(\tau, \eta) + 2\eta \int_0^1 p(\tau_0 - \tau, \eta') r(\eta') \sigma_*(\eta, \eta') \, d\eta' \qquad (52)$$

$$p_2(\tau_0 - \tau, \eta) = p(\tau_0 - \tau, \eta) + 2\eta \int_0^1 p(\tau_0 - \tau, \eta') r(\eta') \rho_*(\eta, \eta') \, d\eta' \qquad (53)$$

The quantities $\sigma_*(\eta, \eta')$ and $\rho_*(\eta, \eta')$ entering these equations represent the brightness coefficient of a medium illuminated from below. These quantities are determined by the equations:

$$\sigma_*(\eta, \zeta) = \sigma(\eta, \zeta) + 2 \int_0^1 \rho(\eta', \zeta) r(\eta') \sigma_*(\eta, \eta') \eta' \, d\eta' \qquad (54)$$

$$\rho_*(\eta, \zeta) = \rho(\eta, \zeta) + 2 \int_0^1 \rho(\eta', \zeta) r(\eta') \rho_*(\eta, \eta') \eta' \, d\eta' \tag{55}$$

which we obtain by inserting Eq. (51) in Eqs. (20) and (21).

Having found the functions $\sigma_*(\eta, \zeta)$ and $\rho_*(\eta, \zeta)$, we can, by way of Eqs. (52) and (53), determine the quantities $p_1(\tau, \eta)$ and $p_2(\tau_0 - \tau, \eta)$ and then, with the aid of Eq. (14), the intensities of radiation emergent from a medium with different radiation sources.

Employing the above-mentioned formulas we can also express the quantities $I(0, \eta)$ and $I(\tau_0, \eta)$ in terms of the quantities $I_0(0, \eta)$ and $I_0(\tau_0, \eta)$ or the intensities of the emergent radiation in the absence of a reflecting surface and the functions σ_* and ρ_*.

First, we assume that the medium is illuminated by parallel rays from above. In this case,

$$f(\tau) = \tau S e^{-\tau/\zeta} + \pi S e^{-\tau_0/\zeta} r(\zeta) e^{-(\tau_0 - \tau)/\zeta} \tag{56}$$

Inserting Eq. (56) in the second of Eqs. (14), we have

$$I(\tau_0, \eta, \zeta) = \pi S \int_0^{\tau_0} e^{-\tau/\zeta} p_2(\tau_0 - \tau, \eta) \frac{d\tau}{\eta}$$

$$+ \pi S e^{-\tau/\zeta} r(\zeta) \int_0^{\tau_0} e^{-(\tau_0 - \tau)/\zeta} p_2(\tau_0 - \tau, \eta) \frac{d\tau}{\eta} \tag{57}$$

Recalling now Eqs. (17) and (22) and expressing $p_2(\tau_0 - \tau, \eta)$ by $p(\tau_0 - \tau, \eta)$ with the aid of Eq. (53) in the first integral of Eq. (57), we obtain

$$I(\tau_0, \eta, \zeta) = S\zeta \Big[\sigma(\eta, \zeta) + 2 \int_0^1 \sigma(\eta', \zeta) r(\eta') \rho_*(\eta, \eta') \eta' \, d\eta'$$

$$+ e^{-\tau_0/\zeta} r(\zeta) \rho_*(\eta, \zeta) \Big] \tag{58}$$

Analogously we find the intensities of radiation emergent from the upper boundary:

$$I(0, \eta, \zeta) = S\zeta \Big[\rho(\eta, \zeta) + 2 \int_0^1 \sigma(\eta', \zeta) r(\eta') \sigma_*(\eta, \eta') \eta' \, d\eta'$$

$$+ e^{-\tau_0/\zeta} r(\zeta) \sigma_*(\eta, \zeta) \Big] + I(\tau_0, \eta, \zeta) r(\eta) e^{-\tau_0/\eta} \tag{59}$$

The last term of this formula takes into account the radiation coming directly from the reflecting surface.

If the sources of radiation are within the medium and the radiation is isotropic, we find, using Eqs. (41), (52), and (53):

$$I(\tau_0, \eta) = I_0(\tau_0, \eta) + 2 \int_0^1 I_0(\tau_0, \eta') r(\eta') \rho_*(\eta, \eta') \eta' \, d\eta' \tag{60}$$

$$I(0, \eta) = I_0(0, \eta) + 2 \int_0^1 I_0(\tau_0, \eta') r(\eta') \sigma_*(\eta, \eta') \eta' \, d\eta'$$

$$+ I(\tau_0, \eta) r(\eta) e^{-\tau_0/\eta} \tag{61}$$

In Eq. (61) we have also added a term which expresses the radiation coming directly from the specular surface.

Thus we see that various problems of the luminescence of a medium with specular boundaries are reduced to the derivation of the functions $\sigma_*(\eta, \zeta)$ and $\rho_*(\eta, \zeta)$ from Eqs. (54) and (55).

The quantities $\sigma(\eta, \zeta)$ and $\rho(\eta, \zeta)$ entering Eqs. (54) and (55), or the brightness coefficients of the medium for $r = 0$, are assumed to be known. Equations (126) in Chapter 6 express these functions of two arguments as the functions $\phi(\eta)$ and $\psi(\eta)$ which depend only on one argument. Utilizing Eqs. (54) and (55) and also the afore-mentioned formulas of Chapter 6, we can express the functions $\sigma_*(\eta, \zeta)$ and $\sigma_*(\eta, \zeta)$ by some auxiliary formulas which depend also only on one argument. We shall do this in the next section for $\tau_0 = \infty$.

6. Medium of Infinitely Large Optical Thickness

From the assumption that the medium with a specular boundary has an infinitely large optical thickness it follows that the light quanta, having suffered some scattering within the medium, and some reflection at the specular surface, will emerge from the medium at the same boundary. To find the intensities of the emergent radiation it is necessary to determine not two functions $\sigma_*(\eta, \zeta)$ and $\rho_*(\eta, \zeta)$ as in the case of finite thickness, but only one, $\rho_*(\eta, \zeta)$, and for this we employ Eq. (55).

The quantity $\rho(\eta, \zeta)$, or the brightness coefficient of a medium without a reflecting surface entering Eq. (55) is, in this case where $\tau_0 = \infty$, defined by the formula:

$$\rho(\eta, \zeta) = \frac{\lambda}{4} \frac{\phi(\eta)\phi(\zeta)}{\eta + \zeta} \tag{62}$$

where the function $\phi(\eta)$ is defined by Eq. (50) of Chapter 6.

We shall now express the required quantities $\rho_*(\eta, \zeta)$ in the form:

$$\rho_*(\eta, \zeta) = \frac{\lambda}{4} \phi(\eta)\phi(\zeta) \left[\frac{A(\eta, \zeta)}{\eta + \zeta} + \frac{B(\eta, \zeta)}{\eta - \zeta} \right] \tag{63}$$

where $A(\eta, \zeta)$ and $B(\eta, \zeta)$ are functions still to be determined.

Inserting Eqs. (62) and (63) into Eq. (55), we obtain

$$\frac{A(\eta, \zeta)}{\eta + \zeta} + \frac{B(\eta, \zeta)}{\eta - \zeta}$$

$$= \frac{1}{\eta + \zeta} + \frac{\lambda}{2} \int_0^1 \phi^2(\eta') r(\eta') \left[\frac{A(\eta, \eta')}{\eta + \eta'} + \frac{B(\eta, \eta')}{\eta - \eta'} \right] \frac{\eta' \, d\eta'}{\eta' + \zeta} \quad (64)$$

Transforming this equation by means of the relations

$$\left. \begin{array}{l} \dfrac{1}{(\eta' + \zeta)(\eta + \eta')} = \left(\dfrac{1}{(\eta' + \zeta)} \dfrac{1}{\eta + \eta'} \right) \dfrac{1}{\eta - \zeta} \\[3mm] \dfrac{1}{(\eta' + \zeta)(\eta - \eta')} = \left(\dfrac{1}{\eta' + \zeta} + \dfrac{1}{\eta' + \zeta} \right) \dfrac{1}{\eta + \zeta} \end{array} \right\} \quad (65)$$

and equating in it separately the terms with the factors $1/(\eta + \zeta)$ and $1/(\eta - \zeta)$, we arrive at the following equations for the determination of $A(\eta, \zeta)$ and $B(\eta, \zeta)$:

$$A(\eta, \zeta) = 1 + \frac{\lambda}{2} \int_0^1 \phi^2(\eta') r(\eta') B(\eta, \eta') \left(\frac{1}{\eta' + \zeta} + \frac{1}{\eta - \eta'} \right) \eta' \, d\eta' \quad (66)$$

$$B(\eta, \zeta) = \frac{\lambda}{2} \int_0^1 \phi^2(\eta') r(\eta') A(\eta, \eta') \left(\frac{1}{\eta' + \zeta} - \frac{1}{\eta + \eta'} \right) \eta' \, d\eta' \quad (67)$$

It is easy to be convinced that the solution of the equations has the form:

$$\left. \begin{array}{l} A(\eta, \zeta) = \alpha(\eta)\alpha(\zeta) - \beta(\eta)\beta(\zeta) \\[2mm] B(\eta, \zeta) = \alpha(\eta)\beta(\zeta) - \alpha(\zeta)\beta(\eta) \end{array} \right\} \quad (68)$$

where $\alpha(\eta)$ and $\beta(\eta)$ are defined by the equations:

$$\alpha(\eta) = 1 + \frac{\lambda}{2} \int_0^1 \phi^2(\eta') r(\eta') \beta(\eta') \frac{\eta' \, d\eta'}{\eta + \eta'} \quad (69)$$

$$\beta(\eta) = \frac{\lambda}{2} \int_0^1 \phi^2(\eta') r(\eta') \alpha(\eta') \frac{\eta' \, d\eta'}{\eta + \eta'} \quad (70)$$

Inserting Eqs. (68) into Eqs. (66) and (67), we obtain the result that the functions $\alpha(\eta)$ and $\beta(\eta)$ must satisfy not only Eqs. (69) and (70) but also the following equations:

$$\alpha(\eta) = 1 + \frac{\lambda}{2} \int_0^1 \phi^2(\eta') r(\eta') \frac{\alpha(\eta)\beta(\eta') - \alpha(\eta')\beta(\eta)}{\eta - \eta'} \eta' \, d\eta' \quad (71)$$

$$\beta(\eta) = \frac{\lambda}{2} \int_0^1 \phi^2(\eta') r(\eta') \frac{\alpha(\eta)\alpha(\eta') - \beta(\eta)\beta(\eta')}{\eta' - \eta} \eta' \, d\eta' \quad (72)$$

That the functions $\alpha(\eta)$ and $\beta(\eta)$ satisfy Eq. (72) is obvious; but to convince ourselves that they satisfy Eq. (71) we proceed as follows.

First we introduce the notation

$$\frac{\lambda}{2}\phi^2(\eta)r(\eta)\eta = K(\eta) \tag{73}$$

with the aid of which we rewrite Eq. (71) in the form:

$$\alpha(\eta) = 1 + \alpha(\eta) \int_0^1 K(\eta')\frac{\beta(\eta')}{\eta - \eta'}\, d\eta' - \beta(\eta) \int_0^1 K(\eta')\frac{\alpha(\eta')}{\eta - \eta'}\, d\eta' \tag{74}$$

Then, recalling Eqs. (69) and (70), we rewrite this as

$$\alpha(\eta) = 1 + \left[1 + \int_0^1 K(\eta'')\beta(\eta'')\frac{d\eta''}{\eta + \eta''}\right] \int_0^1 K(\eta')\frac{\beta(\eta')}{\eta - \eta'}\, d\eta'$$
$$- \int_0^1 K(\eta'')\alpha(\eta'')\frac{d\eta''}{\eta + \eta''} \int_0^1 K(\eta')\frac{\alpha(\eta')}{\eta - \eta'}\, d\eta'$$

or

$$\alpha(\eta) = 1 + \int_0^1 K(\eta')\beta(\eta')\frac{d\eta'}{\eta - \eta'}$$
$$+ \int_0^1\int_0^1 K(\eta')\,K(\eta'')\beta(\eta')\beta(\eta'')\left(\frac{1}{\eta - \eta'} - \frac{1}{\eta + \eta''}\right)\frac{d\eta'\,d\eta''}{\eta' + \eta''}$$
$$- \int_0^1\int_0^1 K(\eta')\,K(\eta'')\alpha(\eta')\alpha(\eta'')\left(\frac{1}{\eta - \eta'} - \frac{1}{\eta + \eta''}\right)\frac{d\eta'\,d\eta''}{\eta' + \eta''}$$

Finally, using Eqs. (69) and (70) again, we obtain the relation:

$$\alpha(\eta) = 1 + \int_0^1 K(\eta')\beta(\eta')\frac{d\eta'}{\eta - \eta'}$$
$$+ \int_0^1 K(\eta')\beta(\eta')[\alpha(\eta') - 1]\frac{d\eta'}{\eta - \eta'}$$
$$- \int_0^1 K(\eta'')\beta(\eta'')[\alpha(\eta'') - 1]\frac{d\eta''}{\eta + \eta''}$$
$$- \int_0^1 K(\eta')\alpha(\eta')\beta(\eta')\frac{d\eta'}{\eta - \eta'} + \int_0^1 K(\eta'')\alpha(\eta'')\beta(\eta'')\frac{d\eta''}{\eta + \eta''},$$

which is an identity.

Thus we have found that the quantity $\rho_*(\eta, \zeta)$ is given by the auxiliary functions $\alpha(\eta)$ and $\beta(\eta)$ by means of the formula:

$$\rho_*(\eta, \zeta) = \frac{\lambda}{4}\phi(\eta)\phi(\zeta)\left[\frac{\alpha(\eta)\alpha(\zeta) - \beta(\eta)\beta(\zeta)}{\eta + \zeta} + \frac{\alpha(\eta)\beta(\zeta) - \alpha(\zeta)\beta(\eta)}{\eta - \zeta}\right] \tag{75}$$

and the functions $\alpha(\eta)$ and $\beta(\eta)$ in turn are given by Eqs. (69) and (70). These equations can easily be solved numerically for every concrete law of light reflection by a surface characterized by the function $r(\zeta)$.

7. SOME APPLICATIONS

Having found the function $\rho_*(\eta,\zeta)$ we can solve various problems of the brightness of a medium with infinitely large optical thickness and with a specular boundary. We now solve some practical problems of this kind.

1. *Overcast sky at sea.* Consider clouds uniformly distributed over the sky when their optical thickness is great. The distribution of brightness over the sky was found in Chapter 3, Section 8. For isotropic light scattering in the clouds, the sky brightness at zenith distance arccos η is given by the formula:

$$I_0(\eta) = C\frac{\phi(\eta)}{1 - k\eta} \tag{76}$$

where C and k are constants.

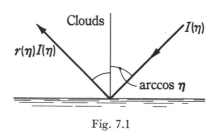

Fig. 7.1

In deriving Eq. (76), however, we have neglected the presence of the surface of the sea in contact with the atmosphere. We now investigate the cloud layers above the sea with its specular reflection of light (Fig. 7.1).

In this case the sky brightness is defined as follows:

$$I(\eta) = C\frac{\phi(\eta)}{1 - k\eta} + 2C\int_0^1 \frac{\phi(\eta')}{1 - k\eta'}r(\eta')\rho_*(\eta, \eta')\eta'\, d\eta' \tag{77}$$

where $r(\eta)$ is the coefficient of radiation reflection by water, given by the formula of Fresnel (see Section 8 of this chapter).

Inserting Eq. (75), obtained earlier for the function $\rho_*(\eta,\zeta)$, into Eq. (77) and employing the equalities

$$\frac{1}{(1-k\eta')(\eta+\eta')} = \left(\frac{1}{\eta+\eta'}+\frac{k}{1-k\eta'}\right)\frac{1}{1+k\eta}$$

$$\frac{1}{(1-k\eta')(\eta-\eta')} = \left(\frac{1}{\eta-\eta'}-\frac{k}{1-k\eta'}\right)\frac{1}{1-k\eta}$$

we find

$$I(\eta) = C\frac{\phi(\eta)}{1-k\eta}$$

$$+ C\frac{\phi(\eta)}{1+k\eta}\frac{\lambda}{2}\int_0^1 \phi^2(\eta')r(\eta')[\alpha(\eta)\alpha(\eta')-\beta(\eta)\beta(\eta')]$$

$$\times \left(\frac{1}{\eta+\eta'}+\frac{k}{1-k\eta'}\right)\eta'\,d\eta'$$

$$+ C\frac{\phi(\eta)}{1-k\eta}\frac{\lambda}{2}\int_0^1 \phi^2(\eta')r(\eta')[\alpha(\eta)\beta(\eta')-\alpha(\eta')\beta(\eta)]$$

$$\times \left(\frac{1}{\eta-\eta'}-\frac{k}{1-k\eta'}\right)\eta'\,d\eta' \tag{78}$$

Recalling Eqs. (71) and (72), we transform Eq. (78) into

$$I(\eta) = C\frac{\phi(\eta)}{1-k\eta}+C\frac{\phi(\eta)}{1+k\eta}[\beta(\eta)+\alpha(\eta)M-\beta(\eta)\mathcal{N}]$$

$$+ C\frac{\phi(\eta)}{1-k\eta}[\alpha(\eta)-1-\alpha(\eta)\mathcal{N}+\beta(\eta)M] \tag{79}$$

where M and $\mathcal{N}$ are constant quantities:

$$\left.\begin{array}{l}M = \dfrac{\lambda}{2}k\int_0^1 \phi^2(\eta')r(\eta')\dfrac{\alpha(\eta')}{1-k\eta'}\eta'\,d\eta' \\[4mm] \mathcal{N} = \dfrac{\lambda}{2}k\int_0^1 \phi^2(\eta')r(\eta')\dfrac{\beta(\eta')}{1-k\eta'}\eta'\,d\eta'\end{array}\right\} \tag{80}$$

Equation (79) can also be rewritten in the form:

$$I(\eta) = C\phi(\eta)\left[\frac{\alpha(\eta)(1-\mathcal{N})+\beta(\eta)M}{1-k\eta}+\frac{\alpha(\eta)M+\beta(\eta)(1-\mathcal{N})}{1+k\eta}\right] \tag{81}$$

This formula becomes much simpler for the case of pure scattering in the cloudy layer. The sky brightness in this case is, in fact,

$$I(\eta) = C\phi(\eta)[\alpha(\eta)+\beta(\eta)] \tag{82}$$

To compute this intensity, $I(\eta)$, it is necessary first to determine the functions $\alpha(\eta)$ and $\beta(\eta)$ for the case when the quantity $r(\eta)$ represents the reflection coefficient of water. In Table 7.1 we give these functions, computed by means of Eqs. (69) and (70) with $\lambda = 1$. In the same table are given the values of the function $r(\eta)$. Here we have assumed that the refractive index n is equal to 1.33.

TABLE 7.1. BRIGHTNESS OF OVERCAST SKY AT SEA

η	0	0.1	0.2	0.3	0.4	0.5	0.6	0.7	0.8	0.9	1.0
$r(\eta)$	1.000	0.543	0.297	0.168	0.097	0.059	0.039	0.028	0.023	0.021	0.020
$\alpha(\eta)$	1.017	1.009	1.007	1.006	1.005	1.004	1.004	1.004	1.003	1.003	1.003
$\beta(\eta)$	0.187	0.118	0.094	0.079	0.068	0.061	0.055	0.050	0.046	0.042	0.039
$I_0(\eta)$	1.00	1.25	1.45	1.64	1.83	2.01	2.19	2.37	2.55	2.73	2.91
$I(\eta)$	1.20	1.41	1.60	1.78	1.96	2.14	2.32	2.50	2.68	2.85	3.03

For comparison we have also given two more quantities in Table 7.1: brightness of the overcast sky without a reflecting surface, $I_0(\eta)$, and brightness of overcast sky with specular reflection of light by the sea, $I(\eta)$.

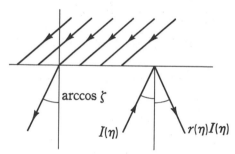

Fig. 7.2

It goes without saying that these formulas do not give the total effect of sea and sky brightness. In reality we should take into account not only the specular reflection of radiation, but also that part of the radiation which emerges from the sea after being scattered in it.

2. *Brightness of the sea.* The light quanta, having entered the sea, suffer scattering as well as specular reflection from the surface, or so-called internal reflection. The optical thickness of the sea can be regarded as infinitely large. Therefore we can find the brightness of the sea by employing the results of the previous section.

We assume that the sea is illuminated by the parallel rays of the sun which are partly reflected and partly refracted. We denote by ζ the cosine of the angle of the incident rays which enter the sea after refraction and by πS the illumination produced by them of the area perpendicular to them immediately under the surface (Fig. 7.2).

In this case the radiation from the external sources enters the medium at the side of the reflecting surface. Therefore, in conformity with the definition of brightness coefficient $\rho_*(\eta, \zeta)$, we find that the intensity of diffuse radiation ascending to the surface of the sea is equal to

$$I(0, \eta, \zeta) = S\rho_*(\eta, \zeta)\zeta \tag{83}$$

To find the intensity of radiation emerging from the sea it is necessary to multiply Eq. (83) by a factor which takes into account the optical phenomena at the boundary of the two media (see Section 8).

The quantity $I(0, \eta, \zeta)$ can also be expressed in the form:

$$I(0, \eta, \zeta) = \frac{\lambda}{4}\phi(\eta)\phi(\zeta)\frac{\eta\delta(\eta)\gamma(\zeta) - \zeta\gamma(\eta)\delta(\zeta)}{\eta^2 - \zeta^2} S\zeta \tag{84}$$

where

$$\gamma(\eta) = \alpha(\eta) + \beta(\eta), \qquad \delta(\eta) = \alpha(\eta) - \beta(\eta) \tag{85}$$

Table 7.2 contains values of these functions which we obtained by solving Eqs. (69) and (70) with $\lambda = 1$. In the same table we give values of $r(\eta)$, or the coefficient of internal light reflection in water.

TABLE 7.2. AUXILIARY FUNCTIONS $\gamma(\eta)$ AND $\delta(\eta)$ WITH $\lambda = 1$

η	0	0.1	0.2	0.3	0.4	0.5	0.6	0.7	0.8	0.9	1.0
$r(\eta)$	1	1	1	1	1	1	1	0.156	0.038	0.022	0.020
$\gamma(\eta)$	3.30	2.73	2.44	2.24	2.09	1.97	1.88	1.80	1.73	1.67	1.63
$\delta(\eta)$	0.30	0.45	0.54	0.60	0.64	0.68	0.71	0.73	0.75	0.77	0.79

The problem of the brightness of the sea was first solved by Ambartsumian in an unpublished work. He applied the method developed in Chapter 3, Section 8. However, his expressions for $I(0, \eta, \zeta)$ and his equations for the auxiliary functions were different from ours.

To determine the total intensities of the radiation emergent from the sea, we have to remember that the sea is illuminated not only by the sun's direct rays but also by the light scattered by the atmosphere. In addition, a rigorous treatment of the problem demands that it be solved simultaneously with that of the brightness of the atmosphere, since the light quanta can pass from sea to atmosphere and back many times.

3. *Medium with uniform distribution of radiation sources.* As the last example of an application we consider a medium of infinitely large optical thickness and with uniformly distributed radiation sources, $B_0 = $ const. We assume that the radiation sources emit energy with equal probability in all directions. For such a case we have shown in

Eq. (79), Chapter 6, Section 3, that the intensity of radiation emergent from the medium without a reflecting surface is equal to

$$I_0(0, \eta) = B_0 \frac{\phi(\eta)}{\sqrt{1-\lambda}} \qquad (86)$$

If, however, the medium has a specular surface with a coefficient of internal reflection $r(\eta)$, the intensity of radiation rising to the surface will be expressed by the formula:

$$I(0, \eta) = B_0 \frac{\phi(\eta)}{\sqrt{1-\lambda}} + 2 \frac{B_0}{\sqrt{1-\lambda}} \int_0^1 \phi(\eta') r(\eta') \rho_*(\eta, \eta') \eta' \, d\eta' \qquad (87)$$

But it follows from Eqs. (71) and (72) that

$$\phi(\eta)\gamma(\eta) = \phi(\eta) + 2 \int_0^1 \phi(\eta') r(\eta') \rho_*(\eta, \eta') \eta' \, d\eta' \qquad (88)$$

Therefore, instead of Eq. (87), we have

$$I(0, \eta) = B_0 \frac{\phi(\eta)}{\sqrt{1-\lambda}} \gamma(\eta) \qquad (89)$$

Equation (89) can be employed in finding the brightness of a liquid with scattering and absorption of the light and with internal sources of radiation.

8. Optical Phenomena at the Boundary of Two Media

In the treatment of the brightness of a medium with a specular surface there are two problems. The first is to compute the reflection of radiation by a surface with radiative diffusion within the medium. This problem has been discussed previously in detail; we were in fact able to find the intensities of radiation, both scattered by the medium and rising to its surface.

The second problem is to determine the intensity of radiation emergent from the medium after the intensity of radiation rising to the surface has been found. This problem is simpler, and we investigate it now.

Let the light quanta fall on the boundary of the two media at the angle θ_1 to the normal. The probability that these quanta are reflected at the same angle θ_1 to the normal is $r(\theta_1)$, and the probability that they pass the boundary is $1 - r(\theta_1)$. In the latter case the quanta change their direction due to the refraction of the light. We denote by θ_2

the angle at which the quanta enter the second medium (angle of refraction), defined by the relation:

$$n \sin \theta_2 = \sin \theta_1 \tag{90}$$

where n is the refractive index of the second medium relative to the first one.

If the incident light is natural and not polarized, the coefficient of reflection $r(\theta_1)$ is given by the following formula of Fresnel:

$$r(\theta_1) = \frac{1}{2} \frac{\sin^2(\theta_2 - \theta_1)}{\sin^2(\theta_1 + \theta_2)} \left[1 + \frac{\cos^2(\theta_1 + \theta_2)}{\cos^2(\theta_2 - \theta_1)} \right] \tag{91}$$

The values of $r(\theta_1)$ computed with this formula are given in Table 7.1 for the case when the rays enter the water from the air; and for the opposite case in Table 7.2.

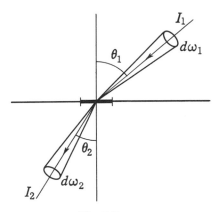

Fig. 7.3

When the radiation enters the water from the air, the angle of refraction changes from 0 to θ_0 as the angle of incidence changes from $0°$ to $90°$. This follows from the relation $n \sin \theta_0 = 1$, which in turn follows from Eq. (90). Here n is the refractive index of water relative to air. Since in this case $n = 1.33$, $\theta_0 = 49°$.

Thus the radiation can enter the air from the water only if the angle of incidence is not larger than θ_0. At the same time, the angle of refraction has all values from $0°$ to $90°$. If the angle of incidence is greater than θ_0, $r(\theta_1) = 1$, that is, the radiation suffers total internal reflection.

Thus, when radiation passes from one medium into another there is a redistribution of radiation over the solid angles. We shall now find the change in radiation intensity due to this effect.

Consider the intensity I_1 of radiation incident on the boundary between two media at an angle θ_1 to the normal within the solid angle $d\omega$ (Fig. 7.3). The amount of energy incident on unit area is $I_1 \cos \theta_1 \, d\omega_1$, and the amount of energy passing through the same area is equal to

$$[1 - r(\theta_1)] I_1 \cos \theta_1 \, d\omega_1$$

On the other side, this amount is equal to $I_2 \cos \theta_2 \, d\omega_2$, where I_2 is the intensity of radiation entering the second medium, θ_2 is the angle formed by the direction of this radiation with the normal, and $d\omega_2$ is the solid angle within which this radiation is propagated. Hence,

$$I_2 \cos \theta_2 \, d\omega_2 = [1 - r(\theta_1)] I_1 \cos \theta_1 \, d\omega_1 \tag{92}$$

Recalling that

$$d\omega_1 = \sin \theta_1 \, d\theta_1 d\phi_1, \qquad d\omega_2 = \sin \theta_2 \, d\theta_2 d\phi_2, \qquad d\phi_1 = d\phi_2$$

we find, instead of Eq. (92),

$$I_2 \cos \theta_2 \sin \theta_2 \, d\theta_2 = [1 - r(\theta_1)] I_1 \cos \theta_1 \sin \theta_1 \, d\theta_1 \tag{93}$$

Furthermore, from Eq. (90), we find

$$n^2 \cos \theta_2 \sin \theta_2 \, d\theta_2 = \cos \theta_1 \sin \theta_1 \, d\theta_1 \tag{94}$$

Thus we finally obtain

$$I_2 = [1 - r(\theta_1)] n^2 I_1 \tag{95}$$

Equation (95) is the required one. It means that the intensity of the radiation that passes through the boundary of two media is equal to the intensity of the radiation rising to the same boundary, multiplied by the factor $[1 - r(\theta_1)] n^2$.

The radiation intensity thus increases by approximately 1.7 times when the radiation enters the water from the air if the angle of incidence is not very large and the factor $1 - r(\theta_1)$ approaches unity.

When radiation passes in the opposite direction the radiation intensity diminishes by approximately the same factor, 1.7. The explanation is that, as the radiation crosses the boundary, the solid angle within which the radiation is propagated is diminished in the former case and increased in the latter.

CHAPTER 8

RADIATION DIFFUSION
WITH A REDISTRIBUTION IN FREQUENCY

In the previous chapters we have assumed that the light scattering occurs without a change in frequency of the light quanta, implying that the radiation intensity for a certain frequency does not depend on the radiation intensities for other frequencies. However, in some instances, there occurs a redistribution of radiation in frequency during an elementary act of scattering. Consequently, here the amount of energy emitted by an elementary volume in a certain frequency depends on the amount of energy absorbed by this volume in other frequencies. Hence, we have to compute simultaneously the radiation intensities in different frequencies.

The most important example of light scattering with a redistribution in frequency is the diffuse radiation in a spectral line. Our earlier computations (see, for example, Chapter 6, Section 4) of absorption line contours in stellar spectra with an assumption that the frequencies of the diffusely propagated quanta do not change can be regarded as correct only to a first approximation.

Now we shall solve a series of problems about the diffusion of radiation with a redistribution in frequency by paying particular attention to the diffuse radiation in a spectral line. In the first section we consider the radiation scattering in a spectral line occurring in an elementary volume. Precisely speaking, we determine the probability that the elementary volume absorbs quanta of the frequency ν_1, but emits them in the frequency ν_2. Further, we consider a diffusion of radiation in a one-dimensional medium with finite optical thickness. At the same time we compare the diffuse radiation with redistribution in frequency and without it. Our results here may be applied to the diffusion of L_α-quanta in the gaseous nebulae and in the interstellar medium, as well as to the diffusion of resonance radiation under dipper ent physical conditions. In the last sections we solved the problem of the luminescence of a medium with infinitely large optical thickness consisting of plane-parallel layers. As an example of the application of our results we compute absorption line contours in stellar spectra for the so-called "total redistribution of radiation in frequency"; in this case the probability that a quantum of a given frequency will be emitted by an elementary volume does not depend on the frequency at which the quantum was absorbed by the same volume.

1. Elementary Act of Scattering

As previously established, the problem of the radiation diffusion in a medium without any change in frequency of the diffusely propagated quanta is reduced to the following equations:

$$\frac{dI_\nu}{ds} = -\sigma_\nu I_\nu + \epsilon_\nu \tag{1}$$

$$\epsilon_\nu = \sigma_\nu \int I_\nu \frac{d\omega}{4\pi} \tag{2}$$

where I_ν is radiation intensity, and ϵ_ν is the emission coefficient and σ_ν the absorption coefficient; the integration of Eq. (2) is carried out with respect to all solid angles. We imply here that pure scattering occurs in the medium with the spherical scattering indicatrix.

If there is a redistribution of radiation in frequency, then instead of Eq. (2), we must write:

$$\epsilon_\nu = \int W(\nu', \nu) \sigma_{\nu'} \, d\nu' \int I_\nu \frac{d\omega}{4\pi} \tag{3}$$

where $W(\nu', \nu) d\nu$ is the probability that having absorbed quanta of frequency ν' the elementary volume emits them in the interval from ν to $\nu + d\nu$.

The function

$$Q(\nu', \nu) = W(\nu', \nu) \sigma_{\nu'} \tag{4}$$

is a volume coefficient of quantum absorption in the frequency ν' with subsequent quantum emission in the frequency ν. It is obvious that

$$\int_0^\infty Q(\nu', \nu) \, d\nu = \sigma_{\nu'} \tag{5}$$

Moreover the function $Q(\nu', \nu)$ should satisfy the condition

$$Q(\nu', \nu) = Q(\nu, \nu') \tag{6}$$

which expresses the principle of reversibility of optical phenomena.

We now consider a particular case of the redistribution of radiation in frequency. Let us assume that the probability of radiation in a certain frequency ν by the elementary quantum volume does not depend on the frequency ν' of the absorbed quantum, that is,

$$Q(\nu', \nu) = W(\nu) \sigma_{\nu'}$$

In this case, using Eq. (6), we find

$$Q(\nu', \nu) = C \sigma_\nu \sigma_{\nu'} \tag{7}$$

where C is a constant. Inserting Eq. (7) into Eq. (5), we obtain

$$C \int_0^\infty \sigma_\nu d\nu = 1 \tag{8}$$

Hence, instead of Eq. (3), we have

$$\epsilon_\nu = \sigma_\nu \frac{\int \sigma_{\nu'} \, d\nu' \int I_{\nu'} \frac{d\omega}{4\pi}}{\int \sigma_{\nu'} \, d\nu'} \tag{9}$$

We shall say, then, that the emission coefficient ϵ_ν in Eq. (9) corresponds to the case of *total redistribution* of radiation in frequency.

Consider now the diffusion of radiation in a spectral line. In this case the process of radiation scattering in the elementary volume is determined by the following essential causes: (1) Radiation damping, (2) Doppler effect caused by thermal motion of the atoms, and (3) pressure effects.

Considering only the first cause we find that the absorption coefficient in the spectral line for one atom is equal to

$$\frac{e^2}{mc} f \frac{\gamma}{(\nu - \nu_0)^2 + \gamma^2}$$

where ν_0 is the frequency in the center of the line, γ is the damping constant, f is the oscillator strength, e is the electron charge, m is its mass, and c is the velocity of light.

For N atoms per unit volume and with a Maxwellian distribution of their velocities, the volume absorption coefficient is defined by the formula:

$$\sigma_\nu = \sigma_0 \frac{a}{\pi} \int_{-\infty}^{+\infty} \frac{e^{-z^2} \, dz}{(x - z)^2 + a^2} \tag{10}$$

where

$$x = \frac{c}{u} \frac{\nu - \nu_0}{\nu_0} \tag{11}$$

is the distance from the line center expressed in Doppler width;

$$a = \frac{\gamma c}{u \nu_0} \tag{12}$$

is the ratio of the natural line width to the Doppler width;

$$\sigma_0 = \sqrt{\pi} \frac{e^2 f}{m u \nu_0} N \tag{13}$$

is the absorption coefficient at the center of the line for $a = 0$; and u is the average thermal velocity of the atom.

Considering simultaneously the pressure effects, we find that the absorption coefficient σ_ν is expressed by the same Eq. (10) with the difference that now γ is the effective damping constant, that is, it expresses the damping due to radiation as well as that due to collision.

In finding the function $Q(\nu', \nu)$, we must distinguish two cases. If the atom density in the medium is great, that is, if collision plays an important part, we may—since there are not yet accurate computations—assume that there is indeed a total redistribution in frequency during an elementary act of scattering. In such a case the function $Q(\nu', \nu)$ is defined by Eq. (7). This very expression will be employed by us in future for problems of absorption line contours in stellar spectra.

If the atom density in the medium is small, as for example in nebulae or interstellar space, we need to consider only the radiation damping and the thermal motion of the atoms in computing the function $Q(\nu', \nu)$. It can be found very easily indeed, and we show this for a resonance line.

Consider radiation of frequency ν_1 falling on an elementary volume and atoms moving with velocities from v to $v - dv$ at angles from θ_1 to $\theta_1 + d\theta_1$ to the direction of incident radiation. The number of atoms per unit volume is given by the Maxwellian formula:

$$dN = \frac{2N}{\sqrt{\pi}u^3}e^{-(v/u)^2}v^2\,dv\,\sin\theta_1\,d\theta_1 \qquad (14)$$

and an average frequency absorbed by them is

$$\nu_0 - \nu_0\frac{v}{c}\cos\theta_1$$

Therefore the volume absorption coefficient of the atoms with frequency ν_1, conditioned by the atoms considered, will be

$$\frac{e^2}{mc}f\frac{\gamma}{[\nu_1 - \nu_0 - \nu_0(v/c)\cos\theta_1]^2 + \gamma^2} \cdot \frac{2N}{\sqrt{\pi}u^3}e^{-(v/u)^2}v^2\,dv\,\sin\theta_1\,d\theta_1 \qquad (15)$$

This formula may be transformed into Eq. (10) if we integrate Eq. (15) with respect to all velocities in all directions of atomic motions and if we make some transformations. We are, however, not interested in all processes of quantum absorption in frequency ν_1 but only in those which are followed by quantum emission in frequency ν_2.

Denoting the angle between the direction of quantum emission and that of the moving atoms by θ_2 and recollecting that for the stationary atoms the frequencies ν_1 and ν_2 coincide because here we consider resonance radiation, we obtain the following formula which connects the quantities ν_2 and θ_2 for given ν_1 and θ_1:

$$\nu_2 - \nu_1 = \nu_0 \frac{v}{c}(\cos\theta_2 - \cos\theta_1) \tag{16}$$

The number of quanta emitted by the atoms considered in the frequency interval ν_2 to $\nu_2 + d\nu_2$ is then

$$\frac{2\pi \sin\theta_2 \, d\theta_2}{4\pi} = \frac{1}{2}\frac{c}{v}\frac{d\nu_2}{\nu_0} \tag{17}$$

Now multiplying out Eqs. (15) and (17) and integrating with respect to v and θ_1, we find the function $Q(\nu_1, \nu_2)$ as follows:

$$Q(\nu_1, \nu_2) = \frac{e^2 f \gamma N}{\sqrt{\pi} m \nu_0 u^3} \int\int \frac{e^{-(v/u)^2} \, v \, dv \sin\theta_1 \, d\theta_1}{[\nu_1 - \nu_0 - \nu_0(v/c)\cos\theta_1]^2 + \gamma^2} \tag{18}$$

The integration of Eq. (18) should be carried out, not with respect to all values of v and θ_1, but only to those which concur with Eq. (16). From this it follows that the quantities v and θ_1 change within the limits:

$$\frac{c}{2}\frac{|\nu_2 - \nu_1|}{\nu_0} \leqslant v < +\infty \tag{19}$$

$$-1 \leqslant \cos\theta_1 \leqslant 1 - \frac{c}{v}\frac{\nu_2 - \nu_1}{\nu_0}, \qquad \text{for} \quad \nu_2 > \nu_1, \tag{20}$$

$$-1 - \frac{c}{v}\frac{\nu_2 - \nu_1}{\nu_0} \leqslant \cos\theta_1 \leqslant 1, \qquad \text{for} \quad \nu_2 < \nu_1. \tag{21}$$

The two last inequalities can be combined:

$$-1 + \frac{c}{v}\frac{|\nu_2 - \nu_1|}{2\nu_0} \leqslant \cos\theta_1 + \frac{c}{v}\frac{\nu_2 - \nu_1}{2\nu_0} \leqslant 1 - \frac{c}{v}\frac{|\nu_2 - \nu_1|}{2\nu_0} \tag{22}$$

Thus, instead of Eq. (12), we have

$$Q(\nu_1, \nu_2) = \frac{e^2 f \gamma N}{\sqrt{\pi} m \nu_0 u^3} \int_{\frac{c}{2}\frac{|\nu_2-\nu_1|}{\nu_0}}^{\infty} e^{-(v/u)^2} v \, dv$$

$$\int_{-1+\frac{c}{v}\frac{|\nu_2-\nu_1|}{2\nu_0}}^{1-\frac{c}{v}\frac{|\nu_2-\nu_1|}{2\nu_0}} \frac{dt}{[(\nu_1+\nu_2)/2 - \nu_0 - \nu_0(v/c)t]^2 + \gamma^2} \tag{23}$$

where we have introduced a new variable of integration

$$t = \cos\theta_1 + \frac{c}{v}\frac{\nu_2 - \nu_1}{2\nu_0} \tag{24}$$

Integrating with respect to t, we obtain

$$Q(\nu_1, \nu_2) = \frac{e^2 f c \mathcal{N}}{\sqrt{\pi} m \nu_0^2 u^3}$$

$$\times \int_{\frac{c}{2}\frac{|\nu_2-\nu_1|}{\nu_0}}^{\infty} e^{-(v/u)^2} dv \left[\text{arctg} \frac{(\nu_1+\nu_2)/2 - \nu_0 + \nu_0(v/c) - |\nu_2-\nu_1|/2}{\gamma} \right.$$

$$\left. - \text{arctg} \frac{(\nu_1+\nu_2)/2 - \nu_0 - \nu_0(v/c) + |\nu_2-\nu_1|/2}{\gamma} \right] \qquad (25)$$

Now introducing the notations,

$$x_1 = \frac{c}{u} \frac{\nu_1 - \nu_0}{\nu_2}, \qquad x_2 = \frac{c}{u} \frac{\nu_2 - \nu_0}{\nu_0} \qquad (26)$$

we replace the function $Q(\nu_1, \nu_2)$ by a new function,

$$q(x_1, x_2) = Q(\nu_1, \nu_2) \frac{u\nu_0}{c} \qquad (27)$$

where $q(x_1, x_2)$ is the quantum absorption coefficient in a dimensionless frequency x_1 together with the subsequent quantum emission in an interval of dimensionless frequencies from x_2 to $x_2 + dx_2$. Having used $v = uz$ and Eqs. (12) and (13), we can rewrite Eq. (25) as follows:

$$q(x_1, x_2) = \frac{\sigma_0}{\pi} \int_{\frac{|x_2-x_1|}{2}}^{\infty} e^{-z^2} \left[\text{arctg} \frac{z + (x_1+x_2)/2 - |x_2-x_1|/2}{a} \right.$$

$$\left. + \text{arctg} \frac{z - (x_1+x_2)/2 - |x_2-x_1|/2}{a} \right] dz \qquad (28)$$

This formula can be greatly simplified by introducing new notations,

$$\frac{x_1 + x_2}{2} = s, \qquad \frac{|x_2 - x_1|}{2} = r \qquad (29)$$

and by employing a new variable of integration $y = z - r$; instead of Eq. (28), we actually find

$$q(x_1, x_2) = \frac{\sigma_0}{\pi} \int_0^{\infty} e^{-(y+r)2} \left[\text{arctg} \frac{y+s}{a} + \text{arctg} \frac{y-s}{a} \right] dy, \qquad (30)$$

which is the final expression for the required function $q(x_1, x_2)$.

We point out the following properties of this function.

1. It is symmetrical with respect to x_1 and x_2;

$$q(x_1, x_2) = q(x_2, x_1) \qquad (31)$$

2. It does not change when the signs of both arguments change:

$$q(x_1, x_2) = q(-x_1, -x_2) \tag{32}$$

3. It satisfies the integral relation:

$$\int_{-\infty}^{+\infty} q(x_1, x_2)\, dx_2 = \sigma_{\nu_1} \tag{33}$$

In Table 8.1 are given the values of q/σ_0 for $a = 0.1$, and in Fig. 8.1 their graphical illustrations.

TABLE 8.1. FUNCTION q/σ_0 FOR $a = 0.1$

r \ s	0	0.2	0.4	0.6	0.8	1.0	1.2	1.4	1.6	1.8	2.0
0	0.694	0.609	0.474	0.346	0.240	0.158	0.100	0.062	0.038	0.023	0.015
0.2	0.521	0.447	0.332	0.230	0.152	0.096	0.059	0.035	0.021	0.013	0.009
0.4	0.371	0.309	0.219	0.145	0.091	0.055	0.032	0.019	0.011	0.007	0.005
0.6	0.248	0.201	0.136	0.085	0.051	0.030	0.017	0.010	0.006	0.004	0.003
0.8	0.156	0.123	0.079	0.047	0.027	0.015	0.009	0.005	0.003	0.002	0.001
1.0	0.092	0.070	0.043	0.026	0.014	0.007	0.004	0.003	0.002	0.001	—
1.2	0.051	0.038	0.023	0.012	0.006	0.004	0.002	0.001	0.001	—	—
1.4	0.026	0.019	0.011	0.005	0.003	0.002	0.001	—	—	—	—
1.6	0.013	0.009	0.005	0.002	0.001	0.001	—	—	—	—	—
1.8	0.006	0.004	0.002	0.001	—	—	—	—	—	—	—
2.0	0.002	0.002	0.001	—	—	—	—	—	—	—	—

We observe that the probability of scattering by the elementary quantum volume in a given frequency depends not only on the frequency of the incident quantum but also on the angle between the directions of the incident and scattered radiation. This probability was found some time ago by Henyey.[1] We could obtain Eq. (30) for the function $q(x_1, x_2)$ by integrating his formula with respect to angle. But we have preferred to do so more simply by employing direct physical considerations.

2. RADIATION DIFFUSION IN A ONE-DIMENSIONAL MEDIUM

Having clarified the laws of radiation redistribution in frequency during an elementary act of scattering, we can now attack the problem of radiation diffusion in a medium with a given law of redistribution in frequency.

[1] L. G. Henyey, The Doppler Effect in Resonance Lines, *Proc. Nat. Acad. Sci.* **26**, 50 (1940).

First we assume that the radiation diffusion occurs in a one-dimensional medium. It is known that a three-dimensional medium consisting of plane-parallel layers can be approximately transformed into a one-dimensional medium. Inasmuch as we are interested primarily in redistribution in frequency and not in angle, such a transformation is the more justified.

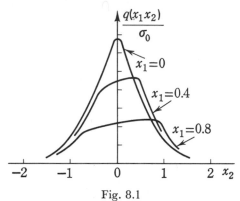

Fig. 8.1

Consider radiation in a spectral line, diffusely propagated along a straight path of length l_0. We shall express l_0 by its optical length. Because the optical length varies with frequency we must be more definite, and we select the frequency for the line center. Denoting this optical length by τ_0, we have

$$\tau_0 = \int_0^{l_0} \sigma_{\nu_0}(l)\, dl \tag{34}$$

where l is the distance of the point in the medium from one of its boundaries. Analogously we can write a similar relation for any point optically distant from a chosen boundary of the medium:

$$\tau = \int_0^l \sigma_{\nu_0}(l)\, dl \tag{35}$$

To simplify writing we shall avail ourselves not of the frequency ν but of the dimensionless frequency x which is defined by Eq. (11) and represents the ratio of the distance from the line center to the Doppler width. In this way the intensities of diffusely propagated radiation in the medium will be functions of τ and x. They will be denoted by $I_1(\tau, x)$ and $I_2(\tau, x)$ corresponding to radiation propagated along the increasing value of τ and in the opposite direction.

With these notations the equations of radiative transfer can be rewritten as follows:

$$\left.\begin{array}{c} \dfrac{dI_1(\tau, x)}{d\tau} = -\alpha(x)\, I_1(\tau, x) + \epsilon(\tau, x), \\[4mm] -\dfrac{dI_2(\tau, x)}{d\tau} = -\alpha(x)\, I_2(\tau, x) + \epsilon(\tau, x). \end{array}\right\} \qquad (36)$$

Here $\epsilon(\tau, x)\,d\tau\,dx$ is the energy emitted on the path from τ to $\tau + d\tau$ in an interval of dimensionless frequency from x to $x + dx$ per unit of time in one direction, but $\alpha(x)$ is the dimensionless absorption coefficient equal to

$$\alpha(x) = \frac{\sigma_\nu}{\sigma_{\nu_0}} \qquad (37)$$

Because the quantities σ_ν and σ_{ν_0} depend on location in the medium only by way of the factor N, the quantity $\alpha(x)$ is independent of location in the medium.

To be able to write the equation of radiative equilibrium, we have to use the function $q(x_1, x_2)$ introduced above, which characterizes the redistribution of the radiation in frequency and within an elementary volume. While transforming $q(x_1, x_2)$ into the dimensionless function

$$\beta(x_1, x_2) = \frac{q(x_1, x_2)}{\sigma_{\nu_0}}, \qquad (38)$$

we can rewrite the equation of radiative equilibrium in the form

$$\epsilon(\tau, x) = \frac{1}{2} \int_{-\infty}^{+\infty} [I_1(\tau, x') + I_2(\tau, x')]\beta(x', x)\, dx' + \epsilon_0(\tau, x), \qquad (39)$$

where $\epsilon_0(\tau, x)\, d\tau dx$ is the energy emitted directly by internal sources along the path from τ to $\tau + d\tau$ in the interval of dimensionless frequency from x to $x + dx$ per unit time in one direction.

We assume that there is no true absorption of the radiated energy in the medium, that is, there are no transitions of atoms from excited states without quantum radiation. Had there been such transitions, and their fraction had been $1 - \lambda$, we should have multiplied the integral in Eq. (39) by λ.

We may obtain one integral equation for the determination of the function $\epsilon(\tau, x)$ by using Eqs. (36) and (39). For this we shall solve Eqs. (36) with respect to I_1 and I_2. Assuming that there is no external radiation, we find

$$\left.\begin{array}{c} I_1(\tau, x) = \displaystyle\int_0^\tau e^{-\alpha(x)(\tau-\tau')}\epsilon(\tau', x)\, d\tau', \\[4mm] I_2(\tau, x) = \displaystyle\int_\tau^{\tau_0} e^{-\alpha(x)(\tau'-\tau)}\epsilon(\tau', x)\, d\tau'. \end{array}\right\} \qquad (40)$$

Inserting Eqs. (40) into Eq. (39) we obtain

$$\epsilon(\tau, x) = \frac{1}{2} \int_{-\infty}^{+\infty} \beta(x', x) \, dx' \int_{0}^{\tau_0} e^{-\alpha(x')|\tau - \tau'|} \epsilon(\tau', x') \, d\tau + \epsilon_0(\tau, x). \qquad (41)$$

Before solving this integral equation we shall simplify it a little. We assume that radiation sources are uniformly distributed in the medium, that is, ϵ_0 is independent of τ, and that the energy radiated by them depends on the frequency as well as on the absorption coefficient $\alpha(x)$. This case of dependence of ϵ_0 on x is realized when the luminiscence of a medium is caused by atoms which in some way emit quanta in the given line. The appearance of L_α quanta in nebulae as a result of photoionizations of hydrogen atoms and subsequent recombinations can furnish an example.

Thus, instead of Eq. (41) we consider the equation,

$$\epsilon(\tau, x) = \frac{1}{2} \int_{-\infty}^{+\infty} \beta(x', x) \, dx' \int_{0}^{\tau_0} e^{-\alpha(x')|\tau - \tau'|} \epsilon(\tau', x') \, d\tau' + \alpha(x) B_0 \qquad (42)$$

where B_0 is a certain constant.

We assume further that the dependence of the absorption coefficient on frequency rests only on thermal motions of atoms, that is,

$$\alpha(x) = e^{-x^2} \qquad (43)$$

With these propositions we now solve the integral equation, Eq. (42), for the following cases; (A) Quanta are diffusely propagated in the medium without change in frequency; (B) diffusion of quanta occurs with total redistribution in frequency; (C) diffusion of quanta occurs with a redistribution in frequency according to the law of Eq. (30).

Case A. For radiation diffusion without redistribution in frequency

$$\beta(x', x) = \delta(x - x')\alpha(x') \qquad (44)$$

where δ is Dirac's function. Therefore, instead of Eq. (42), we have

$$\epsilon(\tau, x) = \frac{1}{2} \int_{0}^{\tau_0} e^{-\alpha(x)|\tau - \tau'|} \epsilon(\tau', x) \, d\tau' + \alpha(x) B_0 \qquad (45)$$

This equation may best be solved by returning to Eqs. (36) and (39) at the start; here the latter takes the following form:

$$\epsilon(\tau, x) = \frac{\alpha(x)}{2}[I_1(\tau, x) + I_2(\tau, x)] + \alpha(x) B_0 \qquad (46)$$

Combining Eqs. (36) and (46) with the condition that

$$I_1(0, x) = 0, \qquad I_2(\tau_0, x) = 0$$

we find

$$\epsilon(\tau, x) = \frac{\alpha^2(x)}{2} B_0[\tau_0 + \alpha(x)\tau(\tau_0 - \tau)] + \alpha(x) B_0 \qquad (47)$$

$$I_1(\tau, x) = \alpha(x) B_0\tau\left[1 + \frac{\alpha(x)}{2}(\tau_0 - \tau)]\right] \qquad (48)$$

$$I_2(\tau, x) = \alpha(x) B_0(\tau_0 - \tau)\left[1 + \frac{\alpha(x)}{2}\tau\right] \qquad (49)$$

These formulas are correct for any form of the function $\alpha(x)$

Case B. For total radiation redistribution in frequency the function $\beta(x', x)$ becomes

$$\beta(x', x) = A\alpha(x)\alpha(x') \qquad (50)$$

where

$$A\int_{-\infty}^{+\infty} \alpha(x) \, dx = 1 \qquad (51)$$

Inserting $\beta(x', x)$ in Eq. (50) into Eq. (42), we obtain

$$\epsilon(\tau, x) = \frac{A}{2}\alpha(x) \int_{-\infty}^{+\infty} \alpha(x') \, dx' \int_0^{\tau_0} e^{-\alpha(x')|\tau - \tau'|}\epsilon(\tau', x') \, d\tau' + \alpha(x) B_0 \quad (52)$$

We observe that the function $\epsilon(\tau, x)$ can be represented as a product

$$\epsilon(\tau, x) = \alpha(x) B(\tau) \qquad (53)$$

where $B(\tau)$ is an unknown function of τ. Inserting Eq. (53) into Eq. (52), we find the following equation for determining this function:

$$B(\tau) = \frac{1}{2} \int_0^{\tau_0} K(|\tau - \tau'|) B(\tau') \, d\tau' + B_0 \qquad (54)$$

where

$$K(\tau) = A \int_{-\infty}^{+\infty} e^{-\alpha(x)\tau}\alpha^2(x) \, dx \qquad (55)$$

In the case where $\alpha(x)$ is given by Eq. (43), the function $K(\tau)$ becomes

$$K(\tau) = \frac{1}{\sqrt{\pi}} \int_{-\infty}^{+\infty} e^{-2x^2 - \tau e^{-x^2}} \, dx \qquad (56)$$

Values of the function $K(\tau)$ for an interval of τ from 0 to 10 are given in Table 8.2. Also given are values of the function

$$L(\tau) = \frac{1}{\sqrt{\pi}} \int_{-\infty}^{+\infty} e^{-x^2 - \tau e^{-x^2}} \, dx \qquad (57)$$

which we shall discuss subsequently.

We point out that for large values of τ the following asymptotic formulas are correct:

$$K(\tau) \simeq \frac{1}{\sqrt{\pi \tau^2} \sqrt{\lg \tau}} \qquad L(\tau) \simeq \frac{1}{\sqrt{\pi \tau} \sqrt{\lg \tau}} \qquad (58)$$

We see that the function $K(\tau)$, which is the kernel of the integral Eq. (54), decreases slowly with increasing τ. This means that a large amount of radiation, coming from other volumes located at great optical distances from the given elementary volume, is reaching it. This is the reason why the integral Eq. (54) cannot be interchanged with the differential equation without loss of accuracy.

This circumstance contrasts sharply with Eqs. (54) and (45), which can be interchanged with a differential equation of the second order, the kernel of which is an exponential function.

TABLE 8.2. FUNCTIONS $K(\tau)$ AND $L(\tau)$

τ	$K(\tau)$	$L(\tau)$	τ	$K(\tau)$	$L(\tau)$	τ	$K(\tau)$	$L(\tau)$
0	0.707	1.000	1.5	0.219	0.381	6.5	0.013	0.063
0.1	0.652	0.932	2.0	0.152	0.289	7.0	0.011	0.057
0.2	0.601	0.869	2.5	0.107	0.225	7.5	0.009	0.052
0.3	0.554	0.812	3.0	0.077	0.180	8.0	0.008	0.048
0.4	0.512	0.758	3.5	0.057	0.147	8.5	0.007	0.044
0.5	0.478	0.709	4.0	0.042	0.122	9.0	0.006	0.041
0.6	0.437	0.664	4.5	0.032	0.104	9.5	0.005	0.038
0.7	0.403	0.662	5.0	0.025	0.090	10.0	0.004	0.036
0.8	0.373	0.583	5.5	0.020	0.079			
0.9	0.345	0.547	6.0	0.016	0.070			
1.0	0.312	0.514						

Equation (54) can be solved numerically for the case $\tau_0 = 10$. These results are given in Table 8.3. Since $B(\tau_0 - \tau) = B(\tau)$, we have given values of $B(\tau)$ only for six values of τ lying between 0 and 5.

TABLE 8.3. VALUES OF THE FUNCTION $B(\tau)$

τ	0	1	2	3	4	5
$B(\tau)$	3.4	4.9	5.9	6.6	7.0	7.2

Case C. In this case the function $\beta(x_1, x_2)$ is defined as

$$\beta(x_1, x_2) = \frac{\sigma_0}{\pi \sigma_{\nu_0}} \int_0^\infty e^{-(y+r)^2} \left[\operatorname{arctg} \frac{y+s}{a} + \operatorname{arctg} \frac{y-s}{a} \right] dy \qquad (59)$$

which follows from Eqs. (30) and (38).

We have agreed to solve the integral Eq. (42) for the case where the absorption coefficient is defined by the Doppler effect due to the thermal motions of atoms. Hence in Eq. (59) we have $a = 0$. With this we find:

$$\beta(x_1, x_2) = \int_{|s|}^{\infty} e^{-(y+r)^2} \, dy \tag{60}$$

or, recollecting Eq. (29),

$$\beta(x_1, x_2) = \int_{|x_2|}^{\infty} e^{-z^2} \, dz \qquad (\text{for } |x_2| > |x_1|) \tag{61}$$

and

$$\beta(x_1, x_2) = \int_{|x_1|}^{\infty} e^{-z^2} \, dz \qquad (\text{for } |x_2| < |x_1|) \tag{62}$$

Thus, in the limiting case $a = 0$, the function $\beta(x_1, x_2)$ has a very simple form. Inserting Eqs. (61) and (62) into Eq. (42), we obtain:

$$\epsilon(\tau, x) = \int_0^x dx' \int_0^{\tau_0} e^{-\alpha(x')|\tau - \tau'|} \epsilon(\tau', x') \, d\tau' \int_x^{\infty} e^{-z^2} \, dz$$

$$+ \int_x^{\infty} dx' \int_{x'}^{\infty} e^{-z^2} \, dz \int_0^{\tau_0} e^{-\alpha(x')|\tau - \tau'|} \epsilon(\tau', x') \, d\tau' + \alpha(x) B_0 \tag{63}$$

This equation may also be rewritten as follows for $\alpha = e^{-x^2}$:

$$\epsilon(\tau, x) = \int_x^{\infty} e^{-z^2} \, dz \int_0^z dx' \int_0^{\tau_0} e^{-|\tau - \tau'|e^{-x'^2}} \epsilon(\tau', x') \, d\tau' + e^{-x^2} B_0 \tag{64}$$

The results of computations in accordance with Eq. (64) and for $\tau_0 = 10$ are given in Table 8.4.

TABLE 8.4. THE FUNCTION $\epsilon(\tau, x)$ FOR $B_0 = 1$

x \ τ	0	1	2	3	4	5
0	3.6	5.3	6.6	7.4	7.9	8.0
0.2	3.4	5.1	6.3	7.1	7.6	7.7
0.4	3.1	4.5	5.6	6.3	6.7	6.8
0.6	2.5	3.6	4.5	5.0	5.4	5.5
0.8	1.9	2.7	3.3	3.7	3.9	4.0
1.0	1.3	1.8	2.2	2.5	2.6	2.7
1.2	0.83	1.1	1.4	1.5	1.6	1.7
1.4	0.48	0.65	0.77	0.86	0.91	0.93
1.6	0.25	0.34	0.40	0.44	0.47	0.48
1.8	0.12	0.16	0.19	0.21	0.22	0.23
2.0	0.05	0.07	0.08	0.09	0.10	0.10

3. Determination of Various Physical Quantities

The results mentioned above enable us to determine the values of several physical quantities, radiation density, light pressure, etc., in the medium. In this section we shall find them for the three cases discussed above, and intercompare them.

Energy emitted per unit volume. Denoting by $\epsilon(\tau)\, d\tau$ the total energy emitted by an elementary cross section of the length $d\tau$ at depth τ per second in one direction, we can obviously write

$$\epsilon(\tau) = \int_{-\infty}^{+\infty} \epsilon(\tau, x)\, dx \tag{65}$$

The total energy emitted by the unit of "volume", that is, by a cross section of length 1 cm per sec in one direction will, however, be equal to $\epsilon(\tau)\, \sigma_{\nu_0}$.

For case A, remembering Eq. (47), we obtain:

$$\epsilon(\tau) = B_0 \frac{\sqrt{\pi}}{2} \left[\frac{\tau_0}{\sqrt{2}} + \frac{\tau(\tau_0 - \tau)}{\sqrt{3}} \right] + B_0 \sqrt{\pi} \tag{66}$$

But for case B, using Eqs. (53) and (65), we have,

$$\epsilon(\tau) = B(\tau)\sqrt{\pi} \tag{67}$$

Values of this function $\epsilon(\tau)$ are given in Table 8.5 for all three cases A, B, C; in comparing them we avail ourselves of the known results of Tables 8.3 and 8.4.

TABLE 8.5. THE FUNCTION $\epsilon(\tau)$ FOR $B_0 = 1$

τ	A	B	C
0	8.0	6.1	6.3
1	12.6	8.7	9.1
2	16.2	10.5	11.2
3	18.8	11.8	12.6
4	20.3	12.5	13.4
5	20.8	12.7	13.7

With the aid of this function we can find the degree of excitation of atoms in the medium. Letting N_1 be the number of atoms in the ground state and N_2 be the number in the excited state per unit volume, we can obviously write

$$2\epsilon(\tau)\sigma_{\nu_0} = N_2 A_{21} h\nu_0 \tag{68}$$

where A_{21} is the Einstein coefficient of the spontaneous transition and h_{ν_0} is the quantum energy. But

$$\sigma_{\nu_0} = N_1 k_{\nu_0} \qquad (69)$$

where k_{ν_0} is the absorption coefficient computed for one atom. Hence,

$$\frac{N_2}{N_1} = \frac{2 k_{\nu_0}}{A_{21} h_{\nu_0}} \, \epsilon(\tau) \qquad (70)$$

We draw particular attention to the fact that the quantity N_2/N_1 appears in investigations of the envelopes of stars of spectral class Be, novae, and others. In these envelopes there first occurs an ionization of hydrogen atoms by the radiation of the star, then recaptures of electrons by the ions, cascading of electrons over the levels, and finally jumps from the second level to the first, producing the $L\alpha$ quanta. Because of the great optical thickness of these envelopes in the $L\alpha$ line they become a great reservoir of $L\alpha$ quanta, which leads to large values of N_2/N_1, and the optical thickness in the Balmer lines reaches unity, and in some cases even more. For the same reason the spectra of these stars show the Balmer series in absorption.

We should point out that the problem of the degree of atomic excitation due to the diffusion of resonance radiation has been investigated earlier in the literature of physics. Biberman[2] derived an integral equation of radiative diffusion in a medium consisting of plane-parallel layers on the assumption of total redistribution in frequency; he solved this equation numerically for different values of the optical thickness of the medium and for different values of the parameter λ which correspond to different effects of collisional damping. He also found the concentration of the excited atoms in dependence on the coordinates and established agreement between theory and experiment.

Radiation density. Let $I(\tau)$ be an average integral intensity of radiation, that is,

$$I(\tau) = \frac{1}{2} \int_{-\infty}^{+\infty} [I_1(\tau, x) + I_2(\tau, x)] \, dx \qquad (71)$$

Then the integral radiation intensity is

$$\sigma_{\nu_0} \rho(\tau) = \frac{2}{c} I(\tau) \qquad (72)$$

For case A,

$$I(\tau) = \frac{\sqrt{\pi}}{2} \left[\tau_0 + \frac{\tau(\tau_0 - \tau)}{\sqrt{2}} \right] B_0 \qquad (73)$$

[2] L. M. Biberman, On the Theory of Diffusion of the Resonance Radiation, *JETF* **17**, 416 (1947).

For case B, remembering Eqs. (40) and (53), we find:

$$I(\tau) = \frac{\sqrt{\pi}}{2} \int_0^{\tau_0} B(\tau') L(|\tau - \tau'|) \, d\tau' \qquad (74)$$

where the function $I(\tau)$ is defined by Eq. (57).

Table 8.6 contains values of this function for these cases with $B_0 = 1$.

TABLE 8.6. AVERAGE INTEGRAL RADIATION INTENSITY $I(\tau)$

τ	A	B	C
0	8.9	8.9	8.9
1	14.5	12.6	12.9
2	18.9	15.4	15.9
3	22.0	17.2	18.0
4	23.9	18.4	19.2
5	24.5	18.7	19.6
$Tc\sigma_{\nu_0}$	193	155	161

Knowledge of the function $\rho(\tau)$ permits us to determine an average duration of quantum stay in the medium, denoted here by T. Since the total amount of radiant energy in the medium is equal to

$$E = \int_0^{\tau_0} \rho(\tau) \, d\tau \qquad (75)$$

and the amount of energy emitted by radiation sources per second is

$$E_0 = 2\sqrt{\pi} B_0 \tau_0 \qquad (76)$$

we have

$$T = \frac{E}{E_0} = \frac{1}{c\sigma_{\nu_0}\tau_0\sqrt{\pi}} \int_0^{\tau_0} I(\tau) \, d\tau \qquad (77)$$

In the last line of Table 8.6. we gave values of the product $Tc\sigma_{\nu_0}$.

Radiation flux. By definition the integral flux of radiation is equal to

$$H(\tau) = \int_{-\infty}^{+\infty} [I_2(\tau, x) - I_1(\tau, x)] \, dx \qquad (78)$$

To find it we employ Eqs. (36) and (39). From Eqs. (36), we obtain:

$$\frac{dH}{d\tau} = \int_{-\infty}^{+\infty} \{\alpha(x)[I_1(\tau, x) + I_2(\tau, x)] - 2\epsilon(\tau, x)\} \, dx \qquad (79)$$

Recollecting Eq. (39), we find:

$$\frac{dH}{d\tau} = -2 \int_{-\infty}^{+\infty} \epsilon_0(\tau, x) \, dx \qquad (80)$$

or

$$H(\tau) = 2 \int_{\tau}^{\tau_0/2} d\tau' \int_{-\infty}^{+\infty} \epsilon_0(\tau', x) \, dx \qquad (81)$$

Here we recollected that $H(\tau_0/2) = 0$.

Because we assumed $\epsilon_0(\tau, x) = \alpha(x)B_0$ we have, instead of Eq. (81):

$$H(\tau) = (\tau_0 - 2\tau) B_0 \sqrt{\pi} \qquad (82)$$

Equations (81) and (82) express the well-known fact that the integrated radiation flux at depth τ is equal to the total amount of energy emitted by radiation sources in a depth interval from τ to $\tau_0/2$. The integrated radiation field does not depend on the form of scattering. In special cases it is the same for the problems A, B, and C.

Light pressure. Let us find the amount of light pressure caused by emission in the given line. We denote by $P(\tau) \, d\tau$ the light pressure on an element of length $d\tau$. We know

$$P(\tau) = \frac{1}{c} \int_{-\infty}^{+\infty} \alpha(x)[I_2(\tau, x) - I_1(\tau, x)] \, dx \qquad (83)$$

The light pressure on a volume element is equal to $P(\tau) \, \sigma_{\nu_0}$.

Employing now Eqs. (36) of radiative transfer and Eq. (71), we obtain

$$P(\tau) = \frac{2}{c} \frac{dI(\tau)}{d\tau} \qquad (84)$$

For problem A,

$$P(\tau) = \frac{B_0}{c} \sqrt{\frac{\pi}{2}}(\tau_0 - 2\tau) \qquad (85)$$

In Table 8.7 we give values of the function $cP(\tau)$ for $B_0 = 1$. We can explain the fact that the light pressure is different in all three cases, although the integral radiation flux is the same, by the different distribution of the radiation flux in frequency.

TABLE 8.7. THE QUANTITY $cP(\tau)$

τ	A	B	C
0	12.5	8.6	9.1
1	10.0	6.6	7.1
2	7.5	4.7	5.1
3	5.0	3.0	3.3
4	2.5	1.4	1.6
5	0	0	0

We should remark that the problem of light pressure caused by $L\alpha$ emission is of great interest in the dynamics of planetary nebulae. Ambartsumian[3] was the first to investigate this problem for a stationary nebula, and almost at the same time Zanstra[4] did so for an expanding nebula with a velocity gradient. They both presupposed that radiation diffusion occurs without change of frequency.

Ten years later the author[5] solved the problem of the $L\alpha$ radiation diffusion in a nebula expanding with a velocity gradient, and with a total redistribution of radiation in frequency. He then showed that even with a small velocity gradient the densities of $L\alpha$ radiation and the light pressure caused by it are many times smaller than those obtained earlier by Ambartsumian and Zanstra.

Still later Zanstra[6] determined the light pressure in a stationary nebula, but with a total redistribution of radiation in frequency. Here he solved integral Eq. (54) for several particular forms of the function $B_0(\tau)$; precisely speaking, he assumed some simple forms of $B(\tau)$ and found $B_0(\tau)$ with the aid of Eq. (54). He found that for τ_0 of the order of 10^4, the light pressure for radiation diffusion with redistribution in frequency (that is, case B) is almost 300 times smaller than the light pressure for radiation diffusion without change of frequency (that is, case A).

Table 8.7 shows that for $\tau = 10$ the ratio of light pressure in case B to that in case A is about $\frac{2}{3}$. In other words, this ratio decreases with increase of the optical thickness τ_0. Table 8.7 shows also that in cases B and C the light pressure is about the same.

Contour of a spectral line. The intensity of the radiation emergent from the medium is equal to

$$I_2(0, x) = \int_0^{\tau_0} e^{-\alpha(x)\tau} \epsilon(\tau, x) \, d\tau \qquad (86)$$

For case A

$$I_2(0, x) = \alpha(x) B_0 \tau_0 \qquad (87)$$

Figure 8.2 shows graphs of the function $I_2(0, x)/B_0$, computed with Eqs. (86) and (87). These graphs represent contours of spectral lines

[3] V. A. Ambartsumian, On the Radiative Equilibrium of a Planetary Nebula, *Bull. Pulk. obs.* **13**, 3 (1933).

[4] H. Zanstra, Radiation Pressure in an Expanding Nebula, *Monthly Notices of the Royal Astronomical Society* **95**, 84 (1934).

[5] V. V. Sobolev, Light Pressure in an Expanding Nebula, *Russian Astronomical J.* **21**, 143 (1944).

[6] H. Zanstra, On Scattering with Redistribution and Radiation Pressure in a Stationary Nebula, *Bull. of the Astr. Inst. Neth.*, XI, No. 401 (1949).

formed by the given medium. We see that the line contours for cases B and C differ very much from the line contour for case A.

We should point out that the diffusion of radiation with redistribution in frequency leads to the same kind of spectral lines as the so-called "self-reversal", and here we should distinguish two processes of formation of emission lines with a central depression.

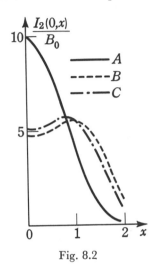

Fig. 8.2

The afore-mentioned results enable us to reach the following conclusions:

1. Various physical quantities obtained for radiation diffusion with redistribution in frequency (cases B and C) differ greatly from those obtained without it (case A). The difference increases with an increase of the optical thickness of the medium, τ_0.

2. The physical quantities for cases B and C are relatively near to one another. But this is true only for smaller values of τ_0 (of the order of 10). How cases B and C will differ as τ_0 increases should be investigated specially.

4. PROBABILITY OF QUANTUM EXIT FROM THE MEDIUM

In Section 2 we investigated the diffusion of radiation with redistribution in frequency by means of the integral equation which defines the emission coefficient $\epsilon(\tau, x)$. We now solve the same problem with the aid of the probability of quantum exit from the medium.[7]

[7] V. V. Sobolev, Diffusion of Radiation with a Redistribution in Frequency, I, *Inform. Leningr. Inst.*, No. 5 (1955); II, No. 11 (1955).

The advantages and drawbacks of each of these methods of solving the problem of radiation diffusion are as follows. The first method enables us to find the radiation field outside as well as within the medium for given radiation sources. To solve the problem for *other* sources we have to solve a new integral equation which differs from the previous one by a free term. The second method permits us to determine *only the intensities* of radiation emergent from the medium. But the probability of quantum exit does not depend on the way in which the quanta appeared in the medium, that is, on the radiation sources. Therefore, having found the probability of quantum exit, we can compute the intensities of the emergent radiation for *any radiation sources*.

In other words, the first method provides us with the following integral equation for the determination of the emission coefficient:

$$\epsilon(\tau, x) = \frac{\lambda}{2} \int_{-\infty}^{+\infty} g(x', x)\alpha(x') \, dx' \int_0^{\tau_0} e^{-\alpha(x')|\tau'-\tau|}\epsilon(\tau', x') \, d\tau' + \epsilon_0(\tau, x) \quad (88)$$

where we have introduced the notation

$$\beta(x', x) = g(x', x)\alpha(x') \quad (89)$$

Equation (88) differs from Eq. (41) only by the factor $\lambda/2$ before the integral; earlier λ was assumed equal to unity.

Having found the quantity $\epsilon(\tau, x)$ from Eq. (88), we can easily compute radiation intensities for any optical depth τ, employing Eqs. (40).

Now we turn our attention to the second method. We denote by $p(\tau, x_1, x_2)dx_2$ the probability that the radiation absorbed at optical depth τ in the form of quanta of frequency x_1 leaves the medium, generally speaking after multiple scattering and redistribution in frequency, in the form of quanta with frequencies in the interval from x_2 to $x_2 + dx_2$. Obviously, the function $p(\tau, x_1, x_2)$ should satisfy the following integral equation:

$$p(\tau, x_1, x_2) = \frac{\lambda}{2} g(x_1, x_2) \, e^{-\alpha(x_2)\tau}$$

$$+ \frac{\lambda}{2} \int_{-\infty}^{+\infty} g(x_1, x)\alpha(x) \, dx \int_0^{\tau_0} e^{-\alpha(x)|\tau'-\tau|}p(\tau', x, x_2) \, d\tau' \quad (90)$$

The first term on the right-hand side expresses here the radiation emergent directly from the given volume, and the second one, that emergent after undergoing scatterings in other volumes.

With a known $p(\tau, x_1, x_2)$, one can easily find the intensities of the emergent radiation for any kind of radiation sources. Let $L(\tau, x')d\tau dx'$ be an amount of energy arriving directly from the radiation sources and absorbed in the medium between τ and $\tau + d\tau$ in the frequency interval $(x', x' + dx')$ per second. Then, corresponding to the boundaries $\tau = 0$ and $\tau = \tau_0$, the intensities of the emergent radiation will be equal to

$$
\left.
\begin{aligned}
I_2(0, x) &= \int_{-\infty}^{+\infty} dx' \int_0^{\tau_0} L(\tau, x') p(\tau, x', x) \, d\tau \\[2mm]
I_1(\tau_0, x) &= \int_{-\infty}^{+\infty} dx' \int_0^{\tau_0} L(\tau, x') p(\tau_0 - \tau, x', x) \, d\tau
\end{aligned}
\right\} \tag{91}
$$

We apply these relations to a medium with external radiation sources. Assuming that the radiation incident on the boundary with $\tau = 0$ has a frequency x_1 and intensity I_0, we can rewrite Eq. (88) as follows:

$$
\epsilon(\tau, x_1, x_2) = \frac{\lambda}{2} \int_{-\infty}^{+\infty} g(x, x_2) \alpha(x) \, dx \int_0^{\tau_0} e^{-\alpha(x)|\tau' - \tau|} \epsilon(\tau', x_1, x) \, d\tau
$$

$$
+ \frac{\lambda}{2} g(x_1, x_2) \alpha(x_1) I_0 e^{-\alpha(x_1)\tau} \tag{92}
$$

Comparing Eqs. (90) and (92) and recollecting the symmetry of the function $\alpha(x_1) g(x_1, x_2)$ we obtain

$$
p(\tau, x_2, x_1) = \frac{\epsilon(\tau, x_1, x_2)}{I_0 \alpha(x_2)} \tag{93}
$$

in other words, the function $\alpha(x_2) p(\tau, x_2, x_1)$ is equal to the emission coefficient in a medium illuminated by radiation of unit intensity. Hence a knowledge of the emission coefficient for a medium under the impact of an external radiation source enables us to determine the luminescence of a medium with radiation sources of any type.

We obtain another interesting result by applying Eq. (93) to the expressions for the intensities of radiation emergent from a medium, for Eqs. (40) provide

$$
\left.
\begin{aligned}
I_2(0, x_1, x_2) &= \int_0^{\tau_0} e^{-\alpha(x_2)\tau} \epsilon(\tau, x_1, x_2) \, d\tau \\[2mm]
I_1(\tau_0, x_1, x_2) &= \int_0^{\tau_0} e^{-\alpha(x_2)(\tau_0 - \tau)} \epsilon(\tau, x_1, x_2) \, d\tau
\end{aligned}
\right\} \tag{94}
$$

On the other hand, if the incident radiation has a frequency x_1 and intensity I_0, we have

$$
L(\tau, x') = I_0 e^{-\alpha(x')\tau} \alpha(x') \delta(x_1 - x') \tag{95}
$$

where δ is Dirac's function. It follows, then, from Eqs. (91) that

$$\left.\begin{aligned}
I_2(0, x_1, x_2) &= I_0 \int_0^{\tau_0} e^{-\alpha(x_1)\tau}\alpha(x_1)p(\tau, x_1, x_2) \, d\tau \\[2em]
I_1(\tau_0, x_1, x_2) &= I_0 \int_0^{\tau_0} e^{-\alpha(x_1)\tau}\alpha(x_1)p(\tau_0 - \tau, x_1, x_2) \, d\tau
\end{aligned}\right\} \quad (96)$$

Comparing Eqs. (94) and (96) and remembering Eq. (93), we find:

$$\left.\begin{aligned}
I_2(0, x_1, x_2) &= I_2(0, x_2, x_1) \\
I_1(\tau_0, x_1, x_2) &= I_1(\tau_0, x_2, x_1)
\end{aligned}\right\} \quad (97)$$

Thus the intensities of diffusely reflected and diffusely transmitted radiation are symmetrical functions of the frequencies x_1 and x_2. This is only a particular case of the principle of reversibility in optical phenomena.

Our results expressed in Eqs. (93) and (97) can be generalized for a three-dimensional medium.

The integral Eq. (90) is not a unique one for computing $p(\tau, x_1, x_2)$, for we can also derive a functional equation for the same purpose.

To derive such a functional equation, we first find the probability of quantum exit at the depth $\tau + \Delta\tau$, or the quantity $p(\tau + \Delta\tau, x_1, x_2)$. Neglecting the terms of the order of $\Delta\tau^2$, we have

$$\begin{aligned}
p(\tau + \Delta\tau, x_1, x_2) = {}& p(\tau, x_1, x_2) \left[1 - \alpha(x_2)\Delta\tau\right] \\
&+ \int p(\tau, x_1, x)\alpha(x)\Delta\tau p(0, x, x_2) \, dx \\
&- \int p(\tau_0 - \tau, x_1, x)\alpha(x)\Delta\tau p(\tau_0, x, x_2) \, dx \qquad (98)
\end{aligned}$$

Here and in future we integrate with respect to x in the interval from $-\infty$ to $+\infty$. Hence,

$$\begin{aligned}
\frac{\partial p(\tau, x_1, x_2)}{\partial \tau} = {}& -\alpha(x_2)p(\tau, x_1, x_2) + \int p(\tau, x_1, x)\varkappa(x)p(0, x, x_2) \, dx \\
&- \int p(\tau_0 - \tau, x_1, x)\alpha(x)p(\tau_0, x, x_2) \, dx_2 \qquad (99)
\end{aligned}$$

The quantities $p(0, x_1, x_2)$ and $p(\tau_0, x_1, x_2)$ entering Eq. (99) can be written as:

$$\left.\begin{aligned}
p(0, x_1, x_2) &= \frac{\lambda}{2}g(x_1, x_2) + \frac{\lambda}{2}\int g(x_1, x)\rho(x, x_2) \, dx \\[1em]
p(\tau_0, x_1, x_2) &= \frac{\lambda}{2}g(x_1, x_2) \, e^{-\alpha(x_2)\tau_0} \\[1em]
&\quad + \frac{\lambda}{2}\int g(x_1, x)\sigma(x, x_2) \, dx
\end{aligned}\right\} \quad (100)$$

where

$$\left.\begin{array}{l}
\rho(x_1, x_2) = \displaystyle\int_0^{\tau_0} p(\tau, x_1, x_2)\alpha(x_1)\, e^{-\alpha(x_1)\tau}\, d\tau \\[4mm]
\sigma(x_1, x_2) = \displaystyle\int_0^{\tau_0} p(\tau_0 - \tau, x_1, x_2)\alpha(x_1)\, e^{-\alpha(x_1)\tau}\, d\tau
\end{array}\right\} \tag{101}$$

The quantity $\rho(x_1, x_2)dx_2$ is the probability that the radiation of frequency x_1 incident on the medium is reflected in the frequency interval $(x_2, x_2 + dx_2)$ and the quantity $\sigma(x_1, x_2)dx_2$ is the probability that the same radiation passes through the medium (after some scattering in it) in the frequency interval $(x_2, x_2 + dx_2)$.

Multiplying Eq. (99) by $e^{-\alpha(x_1)}\alpha(x_1)$ and integrating with respect to τ in the interval $(0, \tau_0)$, we obtain

$$[\alpha(x_1) + \alpha(x_2)]\rho(x_1, x_2) = \alpha(x_1)p(0, x_1, x_2)$$

$$- \alpha(x_1)p(\tau_0, x_1, x_2)\, e^{-\alpha(x_1)\tau_0} + \int \rho(x_1, x)\alpha(x)p(0, x, x_2)\, dx$$

$$- \int \sigma(x_1, x)\alpha(x)p(\tau_0, x, x_2)\, dx \tag{102}$$

Again, multiplying Eq. (99) by $e^{-\alpha(x_1)(\tau_0-\tau)}\alpha(x_1)$ and integrating in the same way, we find correspondingly:

$$[\alpha(x_2) - \alpha(x_1)]\sigma(x_1, x_2) = \alpha(x_1)p(0, x_1, x_2)\, e^{-\alpha(x_1)\tau_0}$$

$$- \alpha(x_1)p(\tau_0, x_1, x_2) + \int \sigma(x_1, x)\alpha(x)p(0, x, x_2)\, dx$$

$$- \int \rho(x_1, x)\alpha(x)p(\tau_0, x, x_2)\, dx \tag{103}$$

Equations (100), (102), and (103) represent a system of four equations with four unknown functions: $p(0, x_1, x_2)$, $p(\tau_0, x_1, x_2)$, $\rho(x_1, x_2)$ and $\sigma(x_1, x_2)$. The last two functions found give the luminescence of a medium with external radiation sources. But the first two functions permit us, in conjunction with Eq. (99), to determine the function $p(\tau, x_1, x_2)$, which in turn leads to the solution for medium luminescence with radiation sources of any type

In general, all these equations are rather involved. However, there are cases in which they can be greatly simplified. We now consider one such case.

5. RADIATION DIFFUSION WITH TOTAL REDISTRIBUTION IN FREQUENCY

Consider a total redistribution in frequency during an elementary act of scattering. In this case the quantity $g(x_1, x_2)$ is independent of x_1 and equal to

$$g(x_1, x_2) = A\alpha(x_2) \tag{104}$$

where A is defined by Eq. (51).

Also the quantity $p(\tau, x_1, x_2)$ is independent of the frequency of the absorbed radiation; we denote it now by $p(\tau, x_2)$. Therefore, instead of Eqs. (99) and (100), we have.

$$\frac{\partial p(\tau, x_2)}{\partial \tau} = -\alpha(x_2)p(\tau, x_2) + p(0, x_2) \int p(\tau, x)\alpha(x)\, dx$$

$$- p(\tau_0, x_2) \int p(\tau_0, -\tau, x)\alpha(x)\, dx \tag{105}$$

$$\left.\begin{array}{l} p(0, x_2) = \dfrac{\lambda}{2}A\alpha(x_2) + \dfrac{\lambda}{2} A \int \alpha(x)\rho(x, x_2)\, dx \\[3mm] p(\tau_0, x_2) = \dfrac{\lambda}{2} A\alpha(x_2)\, e^{-\alpha(x_2)\tau_0} + \dfrac{\lambda}{2} A \int \alpha(x)\sigma(x, x_2)\, dx \end{array}\right\} \tag{106}$$

and Eqs. (102) and (103) can be rewritten as

$$[\alpha(x_1) + \alpha(x_2)]\rho(x_1, x_2) = p(0, x_2) \left[\alpha(x_1) + \int \rho(x_1, x)\alpha(x)\, dx\right]$$

$$- p(\tau_0, x_2) \left[\alpha(x_1)e^{-\alpha(x_1)\tau_0} + \int \sigma(x_1, x)\alpha(x)\, dx\right] \tag{107}$$

$$[\alpha(x_2) - \alpha(x_1)]\sigma(x_1, x_2) = p(0, x_2) \left[\alpha(x_1)\, e^{-\alpha(x_1)\tau_0}\right.$$

$$\left. + \int \sigma(x_1, x)\alpha(x)\, dx\right] - p(\tau_0, x_2)\left[\alpha(x_1) + \int \rho(x_1, x)\alpha(x)\, dx\right] \tag{108}$$

Introducing

$$\left.\begin{array}{l} \phi(x) = A\left[\alpha(x) + \int \rho(x', x)\alpha(x')\, dx'\right] \\[3mm] \psi(x) = A\left[\alpha(x)\, e^{-\alpha(x)\tau_0} + \int \sigma(x', x)\alpha(x')\, dx'\right] \end{array}\right\} \tag{109}$$

and recollecting the symmetry, proved above, of the functions $\rho(x_1, x_2)$ and $\sigma(x_1, x_2)$, together with the fact that

$$p(0, x_2) = \frac{\lambda}{2}\phi(x_2), \quad p(\tau_0, x_2) = \frac{\lambda}{2}\,\psi(x_2) \tag{110}$$

we obtain, instead of Eqs. (107) and (108),

$$
\left.
\begin{aligned}
\rho(x_1, x_2) &= \frac{\lambda}{2A} \frac{\phi(x_1)\phi(x_2) - \psi(x_1)\psi(x_2)}{\alpha(x_1) + \alpha(x_2)} \\[2mm]
\sigma(x_1, x_2) &= \frac{\lambda}{2A} \frac{\psi(x_1)\phi(x_2) - \psi(x_2)\phi(x_1)}{\alpha(x_2) - \alpha(x_1)}
\end{aligned}
\right\}
\tag{111}
$$

Thus the functions $\rho(x_1, x_2)$ and $\sigma(x_1, x_2)$, which depend on two arguments, are expressed by our auxiliary functions $\phi(x)$ and $\psi(x)$ which depend only on one argument.

Inserting Eqs. (111) and Eqs. (109), we find the following equation for computing these functions ϕ and ψ:

$$
\left.
\begin{aligned}
\phi(x) &= A\alpha(x) + \frac{\lambda}{2} \int \frac{\phi(x)\phi(x') - \psi(x)\psi(x')}{\alpha(x') + \alpha(x)} \alpha(x') \, dx' \\[2mm]
\psi(x) &= A\alpha(x) \, e^{-\alpha(x)\tau_0} \\[2mm]
&\quad + \frac{\lambda}{2} \int \frac{\psi(x')\phi(x) - \psi(x)\phi(x')}{\alpha(x) - \alpha(x')} \alpha(x') \, dx'
\end{aligned}
\right\}
\tag{112}
$$

Having solved Eqs. (112), we solve the problem of medium luminescence with external radiation sources with the aid of Eqs. (111). To find the same with internal radiation sources, we have, generally speaking, to find the function $p(\tau, x)$. This can be done in the same manner as we did in Chapter 6, Section 2 in finding the function $p(\tau, \eta)$.

The quantity $p(\tau, x)$ being known, we can find the intensities of the emergent radiation with radiation sources of any type by employing Eqs. (91). In the given case p is independent of x'. Thus Eqs. (91) become

$$
\left.
\begin{aligned}
I_2(0, x) &= \int_0^{\tau_0} L(\tau) p(\tau, x) \, d\tau \\[2mm]
I_1(\tau_0, x) &= \int_0^{\tau_0} L(\tau) p(\tau_0 - \tau, x) \, d\tau
\end{aligned}
\right\}
\tag{113}
$$

where

$$
L(\tau) = \int L(\tau, x) \, dx
\tag{114}
$$

In the case where the energy emitted by radiation sources is proportional to the absorption coefficient in a line, that is,

$$
\epsilon_0(\tau, x) = \alpha(x) \, B_0(\tau)
\tag{115}
$$

we can, while employing Eqs. (113), write

$$\alpha(x)\, B_0(\tau) = \frac{\lambda}{2} A\alpha(x) L(\tau)$$

hence,

$$L(\tau) = \frac{2}{\lambda} \frac{B_0(\tau)}{A} \tag{116}$$

Inserting Eq. (116) into Eqs. (113), we have

$$
\left.
\begin{aligned}
I_2(0, x) &= \frac{2}{\lambda A} \int_0^{\tau_0} B_0(\tau) p(\tau, x)\, d\tau \\[2mm]
I_1(\tau_0, x) &= \frac{2}{\lambda A} \int_0^{\tau_0} B_0(\tau) p(\tau_0 - \tau, x)\, d\tau
\end{aligned}
\right\}
\tag{117}
$$

It is easy to see that if $L(\tau)$ or $B_0(\tau)$ is a polynomial of τ, the intensities of the emergent radiation can be determined without previous knowledge of the function $p(\tau, x)$, directly from Eqs. (105). To do so it is sufficient to multiply Eq. (105) by τ^n and to integrate with respect to τ in the interval $(0, \tau_0)$.

For example, let $B_0 = $ const. It follows from Eqs. (117) that:

$$I_2(0, x) = \frac{2}{\lambda A} B_0 \int_0^{\tau_0} p(\tau, x)\, d\tau \tag{118}$$

and $I_1(\tau_0, x) = I_2(0, x)$. To find the integral of Eq. (118), we integrate Eq. (105) with respect o τ in the interval $(0, \tau_0)$. The result is

$$
p(\tau_0, x) - p(0, x) = -\alpha(x) \int_0^{\tau_0} p(\tau, x)\, d\tau
$$

$$
+ \frac{\lambda}{2}[\phi(x) - \psi(x)] \int \alpha(x)\, dx \int_0^{\tau_0} p(\tau, x)\, d\tau
$$

where

$$
\alpha(x) \int_0^{\tau_0} p(\tau, x)\, d\tau
$$

$$
= \frac{\lambda}{2}[\phi(x) - \psi(x)] \left[1 + \int \alpha(x)\, dx \int_0^{\tau_0} p(\tau, x)\, d\tau \right] \tag{119}
$$

Integrating Eq. (119) with respect to x in the interval $(-\infty, +\infty)$, we find

$$
1 + \int \alpha(x)\, dx \int_0^{\tau_0} p(\tau, x)\, d\tau = \frac{1}{1 - \dfrac{\lambda}{2} \displaystyle\int [\phi(x) - \psi(x)]\, dx} \tag{120}
$$

Using Eqs. (119) and (120) in Eq. (118), we obtain

$$\alpha(x) I_2(0, x) = \frac{B_0}{A} \frac{\phi(x) - \psi(x)}{1 - \frac{\lambda}{2} \int [\phi(x) - \psi(x)] \, dx} \tag{121}$$

Therefore, in our case the intensities of the emergent radiation are very simply expressed by means of the auxiliary functions $\phi(x)$ and $\psi(x)$.

The system of Eqs. (112), defining these functions ϕ and ψ, can easily be solved numerically.

We observe that between these two functions there exists a certain integral relation. To obtain it we integrate the first of Eqs. (112) with respect to x in the interval $(-\infty, +\infty)$ and find

$$\int \phi(x) \, dx = 1 + \frac{\lambda}{2} \int \int \frac{\phi(x')\phi(x) - \psi(x')\psi(x)}{\alpha(x') + \alpha(x)} \alpha(x') \, dx \, dx'$$

$$= 1 + \frac{\lambda}{2} \int \int [\phi(x')\phi(x) - \psi(x')\psi(x)] \, dx \, dx'$$

$$- \frac{\lambda}{2} \int \int \frac{\phi(x')\phi(x) - \psi(x')\psi(x)}{\alpha(x') + \alpha(x)} \alpha(x) \, dx \, dx'$$

Introducing the notations

$$\int \phi(x) \, dx = \phi_0 \qquad \int \psi(x) \, dx = \psi_0 \tag{122}$$

we obtain

$$\phi_0 = 1 + \frac{\lambda}{4}(\phi_0^2 - \psi_0^2) \tag{123}$$

For $\lambda = 1$, we have

$$\phi_0 + \psi_0 = 2 \tag{124}$$

Of extreme interest here is the case of pure scattering. The point is that, for $\lambda = 1$, the system of Eqs. (112) has not one solution only. Employing Eq. (124) it is easy to convince oneself that if the functions $\phi(x)$ and $\psi(x)$ are solutions of Eqs. (112), the functions

$$\phi(x) + \frac{C}{\alpha(x)}[\phi(x) + \psi(x)]$$

$$\psi(x) - \frac{C}{\alpha(x)}[\phi(x) + \psi(x)]$$

will also be solutions, where C is an arbitrary constant.

To remove this indeterminacy we must find an additional relation between ϕ and ψ. We obtain this relation by recalling that for $\lambda = 1$ all quanta emitted by internal radiation sources should leave the medium, that is,

$$\int I_2(0, x) \, dx + \int I_1(\tau_0, x) \, dx = 2 \int dx \int_0^{\tau_0} \epsilon_0(\tau, x) \, d\tau \quad (125)$$

We apply Eq. (125) to the case where $\epsilon_0(\tau, x)$ is defined by Eq. (115) for $B_0 = $ const. In this case Eq. (125) becomes

$$\int I_2(0, x) \, dx = \frac{B_0}{A} \tau_0 \quad (126)$$

But $I_2(0, x)$ is defined in our case by Eq. (121). Consequently, instead of Eq. (126), we obtain

$$\int \frac{\phi(x) - \psi(x)}{\alpha(x)} \, dx = \tau_0 \left\{ 1 - \frac{1}{2} \int [\phi(x) - \psi(x)] \, dx \right\} \quad (127)$$

This is the relation which we should add to the system of Eqs. (112) in order to find the functions $\phi(x)$ and $\psi(x)$, which have a necessary physical meaning, being connected by means of Eqs. (110) with the probability of quantum exit from the medium.

Table 8.8 shows the functions $\phi(x)$ and $\psi(x)$ found by numerical integration of Eqs. (112) and for the case of pure scattering with $\tau_0 = 10$.

TABLE 8.8. THE FUNCTIONS $\phi(x)$ AND $\psi(x)$ FOR $\lambda = 1$, $\tau_0 = 10$

x	0	0.2	0.4	0.6	0.8	1.0	1.2	1.4	1.6	1.8	2.0
$\phi(x)$	0.82	0.80	0.73	0.64	0.52	0.41	0.30	0.21	0.13	0.07	0.03
$\psi(x)$	0.05	0.05	0.05	0.05	0.06	0.08	0.10	0.11	0.08	0.06	0.03

As examples of the application of our results, we may point out the possibility of determining a series of physical quantities which are interesting in practice. For a given medium they are expressed always by the same functions ϕ and ψ for radiation sources of any type, internal as well as external.

1. *Spectrum line contours.* The contours are defined directly by the intensities of the emergent radiation $I_1(\tau_0, x)$ and $I_2(0, x)$. In the case when the radiation sources are uniformly distributed in the medium, or when $\epsilon_0(\tau, x) = \alpha(x) B_0$, the line contours are defined by Eq. (121). The quantity I_2 computed with Eq. (121) and Table 8.8 gives the line contour, shown in Figure 8.2, case B (page)211.

2. *Light pressure at the boundaries of the medium.* At the boundaries of a medium the light pressure, denoted by $P(\tau)\sigma_{\nu_0}$ for unit volume at optical depth τ, will be

$$P(0) = \frac{1}{c} \int \alpha(x) I_2(0, x) \, dx$$

$$P(\tau_0) = \frac{1}{c} \int \alpha(x) I_1(\tau_0, x) \, dx \qquad\qquad (128)$$

where c is the velocity of light. Employing Eqs. (121) and (122), we have, for a uniform distribution of radiation sources:

$$P(0) = P(\tau_0) = \frac{B_0}{cA} \frac{\phi_0 - \psi_0}{1 - \frac{\lambda}{2}(\phi_0 - \psi_0)} \qquad (129)$$

For pure scattering ($\lambda = 1$), this formula becomes

$$P(0) = P(\tau_0) = \frac{2B_0}{cA} \left(\frac{1}{\psi_0} - 1 \right) \qquad (130)$$

Equation (130) can be employed for computing the light pressure caused by $L\alpha$ emission at the boundaries of a nebula.

3. *Number of atoms in the excited state.* The volume emission coefficient is equal to $\epsilon(\tau, x) = \alpha(x) B(x)$ for total redistribution of radiation in frequency. Therefore, for parts of the line distant from the line center, where the absorption is not very important, or, precisely speaking, where the values of x satisfy the inequality $\alpha(x)\tau_0 \ll 1$, we have

$$I_2(0, x) = I_1(\tau_0, x) = \alpha(x) \int_0^{\tau_0} B(\tau) \, d\tau \qquad (131)$$

Since we may consider the intensities of the emergent radiation as known, Eq. (131) enables us to evaluate the integral

$$\int_0^{\tau_0} B(\tau) \, d\tau$$

Obviously, indeed, the total energy emitted by the medium in 1 sec is equal to

$$\frac{2}{A} \int_0^{\tau_0} B(\tau) \, d\tau$$

On the other hand, the same energy can be expressed by $\bar{N}_2 A_{21} h\nu_0$, where $\bar{N}_2$ is the total number of atoms in the excited state

$$\left(\bar{N}_2 = \int_0^{l_0} N_2 \, dl \right)$$

A_{21} is the Einstein coefficient of spontaneous transition in the given line, $h\nu_0$ the quantum energy. From the relation:

$$\frac{2}{A} \int_0^{\tau_0} B(\tau) \, d\tau = \bar{N}_2 A_{21} h\nu_0 \tag{132}$$

we may find the quantity $\bar{N}_2$.

These values of $\bar{N}_2$ enable us to determine the optical depth of the medium in lines for which the excited state is regarded as the lower level. In particular, we can compute the optical depth of a nebula in the Balmer lines when we have at our disposal the intensity of the $L\alpha$ radiation emergent from it.

6. Luminescence of a Medium with Infinitely Large Optical Thickness

Previously we have assumed that the radiation diffusion takes place in a one-dimensional medium. Now we investigate diffusion in a three-dimensional medium consisting of plane-parallel layers. Consider that its optical thickness is infinitely great and that there is complete redistribution of radiation in frequency during an elementary act of scattering.

Since we expect to make a later application of the theory to the problem of line contours in stellar spectra, it is best to assume that absorption occurs not only in the lines but in the continuum. The ratio of the line absorption coefficient σ_ν' to the continuous absorption coefficient κ', that is, σ_ν'/κ', will now be considered to be constant.

We introduce simplifying notations:

$$\frac{\sigma_\nu'}{\displaystyle\int_0^\infty \sigma_\nu' \, d\nu} = \sigma_\nu \qquad \frac{\kappa'}{\displaystyle\int_0^\infty \sigma_\nu' \, d\nu} = \kappa$$

We can express the optical depth in the frequency ν as follows:

$$\tau_\nu = (\sigma_\nu + \kappa)z \tag{133}$$

where

$$\int_0^\infty \sigma_\nu \, d\nu = 1 \tag{134}$$

In the same notation we have also that the fraction of radiation absorbed in a spectral line by a layer of thickness dz in quanta of frequency ν' and scattered by the same layer in quanta of frequencies from ν to $\nu + d\nu$ will be equal to $\sigma_\nu d\nu \sigma_{\nu'} dz$ (for pure scattering).

We solve for the brightness of a given medium by first finding the probability of quantum exit. We denote by $p(z, \nu, \eta)\, d\nu d\omega$ the probability that a quantum absorbed in the given line at depth z emerges from the medium (generally speaking, after multiple scattering) within the frequency interval $(\nu, \nu + d\nu)$ at the angle arccos η to the normal within the solid angle $d\omega$, and by $L(z)$ the amount of energy arriving directly from radiation sources and being absorbed in the line by an elementary volume of cross section 1 cm² and thickness dz, at a depth z, per second. Then it is obvious that the intensity of radiation of frequency ν leaving the atmosphere at the angle arccos η to the normal is equal to

$$I_\nu(0, \eta) = \int_0^\infty L(z)\, p(z, \nu, \eta)\frac{dz}{\eta} \qquad (135)$$

Here we have availed ourselves of the assumption that there is a total redistribution of radiation in frequency, because we suppose that the quantity p is independent of the radiation frequency absorbed by an elementary volume.

Before deriving an equation for determining the quantity $p(z, \nu, \eta)$, we find the probability of quantum exit at the depth $z + \Delta z$, that is the quantity $p(z + \Delta z, \nu, \eta)$. To do this we imagine that the quantum emerges at the depth z and then passes through an additional layer of thickness Δz, with or without absorption in it. Then we obtain the following expression for $p(z + \Delta z, \nu, \eta)$:

$$p(z + \Delta z, \nu, \eta) = p(z, \nu, \eta)\left(1 - \frac{\sigma_\nu + \kappa}{\eta}\Delta z\right)$$
$$+ 2\pi p(0, \nu, \eta)\int \sigma_{\nu'}\, d\nu' \int_0^1 p(z, \nu', \eta')\frac{\Delta z}{\eta'}\, d\eta' \qquad (136)$$

Hence,

$$\frac{\partial p(z, \nu, \eta)}{\partial z} = -p(z, \nu, \eta)\frac{\sigma_\nu + \kappa}{\eta}$$
$$+ 2\pi p(0, \nu, \eta)\int \sigma_{\nu'}\, d\nu' \int_0^1 p(z, \nu', \eta')\frac{d\eta'}{\eta'} \qquad (137)$$

In order to write a similar relation for $p(0, \nu, \eta)$, we have to recall the law of scattering by an elementary volume. For total redistribution of radiation in frequency, the probability of scattering in the frequency interval $(\nu, \nu + d\nu)$ is equal to $\sigma_\nu d\nu$. For the sake of generality, we propose that not all the energy absorbed by an elementary volume in the line is emitted in the same line, but only a certain fraction λ. Then the probability that a quantum absorbed by an elementary volume in a line leaves it in the frequency interval $(\nu, \nu + d\nu)$ within a solid angle $d\omega$ is

$$\frac{\lambda}{4\pi}\sigma_\nu \, d\nu \, d\omega$$

Recollecting what has been stated before, we obtain:

$$p(0, \nu, \eta) = \frac{\lambda}{4\pi}\sigma_\nu + \frac{\lambda}{2}\int \sigma_{\nu'} \, d\nu' \int_0^1 \rho(\nu, \nu', \eta, \eta') \, d\eta' \qquad (138)$$

where

$$\rho(\nu, \nu_1, \eta, \zeta) = \int_0^\infty p(z, \nu, \eta) \, e^{-[(\sigma_{\nu_1}+\kappa)/\zeta)z]}\, \sigma_{\nu_1}\frac{dz}{\zeta} \qquad (139)$$

The quantity $\rho(\nu, \nu_1, \eta, \zeta)d\nu \, d\omega$ represents the probability that the radiation in frequency ν_1 incident on the medium at an angle arccos ζ to the normal is reflected in the frequency interval $(\nu, \nu + d\nu)$ at an angle arccos η to the normal within the solid angle $d\omega$.

We can easily form one equation from Eqs. (137), (138), and (139) for computing the functions $\rho(\nu, \nu_1, \eta, \zeta)$ and $p(0, \nu, \eta)$. Multiplying both sides of Eq. (137) by

$$e^{-(\sigma_{\nu_1}+\kappa)/\zeta}\sigma_{\nu_1}\frac{dz}{\zeta}$$

and integrating in the interval $(0, \infty)$, we find

$$\rho(\nu, \nu_1, \eta, \zeta)\left(\frac{\sigma_\nu + \kappa}{\eta} + \frac{\sigma_{\nu_1} + \kappa}{\zeta}\right)$$

$$= p(0, \nu, \eta)\left[\frac{\sigma_{\nu_1}}{\zeta} + 2\pi\int \sigma_{\nu'} \, d\nu' \int \rho(\nu', \nu_1, \eta', \zeta)\frac{d\eta'}{\eta'}\right] \qquad (140)$$

But physical considerations provide that

$$\rho(\nu, \nu_1, \eta, \zeta)\zeta = \rho(\nu_1, \nu, \zeta, \eta)\eta \qquad (141)$$

(this relation can, by the way, be obtained analogously to Eqs. (97)). Therefore, the term in brackets in Eq. (140) is equal to $(4\pi/\lambda\zeta)p(0, \nu_1, \zeta)$. Consequently, writing

$$p(0, \nu, \eta) = \frac{\lambda}{4\pi}\phi(\nu, \eta)\sigma_\nu \qquad (142)$$

we obtain, instead of, Eq. (140),

$$\rho(\nu, \nu_1, \eta, \zeta)\left(\frac{\sigma_\nu + \kappa}{\eta} + \frac{\sigma_{\nu_1} + \kappa}{\zeta}\right) = \frac{\lambda}{4\pi}\frac{\sigma_\nu\sigma_{\nu_1}}{\zeta}\phi(\nu, \eta)\phi(\nu_1, \zeta) \qquad (143)$$

Thus the quantities $p(0, \nu, \eta)$ and $\rho(\nu, \nu_1, \zeta)$ are expressed by one and the same function $\phi(\nu, \eta)$. As for the function itself, we can determine it by means of the following equation derived from Eq. (138) after the insertion in it of Eqs. (142) and (143):

$$\phi(\nu, \eta) = 1 + \frac{\lambda}{2}\eta \int \mu_{\nu'}\sigma_{\nu'}\, d\nu' \int_0^1 \frac{\phi(\nu, \eta)\phi(\nu', \eta')\, d\eta'}{\eta(\mu_{\nu'} + 1) + \eta(\mu_\nu + 1)} \qquad (144)$$

where $\mu_\nu = \sigma_\nu/\kappa$. It is easy to see that the function $\phi(\nu, \eta)$ depends in reality not on two arguments ν and η, but on one:

$$x = \frac{\eta}{1 + \mu_\nu}$$

(Here the symbol x has a different meaning from that previously used since we did not wish to begin a change in notations accepted in astrophysics.) Hence, instead of Eq. (144),

$$\phi(x) = 1 + \frac{\lambda}{2}x\phi(x) \int_0^1 \frac{\phi(x')}{x + x'}\, K(x')\, dx' \qquad (145)$$

where the function $K(x)$ is defined as

$$K(x) = 2 \int_{\nu(x)}^\infty \mu_\nu\sigma_\nu d\nu \qquad (146)$$

Here $\nu(x) = \nu_0$ if $x < 1/(1 + \mu_{\nu_0})$, and $1/(1 + \mu_{\nu(x)}) = x$ if $x > 1/(1 + \mu_{\nu_0})$ where ν is the central line frequency.

Having found the quantity $p(0, \nu, \eta)$, we can also determine the quantity $p(z, \nu, \eta)$ from Eq. (137). This equation shows that the latter quantity can be written

$$p(z, \nu, \eta) = \frac{\lambda}{4\pi}\sigma_\nu\Phi(z, x) \qquad (147)$$

Inserting Eq. (147) into Eq. (137), we obtain the equation for determining the function $\Phi(z, x)$:

$$\frac{\partial\Phi(z, x)}{\partial z} = -\frac{\kappa}{x}\Phi(z, x) + \frac{\lambda}{2}\phi(x) \int_0^1 \Phi(z, x')\, K(x')\frac{\kappa}{x'}\, dx' \qquad (148)$$

Introducing

$$\frac{\lambda}{2} \int_0^1 \Phi(z, x')\, K(x')\frac{\kappa}{x'}\, dx' = G(z) \qquad (149)$$

and knowing that $\Phi(0, x) = \phi(x)$, we obtain from Eq. (148):

$$\Phi(z, x) = \phi(x)\, e^{-(\kappa/x)z} + \phi(x) \int_0^z G(z')\, e^{-(\kappa/x)(z-z')}\, dz' \qquad (150)$$

Thus the computation of $p(z, \nu, \eta)$ is reduced to the computation of the function $G(z)$. As for this function itself, we can compute it by means of the following integral equation of Volterra type, derived from Eqs. (149) and (150):

$$G(z) = \mathcal{N}(z) + \int_0^z G(z')\mathcal{N}(z-z') \, dz' \qquad (151)$$

where

$$\mathcal{N}(z) = \kappa \frac{\lambda}{2} \int_0^1 \phi(x) \, e^{-(\kappa/x)z} K(x) \, dx \qquad (152)$$

In principle there is no difficulty in solving Eq. (151). But we are not interested in it now, for there are many problems which can be solved well without the function $p(z, \nu, \eta)$ in its explicit form, but by means of Eq. (137). Especially we can solve in this way the problem of line contours in stellar spectra. This we shall now do.

7. ABSORPTION LINE CONTOURS WITH COMPLETELY NONCOHERENT SCATTERING

The formation of absorption lines in stellar spectra with radiation diffusion and without redistribution in frequency, that is, with coherent scattering, was considered in Sections 4 and 5 of Chapter 6. The equation of radiative transfer in such a case has the form:

$$\eta \frac{dI_\nu(z, \eta)}{dz} = (\sigma_\nu + \kappa)I_\nu(z, \eta) - (1 - \epsilon) \frac{\sigma_\nu}{2} \int_{-1}^{+1} I_\nu(z, \eta') \, d\eta'$$
$$- (\kappa + \epsilon \sigma_\nu) B_\nu^*(T) \qquad (153)$$

Analogously we can write the equation of radiative transfer for total redistribution in frequency, or, as we say, for completely noncoherent scattering:

$$\eta \frac{dI_\nu(z, \eta)}{dz}$$
$$= (\sigma_\nu + \kappa) I_\nu(z, \eta) - (1 - \epsilon) \frac{\sigma_\nu}{2} \int_0^\infty \sigma_{\nu'} \, d\nu' \int_{-1}^{+1} I_{\nu'}(z, \eta') \, d\eta'$$
$$- (\kappa + \epsilon \sigma_\nu) B_\nu^*(T) \qquad (154)$$

Our problem, absorption line contours, consists in finding the quantity $I_\nu(0, \eta)$ from Eq. (153) or (154).

But the same quantity can also be found with the aid of the probability of quantum exit from the medium. We have shown this in Chapter 6 for coherent light scattering. In the same manner we now find absorption line contours for completely noncoherent light scattering.

In finding the quantity $I_\nu(0, \eta)$ with the aid of Eq. (135), we first compute the quantity $L(z)$. Since here the radiation sources are internal, the amount of energy in frequency ν emitted by an elementary volume of 1 cm² cross section and thickness dz in unit solid angle per second is equal to

$$(\kappa + \epsilon\sigma_\nu) \, B_\nu^*(T) \, dz \tag{155}$$

As is customary, we write

$$B_\nu^*(T) = B_0(1 + \beta\tau)$$

where τ is the optical depth in the continuum; because $\tau = \kappa z$,

$$B_\nu^*(T) = B_0(1 + \kappa\beta z) \tag{156}$$

We replace the quantity $\kappa + \epsilon_{\sigma_\nu}$, by an arbitrary function of frequency γ_ν in order to be quite general. Then, for the amount of energy emitted by an elementary volume we have, instead of Eq. (155)

$$\gamma_\nu B_0(1 + \kappa\beta z) \, dz \tag{157}$$

The quantity $L(z)$ in our case, with radiation sources distributed in the stellar atmosphere, is

$$L(z) = 2\pi B_0 \int \sigma_{\nu'}\gamma_{\nu'} \, d\nu' \int_0^1 \frac{d\eta'}{\eta'} \int_0^\infty (1 + \kappa\beta z') \, e^{-(\sigma_{\nu'}+\kappa)/\eta'(|z-z'|)} dz' \tag{158}$$

or, after an integration with respect to z',

$$L(z) = 2\pi B_0 \int \frac{\sigma_{\nu'}\gamma_{\nu'} \, d\nu'}{\sigma_{\nu'} + \kappa} [2(1 + \kappa\beta z)$$
$$- \int_0^1 e^{-[(\sigma_{\nu'}+\kappa)/\eta']z} \left(1 - \frac{\kappa\beta\eta'}{\sigma_{\nu'} + \kappa}\right) d\eta'] \tag{159}$$

Replacing now, as before:

$$x' = \frac{\kappa\eta'}{\kappa + \sigma_{\nu'}}$$

we rewrite Eq. (159):

$$L(z) = 4\pi B_0(1 + \kappa\beta z) \int \frac{\sigma_{\nu'}\gamma_{\nu'} \, d\nu'}{\sigma_{\nu'} + \kappa}$$
$$- 2\pi B_0 \int_0^1 e^{-(\kappa/x')z} (1 - \beta x') \, \bar{K}(x') \, dx' \tag{160}$$

where

$$\bar{K}(x) = 2 \int_{\nu(x)}^{\infty} \frac{\gamma_\nu}{\kappa} \sigma_\nu \, d\nu \tag{161}$$

and the lower limit of integration $\nu(x)$ is defined as in the integral Eq. (146).

Now before we make use of Eq. (135) we remark that in writing it we took account only of radiation scattered by the medium. But in other cases of internal radiation sources, we have to take into account also radiation emergent directly from these sources. In our case the intensity of this radiation is equal to

$$\gamma_\nu B_0 \int_0^{\infty} (1 + \kappa\beta z) \, e^{-[(\sigma_\nu + \kappa)/\eta]z} \frac{dz}{\eta}$$

or, after some integration,

$$\frac{\gamma_\nu}{\kappa} B_0 \frac{1 + \beta x}{1 + \mu_\nu}$$

This expression must be added to the right-hand side of Eq. (135). Recalling also Eq. (147) we find the following formula for the determination of the radiation intensity emergent from the stellar atmosphere:

$$I_\nu(0, \eta) = \frac{\lambda}{4\pi} \frac{\sigma_\nu}{1 + \mu_\nu} \int_0^{\infty} L(z) \Phi(z, x) \frac{dz}{x} + \frac{\gamma_\nu}{\kappa} B_0 \frac{1 + \beta x}{1 + \mu_\nu} \tag{162}$$

Now we place Eq. (159) for $L(z)$ into Eq. (162) and obtain

$$I_\nu(0, \eta) = \frac{\gamma_\nu}{\kappa} B_0 \frac{1 + \beta x}{1 + \mu_\nu}$$

$$+ \lambda \frac{\mu_\nu}{1 + \mu_\nu} B_0 \int \frac{\sigma_\nu \gamma_{\nu'} d_{\nu'}'}{\sigma_{\nu'} + \kappa} \int_0^{\infty} (1 + \kappa\beta z) \Phi(z, x) \frac{\kappa dz}{x}$$

$$- \frac{\lambda}{2} \frac{\mu_\nu}{1 + \mu_\nu} B_0 \int_0^1 (1 - \beta x') \bar{K}(x') \, dx \int_0^{\infty} e^{-(\kappa/x')z} \Phi(z, x) \frac{\kappa dz}{x} \tag{163}$$

The integrals of Eq. (163) may readily be found from Eq. (148), which serves for finding the function $\Phi(z, x)$. Accordingly we have:

$$\frac{\kappa}{x} \int_0^{\infty} \Phi(z, x) \, dz = \frac{\phi(x)}{A} \tag{164}$$

and

$$\frac{\kappa^2}{x} \int_0^{\infty} \Phi(z, x) \, z dz = x \frac{\phi(x)}{A} \frac{\lambda}{2} \frac{\phi(x)}{A^2} \int_0^1 \phi(x') \, K(x') x' \, dx' \tag{165}$$

Here

$$A = 1 - \frac{\lambda}{2} \int_0^1 \phi(x) \, K(x) \, dx \tag{166}$$

From Eq. (145), defining the function $\phi(x)$, we find

$$A = \sqrt{1 - \lambda \int \frac{\sigma^2{}_\nu}{\sigma_\nu + \kappa} \, d\nu} \tag{167}$$

The last integral of z in Eq. (163) has been determined previously. From Eqs. (139) and (143), it follows that

$$\int_0^\infty e^{-(\kappa/x)z} \Phi(z, x) \frac{\kappa}{x} \, dz = \frac{\phi(x)\phi(x')}{x + x'} x' \tag{168}$$

Putting the values of these integrals into Eq. (163), we obtain

$$\frac{I_\nu(0, \eta)}{B_0}$$

$$= \lambda \frac{\mu_\nu}{1 + \mu_\nu} \frac{\phi(x)}{A} \left[1 + \beta x + \beta \frac{\lambda}{2A} \int_0^1 \phi(x') \, K(x')x' \, dx' \right] \iint \frac{\sigma_{\nu'}\gamma_{\nu'} \, d\nu'}{\sigma_{\nu'} + \kappa}$$

$$- \frac{\lambda}{2} \frac{\mu_\nu}{1 + \mu_\nu} \phi(x) \int_0^1 \frac{\phi(x')}{x + x'} (1 - \beta x') \, \bar{K}(x')x' \, dx' + \frac{\gamma_\nu}{\kappa} \frac{1 + \beta x}{1 + \mu_\nu} \tag{169}$$

This is the required expression for the intensity of radiation emergent from the star.

In deriving Eq. (169) we made no assumptions about the function γ_ν. Now we propose that $\gamma_\nu = \kappa + \epsilon \sigma_\nu$ and, in addition, $\lambda = 1 - \epsilon$. Then Eq. (169) will give us an expression for $I_\nu(0, \eta)$ corresponding to a solution of Eq. (154).

Inserting the given values of γ_ν and λ into Eq. (169), we find

$$\frac{I_\nu(0, \eta)}{B_0} = \frac{1 + \epsilon\mu_\nu}{1 + \mu_\nu}(1 + \beta x) + (1 - \epsilon)\frac{\mu_\nu}{1 + \mu_\nu} \; \phi(x) \bigg\{ A(1 + \beta x)$$

$$+ A_1\beta - \frac{1}{2} \int_0^1 \frac{\phi(x')}{x + x'} (1 - \beta x')[K_1(x') + \epsilon K(x')]x' \, dx' \bigg\} \tag{170}$$

Here

$$A = \sqrt{\int \frac{1 + \epsilon\mu_\nu}{1 + \mu_\nu} \sigma_\nu \, d\nu} \tag{171}$$

$$A_1 = \frac{1}{2}(1 - \epsilon) \int_0^1 \phi(x')K(x')x' \, dx' \tag{172}$$

$$K_1(x) = 2 \int_{\nu(x)}^\infty \sigma_\nu \, d\nu \tag{173}$$

and the lower limit of integration $\nu(x)$ is taken as before for defining the function $K(x)$.

The quantity $I_\nu(0, \eta)$ represents the intensity of the radiation emergent from the star in the frequency of a spectral line. But in analysing stellar spectra we usually compute the ratio of this quantity to the intensity of radiation emergent from the star in a neighbouring part of the continuum. It is, however, obvious that this ratio is

$$r_\nu(\eta) = \frac{I_\nu(0, \eta)}{B_0(1 + \beta\eta)} \tag{174}$$

Inserting Eq. (170) into Eq. (174) and making some transformations, we obtain:

$$r_\nu(\eta) = \frac{1}{1 + \beta\eta}\left\{\frac{1 + \epsilon\mu_\nu}{1 + \mu_\nu} + \frac{\mu_\nu}{1 + \mu_\nu}\Psi(x) + \beta\left[\frac{1 + \epsilon\mu_\nu}{1 + \mu_\nu}x + \frac{\mu_\nu}{1 + \mu_\nu}\Psi_1(x)\right]\right\} \tag{175}$$

where

$$\Psi(x) = (1 - \epsilon)\phi(x)\left\{A - \frac{1}{2}\int_0^1 \frac{\phi(x')}{x + x'}[K_1(x') + \epsilon K(x')]x'\, dx'\right\} \tag{176}$$

$$\Psi_1(x) = (1 - \epsilon)\phi(x)\left\{Ax + A_1\right.$$

$$\left. + \frac{1}{2}\int_0^1 \frac{\phi(x')}{x + x'}[K_1(x') + \epsilon K(x')]x'^2\, dx'\right\} \tag{177}$$

For the case of an isothermal atmosphere ($\beta = 0$) and in the absence of fluorescence ($\epsilon = 0$), Eq. (175) gives

$$r_\nu(\eta) = \frac{1}{1 + \mu_\nu} + \frac{\mu_\nu}{1 + \mu_\nu}\phi(x)\left[A_0 - \frac{1}{2}\int_0^1 \frac{\phi(x')}{x + x'} K_1(x')x'dx'\right] \tag{178}$$

where

$$A_0 = \sqrt{\int \frac{\sigma_\nu d\nu}{1 + \mu_\nu}} = \sqrt{\int_0^1 K_1(x)\, dx} \tag{179}$$

Equation (178) was derived some time ago[8] using the "principle of invariance." Later Busbridge[9] obtained a generalization of this formula for a linear dependence of $B^*_\nu(T)$ on τ, that is, she obtained Eq. (175) for $\epsilon = 0$. A little later we derived Eq. (175) with the aid of the present method.[10] It is obvious that this method enables us to

[8] V. V. Sobolev, Non-coherent Light Scattering in Stellar Atmospheres, *Russian Astronomical J.* **26**, 129 (1949).

[9] Ida W. Busbridge, Coherent and Non-coherent Scattering in the Theory of Line Formation, *Monthly Notices of the Royal Astronical Soc.* **113**, 52 (1953).

[10] V. V. Sobolev, The Formation of the Absorption Lines with a Non-coherent Light Scattering, *Russian Astronomical J.* **31**, 231 (1954).

derive an even more general form for the quantity $r_\nu(\eta)$ and for taking into account any number of terms in the expansion of $B^*_\nu(T)$ in powers of τ; however, this does not interest us now.

We should observe that in the theory of absorption line formation for coherent scattering, we sometimes consider Eq. (153) with a final term $(\kappa + Q\epsilon\sigma_\nu)B^*_\nu(T)$ instead of $(\kappa + \epsilon\sigma_\nu)B^*_\nu(T)$. Here the factor Q takes into account a possible difference between radiation intensity due to fluorescence and that defined by the Planck formula. Analogously we can change and use Eq. (154) for completely noncoherent scattering. The quantity $I_\nu(0, \eta)$ which corresponds to this case is obtained from Eq. (169) for $\lambda = 1 - \epsilon$ and $\gamma_\nu = \kappa + Q\epsilon\sigma_\nu$.

TABLE 8.9. AUXILIARY FUNCTIONS FOR $a = 0.01$, $\mu_{\nu_0} = 10^4$

x	$K(x)$	$K_1(x)$	$\phi(x)$			$\Psi(x)$			$\Psi_1(x)$		
			$\epsilon=0$	$\epsilon=0.001$	$\epsilon=0.1$	$\epsilon=0$	$\epsilon=0.001$	$\epsilon=0.1$	$\epsilon=0$	$\epsilon=0.001$	$\epsilon=0.01$
0	7000	1.00	1.0	1.0	1.0	0.024	0.038	0.09	0.006	0.005	0.003
0.0000507	7000	1.00	1.6	1.6	1.5	0.038	0.059	0.14	0.010	0.008	0.004
0,000101	5700	0.87	1.9	1.9	1.9	0.047	0.073	0.18	0.012	0.010	0.005
0.000127	2300	0.49	2.1	2.1	2.0	0.052	0.080	0.19	0.013	0.011	0.005
0.000152	1400	0.37	2.3	2.3	2.1	0.056	0.086	0.21	0.014	0.012	0.006
0.000304	250	0.14	3.1	3.0	2.8	0.075	0.115	0.27	0.019	0.016	0.117
0.000457	100	0.088	3.7	3.6	3.2	0.090	0.14	0.32	0.023	0.019	0.009
0.000914	21	0.040	5.0	4.9	4.2	0.125	0.19	0.42	0.032	0.026	0.011
0.00137	88.9	0.027	6.1	5.8	4.8	0.15	0.23	0.48	0.039	0.031	0,013
0.00274	2.1	0.014	8.1	7.7	5.8	0.20	0.30	0.58	0.052	0.041	0.017
0.00412	0.90	0.010	9.5	8.9	6.4	0.24	0.35	0.64	0.062	0.050	0.020
0.00824	0.26	0.0060	12	11	7.2	0.31	0.43	0.73	0.079	0.062	0.025
0.0123	0.115	0.0048	14	12	7.7	0.35	0.48	0.77	0.091	0.071	0.030
0.0246	0.034	0.0035	16	14	8.2	0.43	0.57	0.83	0.11	0.089	0.042
0.0370	0.019	0.0031	18	15	8.5	0.48	0.62	0.86	0.13	0.10	0.054
0.0740	0.0085	0.0025	20	16	8.8	0.56	0.69	0.89	0.17	0.14	0.090
0.111	0.0053	0.0022	21	17	8.9	0.61	0.73	0.92	0.20	0.17	0.125
0.222	0.0018	0.0016	23	18	9.1	0.70	0.81	0.94	0.30	0.28	0.23
0.333	0.0075	0.0012	24	19	9.2	0.76	0.85	0.95	0.40	0.38	0.34
0.667	0.00010	0.0006	25	20	9.3	0.84	0.90	0.96	0.72	0.70	0.67
1.000	0	0	26	20	9.3	0.88	0.93	0.97	1.04	1.03	1.00

We now give an example of the computation of absorption line contours according to Eq. (175). We assume that the line absorption coefficient is defined by radiation damping and Doppler effect, that is, by Eq. (10). Since the quantity σ_ν must satisfy the condition of Eq. (134), we have to assume $\sigma_0 = 1/\sqrt{\pi}$. For the parameter a, which is the ratio of natural broadening to Doppler broadening, we take the value $a = 0.01$. Further we should know the ratio of the absorption coefficient in the line center to that in the continuum. For strong lines this ratio is not very large, and we assume

$$\mu_{\nu_0} = \frac{\sigma_{\nu_0}}{\kappa} = 10^4$$

The results of the computations are given in Table 8.9.

First are given the functions $K(x)$ and $K_1(x)$, determined by Eqs. (146) and (173). Then we give the function $\phi(x)$ for three values of the parameter $\epsilon (\epsilon = 0, 0.001, 0.01)$ computed from Eq. (145). Lastly we give values of the functions $\Psi(x)$ and $\Psi_1(x)$ computed from Eqs. (176) and (177).

Now employing Table 8.9 and Eq. (175), we can compute absorption line contours at any distance arccos η from the center of the disk for the case considered. For this we first determine $x = \eta/(1 + \mu_\nu)$ for a given η in different frequencies, and take values of the functions $\Psi(x)$ and $\Psi_1(x)$ from Table 8.9. Then we use Eq. (175) for determination of line contours with a given parameter β. Such computations will be given later.

8. Comparison of Line Contours

It is interesting to compare line contours formed in stellar spectra by coherent and by completely noncoherent light scattering. For the latter case we use the expression for $r_\nu(\eta)$ in the form of Eq. (175), and for the former that of Eq. (109), Chapter 6, with $\beta_2 = 0$ and $Q = 1$ which becomes

$$r_\nu(\eta) = \frac{\phi_\nu(\eta)}{(1 + \beta\eta)(1 + \mu_\nu)} \left[(1 + \mu_\nu + \beta\eta) \left(\frac{1 + \epsilon\mu_\nu}{1 + \mu_\nu} \right)^{1/2} \right.$$
$$\left. + \frac{\beta}{2}(1 - \epsilon) \frac{\mu_\nu}{1 + \mu_\nu} \alpha_{\nu 1} \right] \qquad (180)$$

where the function $\phi_\nu(\eta)$ is defined by Eq. (50) of Chapter 6 for $\lambda_\nu = (1 - \epsilon) \mu_\nu/(1 + \mu_\nu)$ and $\alpha_{\nu 1}$ is the first moment.

We first compare central line intensities, then the behavior of the quantity $r_\nu(\eta)$ in the internal parts of a line, and finally the same behavior in the outer parts of it.

Central line intensities. It is well known that the problem of the central intensities of absorption lines is one of the most difficult in the theory of the formation of lines in stellar spectra. The original theory, based on the hypothesis of coherent scattering without fluorescence, leads to very small values of the central intensities as compared to the observed ones. Fluorescence itself increases the theoretical values of the central intensities, but for complete agreement with observation we must introduce the afore-mentioned hypothetical factor Q, which is greater than unity. It is therefore of interest to find the central intensities computed with a theory of line formation for completely noncoherent scattering.

First we consider the case $\beta = 0$ and $\epsilon = 0$. Here, for completely noncoherent scattering, the quantity $r_\nu(\eta)$ is defined by Eq. (178).

Compare now the two bracketed terms in Eq. (178). To do this we first find an upper limit for the function $\phi(x)$. From Eq. (145) and with the aid of Eq. (166), we obtain

$$
\phi(x) = \frac{1}{1 - \dfrac{\lambda}{2} x \displaystyle\int_0^1 \frac{\phi(x')}{x + x'} K(x')\, dx'}
$$

$$
< \frac{1}{1 - \dfrac{\lambda}{2} \displaystyle\int_0^1 \phi(x')\, K(x')\, dx'} = \frac{1}{A} \tag{181}
$$

Hence, for $\lambda = 1$,

$$
\frac{1}{2} \int_0^1 \frac{\phi(x')}{x + x'} K_1(x') x'\, dx' < \frac{1}{2 A_0} \int_0^1 K_1(x')\, dx' = \frac{1}{2} A_0 \tag{182}
$$

Thus the second term in brackets is at least half the first one; consequently it can be neglected in estimating the order of magnitude of central line intensity. This is very advantageous because, for computation of the second term, we should know the function $\phi(x)$, but we do not need it for the first term.

Apropos of the factor before the bracket, it is of the order of unity for very small values of x, and in the center of the line

$$
x \leqslant \frac{1}{1 + \mu_{\nu_0}}
$$

Thus we make the following estimation of the central intensity of an absorption line with completely noncoherent scattering:

$$
r_{\nu_0} \approx A_0 \tag{183}
$$

Now, using Eq. (10) for the absorption coefficient, we calculate A_0 and obtain

$$
r_{\nu_0} \approx \left(\frac{a}{\mu_{\nu_0}} \right)^{1/4} \tag{184}
$$

To estimate r_{ν_0} for coherent scattering, we should employ Eq. (180). For $\beta = 0$ and $\epsilon = 0$, it gives

$$r_\nu(\eta) = \frac{\phi\nu(\eta)}{\sqrt{1+\mu_\nu}}$$ (185)

and because the function $\phi_\nu(\eta)$ varies only within small limits $(1, 2.9)$ we find a central intensity of the order of

$$r_{\nu_0} \approx \frac{1}{\sqrt{\mu_{\nu_0}}}$$ (186)

We see that the expressions of r_{ν_0} for coherent and for completely noncoherent scattering differ greatly. Placing $a = 0.01$ and $\mu_{\nu_0} = 10^4$ into Eqs. (184) and (186), we find that the ratio of central intensities for completely noncoherent scattering to that for coherent scattering is about 3; an accurate value is 2.5 for the limb and 1.6 for the center of the disk. This ratio increases, however, with an increase in the parameters a and μ_{ν_0}. For example, for $a = 0.01$ and $\mu_{\nu_0} = 10^6$ it becomes of the order of 10. In other words, central intensities of absorption lines may be much larger for completely noncoherent than for coherent scattering.

Consider now $\epsilon = 0$ but $\beta \neq 0$ in Eqs. (175) and (180). Eq. (180) shows that its terms containing the factor β do not influence the central intensities of absorption lines at all. This is because coherent scattering causes the formation of the central parts of the line in the very highest layers of the atmosphere where the deviation of $B^*_\nu(T)$ from B_0 is very small. But for noncoherent scattering the energy absorbed in the external parts of a line may be emitted in its central region, and actually the probability of such an emission is very great for completely noncoherent scattering. Inasmuch as the amount of such energy greatly depends on whether the quantity $B^*_\nu(T)$ is constant, or a linear function of τ, the calculation of the terms with the factor β in Eq. (180) becomes markedly sensitive to the values of the central intensities of the absorption lines. For example, Table 8.9 shows that for $\epsilon = 0$ and for small values of x, the values of $\Psi_1(x)$ are approximately four times smaller than those of $\Psi'(x)$. This means that the quantity $I_\nu(0)$ is about twice as large for $\beta = 4$ as for $\beta = 0$. Consequently, the factor by which the quantity $B^*_\nu(T)$ deviates from B_0 increases the central intensities of absorption lines even more for noncoherent than for coherent scattering.

Finally we propose $\epsilon \neq 0$, that is, we consider an effect of fluorescence on the central intensities of absorption lines.

As before, to estimate the order of magnitude of r_{ν_0} for noncoherent scattering, we consider only the first term in braces in Eq. (170) and neglect the rest. Then we obtain

$$r_{\nu_0} \approx \frac{\phi(x_0)}{1+\beta\eta} \sqrt{\int \frac{1+\epsilon\mu_\nu}{1+\mu_\nu}\sigma_\nu\, d\nu} \tag{187}$$

where $x_0 = \eta/(1+\mu_{\nu_0})$ or, after an integration,

$$r_{\nu_0} \approx \frac{\phi(x_0)}{1+\beta\eta} \sqrt{\left(\frac{a}{\mu_{\nu_0}}\right)^{1/2} + \epsilon} \tag{188}$$

Apropos of the terms that are neglected, we know that they cannot affect the order of magnitude of r_{ν_0}. Indeed,

$$\frac{1}{2}\int_0^1 \frac{\phi(x')}{x+x'} K_1(x')x'\, dx < \frac{1}{2A}\int_0^1 K_1(x')\, dx' = \frac{1}{2}\left(\frac{A_0}{A}\right)^2 A \tag{189}$$

and

$$\frac{\epsilon}{2}\int_0^1 \frac{\phi(x')}{x+x'} K(x')x'\, dx' \leqslant \frac{\epsilon}{2}\int_0^1 \phi(x')\, K(x')\, dx' < \frac{\epsilon}{1-\epsilon} \tag{190}$$

The other neglected terms with the factor β may slightly increase the value of r_{ν_0} as given by Eq. (188). But because the factor β cannot be very large, the terms cannot change the order of r_{ν_0} (see Table 8.9).

For coherent scattering we now find from Eq. (180):

$$r_{\nu_0} \approx \frac{\phi_{\nu_0}(\eta)}{1+\beta\eta} \sqrt{\frac{1}{\mu_{\nu_0}} + \epsilon} \tag{191}$$

If we compare Eqs. (191) and (188), knowing that the functions $\phi(x)$ and $\phi_\nu(\eta)$ are equal to unity at the limb of the star and increase more or less the same rate from the limb to the center, we may draw the following conclusions.

For $\epsilon = 0$, as we showed earlier, the central intensities are considerably larger for noncoherent scattering than for coherent. It goes without saying that here $(a/\mu_{\nu_0})^{1/2} \gg 1/\mu_{\nu_0}$ is true, as is always correct for strong lines.

If

$$\epsilon \ll \left(\frac{a}{\mu_{\nu_0}}\right)^{1/2} \tag{192}$$

the quantity r_{ν_0} remains the same as for $\epsilon = 0$ for noncoherent scattering, but for coherent scattering it may increase markedly. Nevertheless, with the fulfilment of the inequality of Eq. (192), the quantity r_{ν_0} will always be greater for noncoherent than for coherent scattering.

If

$$\epsilon \gg \left(\frac{a}{\mu_{\nu_0}}\right)^{1/2} \qquad (193)$$

the fluorescence plays a predominant part in the formation of the central regions of the absorption line, not only with coherent, but with non-coherent scattering as well. In this case the quantity r_{ν_0} will be of the same order for both forms of scattering.

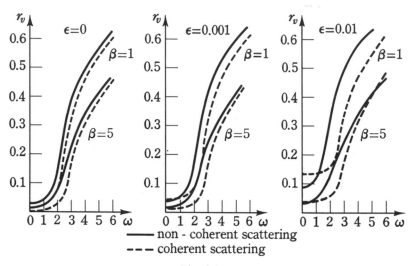

— non - coherent scattering
--- coherent scattering

Fig. 8.3

As stated previously, the theory of coherent scattering neglecting fluorescence gives very low values for the central intensities as compared to those observed. By allowing for fluorescence we improve the situation markedly. But only when ϵ is large do the theoretical and observational values of r_{ν_0} appear to be near each other. However, when ϵ is small, which is actually the case for many lines in the solar spectrum, theory still differs greatly from observation even when fluorescence is allowed for.

These results enable us to conclude that, in the question of the central intensities of absorption lines, the theory of noncoherent scattering agrees better with observation than the theory of coherent scattering. However, when ϵ is large, the quantity r_{ν_0} for noncoherent scattering becomes of about the same order as for coherent scattering, that is, it does not differ markedly from the observed value. But when ϵ is small, the noncoherent scattering gives much larger values for the quantity r_{ν_0} than coherent scattering, that is, it approaches observation more closely.

Internal portions of the line. For noncoherent scattering the line contour is defined by Eq. (175). Employing this and Table 8.9 we have computed a series of line contours for $a = 0.01$ and $\mu_{\nu_0} = 10^4$. These contours are given in Fig. 8.3. We give there also for comparison the line contours computed by Eq. (180) for coherent scattering.

Figure 8.3 shows that the internal portions of the line differ markedly from one another for coherent and noncoherent scattering. This difference is especially great for large values of ϵ. Although in this case the central intensities are near to each other, the lines themselves appear much sharper for noncoherent than for coherent scattering.

This conclusion, based on a study of line contours in particular cases, is also correct for other values of the parameters entering into the expression for $r_\nu(\eta)$. For coherent scattering the quantity $r_\nu(\eta)$ is proportional to the function $\phi_\nu(\eta)$ which does not change appreciably in the central parts of the line. Therefore, it follows from Eq. (180) that the quantity $r_\nu(\eta)$ is nearly constant at first, in an interval of frequency for which $\mu_\nu > 1/\epsilon$, and then increases rapidly as $\mu_\nu^{-1/2}$. Equation (179) shows that for noncoherent scattering the quantity $r_\nu(\eta)$ in the central parts of a line is approximately proportional to the function $\phi(x)$, which increases very rapidly with an increase of x. That is why the quantity $r_\nu(\eta)$ also increases rapidly as we go away from the center of the line. This explains the great sharpness of the absorption lines for noncoherent scattering as compared to the case for coherent scattering.

It appears that observation furnishes lines still sharper than those derived from the theory of coherent scattering. However, a detailed comparison between theory and observation is still difficult, for the observations are not very reliable, and in addition there are difficulties in determining the parameters a, μ_{ν_0}, ϵ, and β for each line.

External portions of a line. In the extreme portions of a line the quantity $r_\nu(\eta)$ changes proportionately to μ_ν. Therefore, to characterize a given part of a line we may utilize a quantity that is independent of frequency, namely:

$$C(\eta) = \lim_{\mu_\nu \to 0} \frac{1 - r_\nu(\eta)}{\mu_\nu} \tag{194}$$

For coherent scattering this becomes:

$$C(\eta) = \frac{3}{2} - \frac{\epsilon}{2} - \frac{1}{2}(1 - \epsilon)\eta \lg\frac{1 + \eta}{\eta} - \frac{1}{1 + \beta\eta}\left[1 + \frac{\beta}{4}(1 - \epsilon)\right] \tag{195}$$

This formula can be derived from Eq. (111) of Chapter 6 for $Q = 1$ and $\beta_2 = 0$.

For noncoherent scattering, we find from Eq. (175):

$$C(\eta) = 1 - \epsilon + \frac{\beta\eta}{1+\beta\eta} - \frac{\Psi(x) + \beta\Psi_1(\eta)}{1+\beta\eta} \qquad (196)$$

We should point out that for values of η which are not very small, say for $\eta > 0.1$, we can keep approximately only the first term in braces and assume $\phi(\eta) \approx 1/A$ in Eqs. (176) and (177) which serve for the determination of the functions $\Psi(x)$ and $\Psi_1(x)$. Instead of Eq. (196) we then obtain approximately:

$$C(\eta) \approx \frac{\beta\eta}{1+\beta\eta} \qquad (197)$$

Needless to say, this transition is valid only for values of β not very close to zero.

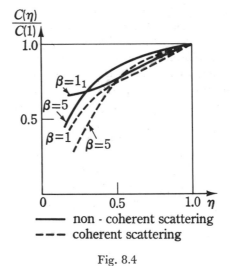

Fig. 8.4

It is easy to see that Eq. (197) gives precise values of the quantity $C(\eta)$ for $\epsilon = 1$, that is, when the terms that correspond to radiation scattering in a spectrum line are absent from Eqs. (153) and (154). Consequently the behavior of the far wings of the line appears to be approximately the same with noncoherent scattering as without any scattering.

In Fig. 8.4 are given graphs of the function $C(\eta)/C(1)$, computed for coherent scattering with Eq. (195) and for noncoherent scattering with Eq. (196), making use of Table 8.9. The graphs refer to $\epsilon = 0$; they differ little from those for $\epsilon = 0.001$ and $\epsilon = 0.01$.

For coherent as well as for noncoherent scattering, the quantity $C(\eta)/C(1)$ depends essentially on the parameter β. The graphs are drawn for $\beta = 1$ and $\beta = 5$, corresponding to two extreme observational regions of the solar spectrum, the red and the violet.

Figure 8.4 shows that the quantities $C(\eta)/C(1)$ are markedly different for coherent and noncoherent scattering. Comparing them now with the observed quantities found by Houtgast[11] for many lines, we see that theory agrees better with observation for noncoherent than for coherent scattering, although there is not complete agreement. Analogous results were obtained by Savedoff,[12] who computed the quantity $C(\eta)/C(1)$ for noncoherent scattering, and for another case $(a \to \infty,$ $\mu_{v_0} = 4.10^6)$ by another method. Houtgast[11] found still earlier from his own observations that the change in the far wings going from the center to the limb can be explained only by noncoherent scattering.

In conclusion we should say that recently the problem of the formation of absorption lines in stellar spectra has become very fashionable among astrophysicists. We may mention the work of Stibbs,[13] who has considered the problem of the formation of absorption lines for partially coherent scattering and for partially noncoherent scattering, as well as the investigations of Miyamoto[14] and Labs,[15] who dealt with an approximate solution of the problem indicated above for noncoherent scattering.

[11] J. Houtgast, *The Variations in the Profiles of Strong Fraunhofer Lines*, Utrecht (1942).

[12] M. P. Savedoff, Formation of Absorption Lines by Noncoherent Scattering, *Astrophysical J.* **115**, 509 (1952).

[13] D. W. N. Stibbs, On a Problem in the Theory of Formation of Absorption Lines, *Monthly Notices of the Royal Astronomical Soc.* **113**, 493 (1953).

[14] S. Miyamoto, On the Calculation of Noncoherent Contours, *Publ. Astr. Soc. Japan* **6**, No. 9 (1954); **7**, No. 1 (1955).

[15] D. Labs, Untersuchungen zur inkohärenten Streuung in Fraunhoferlinien, *Zs. f. Astroph.* **28**, 150 (1951); **34**, 173 (1954).

CHAPTER 9

NONSTATIONARY RADIATION FIELD

In this chapter we consider the problem of luminescence of a medium under the impact of radiation sources of variable intensity. At the present time this problem is not yet well investigated, although we encounter it often in astrophysics and physics.

In solving this problem we should consider two cases. When the average time of quantum existence in medium is small in comparison with the interval of time in which intensity of radiation sources is conspicuously changing, we may assume that there is radiative equilibrium at every moment in the medium. In this case the nonstationary processes of luminescence are reduced to stationary ones. For example, in determining the brightness of the sky during the day it is sufficient to find its brightness for a definite position of the Sun and then to take into account the zenith distance of the Sun during the day in our final formulas. Another example can be furnished by the brightness of the envelope of a nova. An amount of energy arriving from the star at its envelope changes in time due to a change of star brightness and to a recession of the envelope from the star. Nevertheless, we may conventionally analyze the spectrum of the envelope by employing formulas derived with an assumption that radiative equilibrium occurs in the envelope.

However, an opposite case may also occur, namely when, during the average time of quantum existence in a medium, the intensity of radiation causing the brightness of the medium changes greatly. The glaring example of this case is a gradual brightening of the medium when radiation sources are suddenly switched on, or a dimming of the medium when they are suddenly switched off. Similar phenomena are encountered in astrophysics; for example, a luminescence of a nebula due to the sudden brightening or dimming of a star during a long interval of time after the star has ceased to illuminate it for some reason. The presence of such phenomena makes it necessary to work out a theory of radiation diffusion with nonstationary processes.

In this chapter we first analyze the nonstationary luminescence of a medium with the aid of the radiative transfer equation. Then, the same problem is analyzed by means of the probability of quantum exit from the medium during a certain interval of time after it has been absorbed at a given optical depth. Finally, we apply our results to the brightness of novae and nebulae.

1. Equation Defining the Function $B(\tau, t)$

As we stated, in the theory of nonstationary radiation diffusion the fundamental part is played by the average duration of quantum existence in the medium. Therefore, before everything else we investigate the causes which condition this duration.

First, the light quantum spends some time directly on the act of scattering. Regarding scattering as absorption with a subsequent emission of a light quantum, we may say that the quantum remains in a state of absorption for a certain time. Let an average value of this time be t_1, and the probability that the quantum is emitted in the time interval $(t, t+dt)$ be

$$e^{-t/t_1} \frac{dt}{t_1} \tag{1}$$

Secondly, the light quantum remains for a certain time on its path between scatterings. It is known that the probability of quantum absorption within its path interval $(s, s+ds)$ is

$$e^{-nks} nk \, ds$$

where n in the number of scattering particles in 1 cm³, and k is the scattering coefficient for one particle. But $s = ct$, where c = velocity of light. Therefore, the probability of quantum absorption in time interval $(t, t+dt)$ is

$$e^{-t/t_2} \frac{dt}{t_2} \tag{2}$$

where $t_2 = 1/cnk$. The quantity t_2 is an average time spent by a quantum on its path between two consecutive scatterings.

It is important to realize that the quantities t_1 and t_2 are usually of different order. As an example we consider the scattering of radiation in a spectral line. Here we can assume $t_1 \approx 10^{-8}$ sec, $t_2 \approx 100/n$ sec. Consequently, the quantities t_1 and t_2 are of the same order only when $n \approx 10^{10}$ cm⁻³. But as a rule in practice we have either: (1) $t_1 \gg t_2$ for $n \gg 10^{10}$, or (2) $t_1 \ll t_2$ for $n \ll 10^{10}$. Needless to say, in our physical laboratories we have the first alternative because we cannot make the concentration of atoms very small. In contrast, many astronomical objects—nova envelopes, planetary nebulae, interstellar medium—exhibit the second alternative. It is of course reasonable to treat these two alternatives separately in what follows.

It goes without saying that to find an average time of quantum existence in a medium we have only to multiply the quantity $t_1 + t_2$ by the average number of scatterings suffered by the quantum. Clearly the latter quantity can be obtained from a theory of radiation diffusion and we shall determine it. At the present time we remark only that an average number of quantum scatterings in a medium may be very large indeed, so that an average time of quantum existence in the medium may, even for radiation scattering in a spectral line under laboratory conditions—that is, when $t_1 + t_2 \approx 10^{-8}$ sec—become a completely observable quantity. But as far as planetary nebulae and other astronomical objects are concerned the average time of quantum existence in them may reach tens and hundreds of years.

In solving the problem of nonstationary radiation diffusion, we first employ the radiative transfer equation. However, we cannot use it in its earlier form for our case of a nonstationary radiation field, and we must derive a more general form of radiative transfer which defines the variation of radiation intensity due to change of distance along the ray, as well as to the change in time.

Consider an elementary area of size $d\sigma$ perpendicular to the direction of radiation. Denoting by $I(s, t)$ the radiation intensity incident on the area within a solid angle $d\omega$ in a time interval $(t, t + dt)$, we write, for the amount of energy incident on the area, $I(s, t)\, d\sigma d\omega dt$. Correspondingly, the amount of energy incident on another area of the same size at the distance ds from the first one will be $I(s + ds, t + dt) \times d\sigma d\omega dt$. The difference between these amounts of energy is due to energy absorption in the volume $d\sigma ds$, as well as to energy emission by the same volume. Denoting $\alpha(s)$ the volume absorption coefficient and by $\epsilon(s, t)$ the volume emission coefficient, we may write:

$$I(s + ds, t + dt)\, d\sigma d\omega dt - I(s, t)\, d\sigma d\omega dt$$
$$= -\ \alpha(s)\ dsI(s, t)\ d\sigma d\omega dt + \epsilon(s, t)\ d\sigma ds d\omega dt$$

Hence,

$$\frac{\partial I(s, t)}{\partial s}\, ds + \frac{\partial I(s, t)}{\partial t}\, dt = -\ \alpha(s)\ dsI(s, t) + \epsilon(s, t)\ ds$$

or recollecting $ds = cdt$,

$$\frac{\partial I(s, t)}{\partial s} + \frac{1}{c}\frac{\partial I(s, t)}{\partial t} = -\alpha(s)I(s, t) + \epsilon(s, t) \tag{3}$$

This is in fact the required equation of radiative transfer for the case of a nonstationary field.

For simplicity we assume that radiation diffusion occurs in a one-dimensional medium. Denoting by $I_1(\tau, t)$ and $I_2(\tau, t)$ intensities of radiation coming from an optical depth τ at a moment of time t and corresponding respectively to directions of increasing and decreasing depth $(d\tau = \alpha\, ds)$, we find that the radiative transfer equation has the form:

$$\left.\begin{aligned}
\frac{\partial I_1}{\partial \tau} - \frac{1}{\alpha c}\frac{\partial I_1}{\partial t} &= -I_1 + \frac{\epsilon}{\alpha} \\[2ex]
-\frac{\partial I_2}{\partial \tau} + \frac{1}{\alpha c}\frac{\partial I_2}{\partial t} &= -I_2 + \frac{\epsilon}{\alpha}
\end{aligned}\right\} \tag{4}$$

Setting $\epsilon = \alpha B$ and remembering $\alpha = nk$, we have, instead of Eqs. (4),

$$\left.\begin{aligned}
\frac{\partial I_1}{\partial \tau} + t_2\frac{\partial I_1}{\partial t} &= -I_1 + B \\[2ex]
-\frac{\partial I_2}{\partial \tau} + t_2\frac{\partial I_2}{\partial t} &= -I_2 + B
\end{aligned}\right\} \tag{5}$$

Assuming now that the probability of the quantum "lifetime" is equal to λ, and that the probability of emission during a certain time interval after absorption is defined by the above given law, Eq. (1), for an elementary act of scattering, we can write the function $B(\tau, t)$ as follows:

$$B(\tau, t) = \frac{\lambda}{2}\int_0^t [I_1(\tau, t') + I_2(\tau, t')]e^{-(t-t')/t_1}\frac{dt'}{t_1} \tag{6}$$

For $n = \text{const}$, which means $t_2 = \text{const}$, the system of Eqs. (5) and (6) can easily be reduced to one differential equation for a determination of the function $B(\tau, t)$, namely:

$$t_1\frac{\partial^3 B}{\partial \tau^2 \partial t} + \frac{\partial^2 B}{\partial \tau^2}$$
$$= t_1 t_2^2\frac{\partial^3 B}{\partial t^3} + (2t_1 t_2 + t_2^2)\frac{\partial^2 B}{\partial t^2} + [t_1 + (2-\lambda)t_2]\frac{\partial B}{\partial t} + (1-\lambda)B \tag{7}$$

It is clear that we should also add to Eq. (7) initial boundary conditions which will take into account the location and effect of the light sources.

Having determined the function B from Eq. (7) we can find the quantities I_1 and I_2 by employing Eqs. (5). In particular, we may find the intensities of radiation emergent from the medium, $I_1(\tau_0, t)$ and $I_2(0, t)$, which interest us.

As stated previously, the quantities t_1 and t_2 may be of different order. We therefore analyze two special cases of Eq. (7).

If $t_1 \gg t_2$, then, denoting t/t_1 by u and neglecting terms with t_2/t_1, we find

$$\frac{\partial^3 B}{\partial \tau^2 \partial u} + \frac{\partial^2 B}{\partial \tau^2} = \frac{\partial B}{\partial u} + (1-\lambda)B \tag{8}$$

For an opposite case when $t_1 \ll t_2$, denoting t/t_2 by u and neglecting terms with t_1/t_2, we find

$$\frac{\partial^2 B}{\partial \tau^2} = \frac{\partial^2 B}{\partial u^2} + (2 - \lambda)\frac{\partial B}{\partial u} + (1 - \lambda)B \tag{9}$$

We observe that Eqs. (8) and (9) resemble the usual equations of thermoconductivity:

$$\frac{\partial^2 B}{\partial \tau^2} = \frac{\partial B}{\partial u} + (1 - \lambda)B \tag{10}$$

In this connection we should remark that Compton[1] attempted to treat nonstationary processes of radiation diffusion with the aid of Eq. (10). However, Milne[2] showed that such a treatment may lead to results that are physically absurd. Having considered this, he derived and solved Eq. (8) for $\lambda = 1$. His equation is a special case of Eq. (7), derived here by us. However, we shall not solve this equation now for we shall need it only for a comparison with other equations derived subsequently.

2. Integral Equation for the Function $p(\tau, t)$

The problem of nonstationary luminescence of a medium may be solved by another method based on the probability of quantum exit from the medium.[3]

We denote by $p(\tau, t - t')\, dt$ the probability that the light quantum absorbed at the optical depth τ in a moment of time t' emerges from the medium in the time interval $(t, t + dt)$. It is obvious, if the quantity p is found, that the intensity of the emergent radiation may be obtained by means of some integrations for any kind of light sources affecting the medium. Indeed, denoting by $L(\tau, t')\, d\tau dt'$ an amount of energy coming directly from light sources and absorbed at the optical depth interval $(\tau, \tau + d\tau)$ in the time interval $(t', t' + dt')$, we obtain the intensities of radiation emergent from the medium as follows:

$$\left.\begin{aligned} I_2(0, t) &= \int_0^{\tau_0} d\tau \int_0^t L(\tau, t')p(\tau, t - t')\, dt' \\[2mm] I_1(\tau_0, t) &= \int_0^{\tau_0} d\tau \int_0^t L(\tau, t')p(\tau_0 - \tau, t - t')\, dt' \end{aligned}\right\} \tag{11}$$

[1] K. T. Compton, Some Properties of Resonance Radiation and Excited Atoms, *Phil. Mag.* **45**, 750 (1923).

[2] E. A. Milne, *J. Lond. Math. Soc.* **1**, 1 (1926).

[3] V. V. Sobolev, On the Theory of the Non-stationary Radiation Field, I, *Russian Astronomical J.* **29**, Bulletin 4 (1952).

The fact that in this method we need to know only one and the same function $p(\tau, t)$ for the solution of any problem of the luminescence of a medium is a great advantage of this method over the one previously considered.

In deriving an equation defining the probability of quantum exit from a medium, we first investigate a case when a quantum remains in a state of absorption during a diffusion in the medium, that is, $t_1 \gg t_2$. As before, we replace the variable t by another variable $u = t/t_1$. Generally speaking, the quantity $p(\tau, u)$ consists of two parts: the probability of quantum exit without a scattering on its path, and the probability of quantum exit after a series of scatterings. The first part is obviously equal to $(\lambda/2)e^{-\tau-u}$ in this case. To determine the second part, we multiply the quantity $(\lambda/2)e^{-|\tau-\tau'|-u'}d\tau'du'$ by $p(\tau', u-u')$ and integrate the product with respect to τ' over an interval $(0, \tau_0)$ and with respect to u' over an interval $(0, u)$. As a result, we have

$$p(\tau, u) = \frac{\lambda}{2}e^{-\tau-u} + \frac{\lambda}{2}\int_0^{\tau_0} e^{-|\tau-\tau'|}\, d\tau' \int_0^u e^{-u'}p(\tau', u-u')\, du' \quad (12)$$

This is in fact the required integral equation defining the function $p(\tau, u)$ for the case $t_1 \gg t_2$.

In the other case, $t_2 \gg t_1$, we introduce a new variable $u = t/t_2$. Obviously, here the light quantum absorbed at the optical depth τ emerges from the medium without a scattering on its path during a time exactly equal to τ. Therefore, the corresponding term in the expression for $p(\tau, u)$ will be equal to $(\lambda|2)e^{-\tau}\delta(\tau, u)$ where $\delta(\tau, u)$ is the so-called "δ function". To obtain the second term relative to the scattering on the path we have to multiply the quantity $(\lambda/2)e^{-|\tau-\tau'|}\, d\tau'$ by $p(\tau', u-|\tau-\tau'|)$ and integrate the product with respect to τ' over an interval $(0,(\tau+u)/2)$ for $(\tau+u)/2 < \tau_0$ and $(0, \tau)$ for $(\tau+u)/2 > \tau_0$. For an upper limit we take the quantity $(\tau-u)_/2$, that is, we assume $\tau_0 = \infty$. Thus we find

$$p(\tau, u) = \frac{\lambda}{2}e^{-\tau}\delta(\tau, u) + \frac{\lambda}{2}\int_0^{(\tau+u)/2} e^{-|\tau-\tau'|}p(\tau', u-|\tau-\tau'|)\, d\tau' \quad (13)$$

This is the integral equation which defines the function $p(\tau, u)$ for the case $t_2 \gg t_1$.

Analogously, we can derive an integral equation defining the function $p(\tau, t)$; for the general case, namely, for $\tau_0 = \infty$, we have

$$p(\tau, t) = \frac{\lambda}{2}e^{-\tau-(t-t_2\tau)/t_1}$$

$$+ \frac{\lambda}{2}\int_0^{(1/2)[\tau+(t/t_2)]} e^{-|\tau-\tau'|}\, dv' \int_{t_2|\tau-\tau'|}^{t-t_2\tau'} e^{-(t'-t_2|\tau-\tau'|)/t_1}p(\tau', t-t')\frac{dt'}{t_1} \quad (14)$$

From these integral equations we can easily derive differential equations for the function $p(\tau, t)$. It appears that this function satisfies the same differential equation which is satisfied by the function $B(\tau, t)$ for certain initial and boundary conditions. In other words, the function $p(\tau, t)$ is equal to the function $B(\tau, t)$ for a particular case of luminescence of a medium (see for comparison Chapter 6, Section 2).

The integral equations for the function $p(\tau, t)$ given above may be solved without special difficulties. We limit ourselves to the case $t_1 \gg t_2$ or to a solution of Eq. (12).

From Eq. (12) it follows that the function $p(\tau, u)$ must satisfy the following differential equation:

$$\frac{\partial^3 p}{\partial \tau^2 \partial u} + \frac{\partial^2 p}{\partial \tau^2} = \frac{\partial p}{\partial u} + (1 - \lambda)p \tag{15}$$

with an initial condition

$$p(\tau, 0) = \frac{\lambda}{2} e^{-\tau} \tag{16}$$

and with boundary conditions

$$\left. \begin{array}{ll} p = \dfrac{\partial p}{\partial \tau} & \text{for} \quad \tau = 0 \\[3mm] p = -\dfrac{\partial p}{\partial \tau} & \text{for} \quad \tau = \tau_0 \end{array} \right\} \tag{17}$$

Let us find a particular solution of differential Eq. (15) in the form of a product $\Phi(\tau)\Psi(u)$. From Eq. (15) we obtain

$$\Phi(\tau) = C \cos x\tau + D \sin x\tau \tag{18}$$

$$\Psi(u) = e^{-[1-\lambda/(1+x^2)]u} \tag{19}$$

where C, D, and x are arbitrary constants. To fulfil boundary conditions it is necessary to set

$$Dx = C \tag{20}$$

$$\operatorname{tg} x\tau_0 = \frac{2x}{x^2 - 1} \tag{21}$$

Denoting by $x_1, x_2, ..., x_k, ...$ the roots of Eq. (21), we find that the general solution of Eq. (15) which satisfies boundary conditions has the form

$$p(\tau, u) = \sum_{k=1}^{\infty} D_k(x_k \cos x_k\tau + \sin x_k\tau) e^{-[1-\lambda/(1+x_k^2)]u} \tag{22}$$

The coefficients D are found from the initial condition:

$$\frac{\lambda}{2}e^{-\tau} = \sum_1^\infty D_k(x_k \cos x_k\tau + \sin x_k\tau) \qquad (23)$$

Multiplying both sides of this relation by $x_k \cos x_k + \sin x_k\tau$ and integrating with respect to τ over the interval $(0, \tau_0)$, we find

$$D_k = \frac{\lambda x_k}{[1 + (\tau_0/2)(1 + x_k^2)](1 + x_k^2)} \qquad (24)$$

Inserting Eq. (24) into Eq. (22), we obtain

$$p(\tau, u) = \lambda \sum_1^\infty \frac{x_k(x_k \cos x_k\tau + \sin x_k\tau)}{[1 + (\tau_0/2)(1 + x_k^2)](1 + x_k^2)} e^{-[1 - \lambda/(1 + x_k^2)]u} \qquad (25)$$

For $\tau_0 = \infty$ there remains only the first of the boundary conditions in Eq. (17) which is fulfilled by a superposition of the connection [Eq. (20)] between the coefficients C and D. Thus for the function $p(\tau, u)$, we find

$$p(\tau, u) = \int_0^\infty D(x)(x \cos x\tau + \sin x\tau)e^{-[1 - \lambda/(1 + x^2)]u} \, dx \qquad (26)$$

Here the function $D(x)$ should be determined from the initial condition,

$$\frac{\lambda}{2}e^{-\tau} = \int_0^\infty D(x)(x \cos x\tau + \sin x\tau) \, dx \qquad (27)$$

It appears that

$$D(x) = \frac{2}{\pi}\lambda\frac{x}{(1 + x^2)^2} \qquad (28)$$

Consequently, the function $p(\tau, u)$ for $\tau_0 = \infty$ is

$$p(\tau, u) = \frac{2}{\pi}\lambda \int_0^\infty (x \cos x\tau + \sin x\tau)e^{-[1 + \lambda/(1 + x^2)]u}\frac{x \, dx}{(1 + x^2)^2} \qquad (29)$$

Equations (25) and (26) express the probability of quantum exit from the medium. As stated previously, a substitution of these expressions for $p(\tau, u)$ in Eqs. (11) may provide the solution of any problem in the luminescence of a medium.

3. Average Time of Quantum Existence in Medium

In practice there is great interest in determining the average time of quantum existence in a medium; we denote this time by $\bar{t}$. It is evident that

$$\bar{t} = (t_1 + t_2)\bar{z} \qquad (30)$$

when $\bar{z}$ is an average number of scatterings suffered by the quantum during its diffusion in the medium. Since the quantities t_1 and t_2 are supposed to be known, the problem is reduced to a determination of the quantity $\bar{z}$. Clearly this quantity does not depend on the mechanism of scattering but does depend only on the optical thickness of the medium τ_0 and the parameter λ (for given light sources).

It is obvious that for a determination of the quantity $\bar{z}$ in a given medium and for any kind of light sources affecting it, we need only to find two functions:

$$P(\tau) = \int_0^\infty p(\tau, u) \, du \tag{31}$$

and

$$\mathcal{Z}(\tau) = \int_0^\infty p(\tau, u) u \, du \tag{32}$$

Denoting by $K(\tau) d\tau$ the number of quanta arriving from a light source and absorbed between optical depths τ and $\tau + d\tau$, we obtain

$$\bar{z} = \frac{\displaystyle\int_0^{\tau_0} \mathcal{Z}(\tau) K(\tau) \, d\tau}{\displaystyle\int_0^{\tau_0} P(\tau) K(\tau) \, d\tau} \tag{33}$$

To derive an equation for the functions $P(\tau)$ and $\mathcal{Z}(\tau)$, we may employ, as an example, Eq. (12) or (13) which define the function $p(\tau, u)$. From this we easily find

$$P(\tau) = \frac{\lambda}{2} e^{-\tau} + \frac{\lambda}{2} \int_0^{\tau_0} e^{-|\tau - \tau'|} P(\tau') \, d\tau' \tag{34}$$

$$\mathcal{Z}(\tau) = P(\tau) + \frac{\lambda}{2} \int_0^{\tau_0} e^{-|\tau - \tau'|} \mathcal{Z}(\tau') \, d\tau' \tag{35}$$

Clearly Eqs. (34) and (35) might have been obtained even from physical considerations directly without considering the time rate of the diffusion process.

From the integral Eqs. (34) and (35) it follows that the function $P(\tau)$ satisfies a differential equation

$$\frac{d^2 P(\tau)}{d\tau^2} = (1 - \lambda) P(\tau) \tag{36}$$

with boundary conditions

$$P(0) = P'(0) + \lambda, \qquad P(\tau_0) = -P'(\tau_0) \tag{37}$$

and the function $\mathcal{Z}(\tau)$ satisfies a differential equation

$$\frac{d^2\mathcal{Z}(\tau)}{d\tau^2} = (1-\lambda)\mathcal{Z}(\tau) - \lambda P(\tau) \tag{38}$$

with boundary conditions

$$\mathcal{Z}(0) = \mathcal{Z}'(0) + \lambda, \qquad \mathcal{Z}(\tau_0) = -\mathcal{Z}'(\tau_0) \tag{39}$$

Of the greatest interest in practice is the case of pure scattering, $\lambda = 1$. In this case, the above equations provide

$$P(\tau) = \frac{1 + \tau_0 - \tau}{2 + \tau_0} \tag{40}$$

$$\mathcal{Z}(\tau) = 1 + \frac{\tau_0^3 + 3\tau_0^2 - 6}{3(2+\tau_0)^2}(1+\tau) - \frac{1+\tau_0}{2(2+\tau_0)}\tau^2 + \frac{\tau^3}{6(2+\tau_0)} \tag{41}$$

To obtain an average number of scatterings for one light source or another we have to insert these expressions of P and $\mathcal{Z}$ in Eq. (33).

We now give some examples. When the light source is within the medium at the optical depth τ the average number of scatterings is obtained from the simple division of Eq. (41) by Eq. (40). If light sources are uniformly distributed in the medium we should first integrate Eqs. (40) and (41) with respect to τ from 0 to τ_0 and then divide one by another in order to find the quantity $\bar{z}$ in accordance with the Eq. (33). As a result, we have

$$\bar{z} = \frac{24(1+\tau_0) + 8\tau_0^2 + \tau_0^3}{12(2+\tau_0)} \tag{42}$$

We might as well find an average number of scatterings suffered by the quantum while passing the medium and by the quantum reflected by it. Denoting the former number by $\bar{z}_1$ and the latter by $\bar{z}_2$, we easily find

$$\bar{z}_2 = \frac{\displaystyle\int_0^{\tau_0} \mathcal{Z}(\tau) e^{-\tau}\, d\tau}{\displaystyle\int_0^{\tau_0} P(\tau) e^{-\tau}\, d\tau} = \frac{\mathcal{Z}(0) - P(0)}{P(0) - (\lambda/2)} \tag{43}$$

$$\bar{z}_1 = \frac{\displaystyle\int_0^{\tau_0} \mathcal{Z}(\tau) e^{-(\tau_0-\tau)}\, d\tau}{\displaystyle\int_0^{\tau_0} P(\tau) e^{-(\tau_0-\tau)}\, d\tau + e^{-\tau_0}} = \frac{\mathcal{Z}(\tau_0) - P(\tau_0)}{P(\tau_0)} \tag{44}$$

(in the denominator of Eq. (44) we added the term $e^{-\tau_0}$ taking into account quanta transmitted without scatterings).

Employing now the expressions for $P(\tau)$ and $\mathcal{Z}(\tau)$, we obtain from Eqs. (43) and (44):

$$\bar{z}_2 = \frac{2}{3} \cdot \frac{3 + 3\tau_0 + \tau_0^2}{2 + \tau_0} \tag{45}$$

$$\bar{z}_1 = \frac{\tau_0}{6} \cdot \frac{6 + 6\tau_0 + \tau_0^2}{2 + \tau_0} \tag{46}$$

It is interesting that the quantities $\bar{z}_1$ and $\bar{z}_2$ can be found even without a knowledge of the function $\mathcal{Z}(\tau)$. Actually, the integral

$$\int_0^{\tau_0} \mathcal{Z}(\tau) e^{-\tau} \, d\tau$$

may be regarded as the intensity of radiation emergent from a medium for which the function $B(\tau)$ is equal to $\mathcal{Z}(\tau)$. But in such a case the quantity $(2/\lambda) P(\tau) d\tau$, in accordance with Eq. (35), represents an amount of energy coming from the light sources and absorbed between the optical depths τ and $\tau + d\tau$. Hence, this intensity may be rewritten as follows:

$$\frac{2}{\lambda} \int_0^{\tau_0} P^2(\tau) \, d\tau$$

Consequently, the quantity $\bar{z}_2$ becomes

$$\bar{z}_2 = \frac{\displaystyle\int_0^{\tau_0} P^2(\tau) \, d\tau}{P(0) - (\lambda/2)} \tag{47}$$

Analogously, the quantity $\bar{z}_1$ becomes

$$\bar{z}_1 = \frac{\displaystyle\int_0^{\tau_0} P(\tau) P(\tau_0 - \tau) \, d\tau}{P(\tau_0)} \tag{48}$$

We should say that Ambartsumian[4] proposed another method for determining the average number of scatterings suffered by a quantum in a medium. He obtained in fact the following formula for computing the quantity $\bar{z}$:

$$\bar{z} = \lambda \frac{\partial \lg I}{\partial \lambda} \tag{49}$$

where I is an intensity of radiation emergent from medium. Ter-

[4] V. A. Ambartsumian, On the Number of Scatterings for Diffusion of Protons in a Turbid Medium, *DAN Arm. SSR* **8**, No. 3 (1948).

Mikaelian[5] computed $\bar{z}_1$ and $\bar{z}_2$ while employing the formula of Ambartsumian, and arrived at the same Eqs. (45) and (46).

As an example of the application of the formulas obtained in this section, consider the diffusion of L_α emission in planetary nebulae. It is known that L_α quanta occur in a nebula as a result of photoionization of hydrogen atoms and subsequent recombination. To determine an average number of scatterings in this case we apply Eq. (42). For $\tau_0 \gg 1$ this gives $\bar{z} = \tau_0^2/12$. To go over from a one-dimensional medium to a three-dimensional one, we should write $3\tau_0^2$ instead of τ_0^2 (see Chapter 2, Section 2). Therefore, instead of the last expression for $\bar{z}$, we have $\bar{z} = \tau_0^2/4$. Because, in a nebula, $t_1 \ll t_2$ but $t_2 = 1/nck$, where k is the scattering coefficient computed for one atom, the average time $\bar{t}$ of L_α quantum existence in a nebula becomes

$$\bar{t} = \frac{\tau_0^2}{4nck} \tag{50}$$

We may assume $\tau_0 \approx 10^4$ and $n \approx 1$. Hence $\bar{t}$ becomes a magnitude of the order of 300 years.

In reality in computing the quantity $\bar{t}$ we should take into account the noncoherent scattering and also the quantum exit from the medium due to the Doppler effect, in view of the presence of a velocity gradient. In this case, as was shown in Chapter 8, the magnitude of $\bar{t}$ may be greatly reduced as compared with that computed by Eq. (50). Nevertheless, even with a consideration of these two processes the L_α quantum existence in a nebula may be of a rather long duration.

4. FUNCTIONAL EQUATIONS FOR THE FUNCTION $p(\tau, t)$

In Section 2 we derived and solved integral and differential equations for determination of the probability of quantum exit from medium. For the same purpose we now form functional equations.

For the sake of simplicity we assume that quantum diffusion occurs in a one-dimensional medium with an infinitely large optical thickness. Again we limit ourselves to the case when the average time of quantum existence in the absorption state considerably surpasses the average time of quantum existence on the path between the two consecutive scatterings, that is, $t_1 \gg t_2$.

To obtain a functional equation for defining the function $p(\tau, u)$ we first find the probability of quantum exit from the medium with an optical depth $\tau + \Delta\tau$, that is, the quantity $p(\tau + \Delta\tau, u)$. For this purpose we shall regard the quantum exit at the depth $\tau + \Delta\tau$ as a quantum

[5] M. L. Ter-Mikaelian, One-Dimensional Case in the Problem of a Number of Scatterings for Diffusion of Photons, *DAN Arm. SSR* **8**, No. 4 (1948).

exit at the depth τ with a subsequent passage through an additional layer of thickness $\Delta\tau$, with or without scattering in this layer. Obviously the probability of quantum exit without scattering in the additional layer is equal to $p(\tau, u)(1 - \Delta\tau)$. On the other hand, the probability of quantum exit with scattering in the additional layer can be obtained by multiplying the quantity $p(\tau, u')\Delta\tau$ by $p(0, u - u')du'$ and then integrating the product with respect to u' within the limits from 0 to u. As a result, we find

$$p(\tau + \Delta\tau, u) = p(\tau, u)(1 - \Delta\tau) + \Delta\tau \int_0^u p(\tau, u')p(0, u - u') \, du' \qquad (51)$$

Hence,

$$\frac{\partial p(\tau, u)}{\partial \tau} = -p(\tau, u) + \int_0^u p(\tau, u')p(0, u - u') \, du' \qquad (52)$$

Clearly Eq. (52) does not yet define the function $p(\tau, u)$ completely. We see this even from the fact that the mechanism of scattering is not implicit in Eq. (52). We assume that during an elementary act of scattering the probability of quantum "lifetime" is equal to λ, and that the probability of quantum emission in the time interval $(u, u + du)$ after an absorption is equal $e^{-u}du$. Then the quantity $p(0, u)$ becomes

$$p(0, u) = \frac{\lambda}{2}e^{-u} + \frac{\lambda}{2}\int_0^u e^{-u'}\rho(u - u') \, du' \qquad (53)$$

where

$$\rho(u) = \int_0^\infty e^{-\tau}p(\tau, u) \, d\tau \qquad (54)$$

The quantity $\rho(u)du$ represents the probability of quantum reflection by the medium in a time interval $(u, u + du)$ after the quantum fell on it.

We can easily obtain a single equation for the function $\rho(u)$ from Eqs. (52), (53), and (54) by multiplying both sides of Eq. (52) by $e^{-\tau}d\tau$ and integrating from 0 to ∞. Having done so, we find

$$-p(0, u) + \rho(u) = -\rho(u) + \int_0^u \rho(u')p(0, u - u') \, du' \qquad (55)$$

or after a differentiation with respect to u,

$$2\rho'(u) = p'(0, u) + \frac{\lambda}{2}\rho(u) + \int_0^u \rho(u')p'(0, u - u') \, du' \qquad (56)$$

But Eq. (53) provides that

$$p'(0, u) + p(0, u) = \frac{\lambda}{2} \rho(u) \qquad (57)$$

Inserting Eq. (57) into Eq. (56), we arrive at the required equation defining the function $\rho(u)$:

$$\rho'(u) + \left(1 - \frac{\lambda}{2}\right)\rho(u) = \frac{\lambda}{4}\int_0^u \rho(u')\rho(u-u')\,du' \tag{58}$$

To solve Eq. (58) we apply the Laplacean operator. Denoting

$$\bar{\rho}(s) = \int_0^\infty e^{-su}\rho(u)\,du \tag{59}$$

we obtain from Eq. (58):

$$-\frac{\lambda}{4} + s\bar{\rho}(s) + \left(1 - \frac{\lambda}{2}\right)\bar{\rho}(s) = \frac{\lambda}{4}\bar{\rho}^2(s) \tag{60}$$

or

$$\bar{\rho}(s) = \frac{2}{\lambda}(s+1) - 1 - \frac{2}{\lambda}\sqrt{(s+1)^2 - \lambda(s+1)} \tag{61}$$

Following the usual rules of operator calculus, we find from Eq. (61):

$$\rho(u) = \frac{2}{\pi}\lambda \int_0^1 e^{-(1-\lambda y)u}\sqrt{y(1-y)}\,dy \tag{62}$$

Having found the function $\rho(u)$, we can find analogously the function $p(\tau, u)$ also. Having applied the Laplacean operator to Eq. (52), we obtain

$$\frac{\partial \bar{p}(\tau, s)}{\partial \tau} = -\bar{p}(\tau, s)[1 - \bar{p}(0, s)] \tag{63}$$

Hence,

$$\bar{p}(\tau, s) = \bar{p}(0, s)e^{-\tau[1-p(0,s)]} \tag{64}$$

But the insertion of Eq. (62) into Eq. (53) makes the function $p(0, u)$ equal to

$$p(0, u) = \frac{\lambda}{\pi}\int_0^1 e^{-(1-\lambda y)u}\sqrt{\frac{1-y}{y}}\,dy \tag{65}$$

Hence,

$$\bar{p}(0, s) = 1 - \sqrt{1 - \frac{\lambda}{1+s}} \tag{66}$$

Placing Eq. (66) into Eq. (64), we find

$$\bar{p}(\tau, s) = \left(1 - \sqrt{1 - \frac{\lambda}{1+s}}\right)e^{-\tau\sqrt{1-[\lambda/(1+s)]}} \tag{67}$$

A solution of Eq. (67) is of the form:

$$p(\tau, u) = \frac{\lambda}{\pi}\int_0^1 e^{-(1-\lambda)u}\left(\sin\tau\sqrt{\frac{1-y}{y}} + \sqrt{\frac{1-y}{y}}\cos\tau\sqrt{}\right)dy\sqrt{\frac{1-y}{y}} \tag{68}$$

Having made here the substitution $y = 1/(1+x^2)$, we arrive at Eq. (29).

With the aid of the function $\rho(u)$ derived above, we are able to solve easily any problem in the luminescence of a medium illuminated by external light sources. If we let $I_0(u)$ be an intensity of radiation incident on a boundary of the medium from external light sources and $I(u)$ be an intensity of radiation emergent from the medium, we may evidently express the latter quantity $I(u)$ by means of the former $I_0(u)$ as follows:

$$I(u) = \int_0^u I_0(u')\rho(u-u')\, du' \qquad (69)$$

Assuming, for example, that during a time interval from $-\infty$ to 0 the intensity of radiation incident on the boundary of the medium remains constant, the illumination of the medium ceases. Then applying Eq. (69), the dimming of the medium will proceed in accordance with the law

$$I(u) = I_0 \int_u^\infty \rho(u)\, du \qquad (70)$$

Functional values of $\rho(u)$ are given in Table 9.1 for different values of the parameter λ and with an inaccuracy up to 2%.

TABLE 9.1. FUNCTION $\rho(u)$

u \ λ	0.1	0.2	0.3	0.4	0.5	0.6	0.7	0.8	0.9	1.0
0.0	0.025	0.049	0.074	0.099	0.123	0.148	0.173	0.197	0.222	0.246
0.2	0.020	0.041	0.062	0.084	0.106	0.129	0.152	0.175	0.199	0.223
0.4	0.017	0.035	0.053	0.072	0.092	0.112	0.133	0.156	0.179	0.203
0.6	0.014	0.029	0.045	0.060	0.079	0.098	0.116	0.139	0.161	0.185
0.8	0.011	0.024	0.038	0.052	0.068	0.085	0.104	0.125	0.145	0.168
1.0	0.009	0.020	0.032	0.045	0.059	0.073	0.091	0.111	0.131	0.154
1.2	0.008	0.017	0.027	0.038	0.051	0.065	0.081	0.099	0.119	0.141
1.4	0.006	0.014	0.023	0.033	0.044	0.057	0.072	0.089	0.108	0.129
1.6	0.005	0.012	0.019	0.028	0.038	0.050	0.063	0.079	0.098	0.119
1.8	0.004	0.010	0.016	0.024	0.033	0.044	0.056	0.071	0.089	0.110
2.0	0.004	0.008	0.014	0.020	0.028	0.038	0.050	0.064	0.081	0.102
2.2	0.004	0.007	0.012	0.017	0.024	0.033	0.044	0.053	0.074	0.095
2.4	0.003	0.006	0.010	0.015	0.021	0.029	0.039	0.052	0.068	0.088
2.6	0.003	0.005	0.008	0.013	0.018	0.026	0.035	0.047	0.061	0.082
2.8	0.002	0.004	0.007	0.011	0.016	0.023	0.031	0.043	0.057	0.076
3.0	0.002	0.003	0.006	0.009	0.014	0.020	0.028	0.040	0.053	0.071

We observe that for large u we have the following asymptotic representation:

$$\rho(u) = \frac{1}{u\sqrt{\pi\lambda u}} e^{-(1-\lambda)u} \qquad (71)$$

5. DIMMING OF THE MEDIUM

Knowledge of the function $p(\tau, u)$ enables us to solve any problem of luminescence for a given medium. Here we explore problems of medium dimming, that is, medium luminescence after radiation sources are shut off. As in the preceding section, we assume that $t_1 \gg t_2$ and we count the time from the moment when the radiation sources are shut off.

This problem may easily be solved in the following two instances.

1. We know the action of light sources during the entire time prior to their shutoff. In this case for the intensity of radiation emergent from medium, we have

$$I(u) = \int_0^\infty d\tau \int_{-\infty}^0 L(\tau, u')p(\tau, u-u') \, du' \tag{72}$$

where $L(\tau, u')d\tau du'$ is the energy coming directly from the light sources and absorbed between the optical depths τ and $\tau + d\tau$ in a time interval $(u', u' + du')$.

If the radiation sources are stationary, that is, the function L does not depend on u, we obtain, instead of Eq. (72),

$$I(u) = \int_0^\infty L(\tau) \, d\tau \int_0^\infty p(\tau, u') \, du' \tag{73}$$

Assume, for example, that the radiation falls on the medium from outside and with a constant intensity I_0. Then

$$L(\tau) = I_0 e^{-\tau}$$

and from Eq. (73) follows Eq. (70).

2. We know the distribution of energy in the medium at the moment when the light sources are shut off. In this case,

$$I(u) = \int_0^\infty R(\tau)p(\tau, u) \, d\tau \tag{74}$$

where $R(\tau)d\tau$ is the amount of energy enclosed between the optical depths from τ to $\tau + d\tau$ at the moment of time $u = 0$. It is obvious that the quantity $R(\tau)$ is connected with the function $B(\tau)$ by means of the relation

$$R(\tau) = \frac{2}{\lambda}B(\tau)$$

Assume, for example, that at the moment the light source is shut off,

$$R(\tau) = a_0 + a_1\tau \tag{75}$$

Then from Eq. (74),

$$I(u) = a_0 A_0(u) + a_1 A_1(u) \tag{76}$$

where

$$\left.\begin{aligned}
A_0(u) &= \int_0^\infty p(\tau, u)\,d\tau \\[2mm]
A_1(u) &= \int_0^\infty p(\tau, u)\tau\,d\tau
\end{aligned}\right\} \tag{77}$$

We first find the quantity $A_0(u)$. It appears that we do not have to know the function $p(\tau, u)$ but only the function $p(0, u)$. Indeed, Eq. (52) provides

$$-p(0, u) = -A_0(u) + \int_0^u A_0(u')p(0, u-u')\,du' \tag{78}$$

or, applying the Laplacean operator,

$$\bar{A}_0(s) = \frac{\bar{p}(0, s)}{1 - \bar{p}(0, s)} \tag{79}$$

Assuming that pure scattering occurs in the medium and inserting the value $\bar{p}(0, s)$ of Eq. (66) for $\lambda = 1$ in Eq. (79), we find

$$\bar{A}_0(s) = \sqrt{1 + \frac{1}{s}} - 1 \tag{80}$$

A solution of this equation has the form:

$$A_0(u) = \frac{1}{\pi} \int_0^1 e^{-yu} \sqrt{\frac{1-y}{y}}\,dy \tag{81}$$

Analogously, we find the quantity $A_1(u)$, namely:

$$A_1(u) = 1 - A_0(u) \tag{82}$$

Consequently the required radiation intensity $I(u)$ is equal to

$$I(u) = a_1 + \frac{a_0 - a_1}{\pi} \int_0^1 e^{-yu} \sqrt{\frac{1-y}{y}}\,dy \tag{83}$$

6. Brightness of a Nova
After Its Envelope Has Been Torn Off

Equation (83) may now be applied to one of the interesting problems connected with the question of brightness of novae. It is well known that during the outburst of a nova its envelope is first torn off and then gradually is dispersed into space. The question arises: What happens to the nova brightness after the separation of the envelope?

Consider this problem for a one-dimensional medium. Assuming that the medium has an infinitely large optical depth, we find that in a stationary state of the given medium the function $R(\tau) = 2B(\tau)$ is defined by the following formula:

$$R(\tau) = H(1+\tau) \qquad (84)$$

where H is the radiation flux.

Denoting now the optical thickness of the ripped-off layer by τ_* we find that the function $R(\tau)$ at the moment of envelope separation is equal to

$$R(\tau) = H(1+\tau_*+\tau) \qquad (85)$$

where τ is an optical depth counted from the new boundary of the medium.

After the separation of a layer of thickness τ_* the brightness of the medium will fall and at the same time the energy distribution in the medium will go over from Eq. (85) to Eq. (84).

By applying Eq. (83) to a case when the energy distribution in the medium is represented by Eq. (84), we obtain, as was expected,

$$I(u) = H \qquad (86)$$

However, when, at the initial moment of time, the energy distribution in the medium is given by Eq. (85), this quantity $I(u)$ will be equal to

$$I(u) = H\left(1+\frac{\tau_*}{\pi}\int_0^1 e^{-yu}\sqrt{\frac{1-y}{y}}\,dy\right) \qquad (87)$$

For large values of u, instead of Eq. (87), we have

$$I(u) = H\left(1+\frac{\tau_*}{\sqrt{\pi u}}\right) \qquad (88)$$

Equation (88) gives the required solution, that is, it defines the amount of energy emitted by the medium after the separation from it of a layer with optical thickness τ_*.

To be able to apply this formula to new stars, we have to know physical conditions at the place of envelope separation from the star. To determine these is difficult at the present time. We have made[6] approximate estimations and found that the optical thickness of the

[6] V. V. Sobolev, On the Theory of the Non-stationary Radiation Field, II, *Russian Astronomical J.* **29**, Bulletin 5 (1952).

envelope at the moment of separation is of the order of 10^8, the temperature at the point of separation of the order of 5×10^6 degrees, and the atom concentration of the order 2×10^{23} cm^{-3}. With these conditions, the quantity t_1 appears to be of the order of 10^{-8} sec, and with it $t_1 \gg t_2$.

Equation (88) enables us to determine the change of brightness of the star itself after the envelope separates from it. Let us find, for example, the brightness of the star several days after the original outburst. Because $u = t/t_1$, $t = 10^6$ sec, $t_1 = 10^{-8}$ sec, we put $u = 10^{14}$ and $t_* = 10^8$ in Eq. (88) and find that at the given time the star brightness is only about 10 times greater than the brightness before the outburst. In other words, the stellar surface temperature, which is 5,000,000° at the beginning of the outburst, decreases approximately to 100,000° at this time. If, however, we remember that after the envelope separation there begins an ejection of stellar matter which forms an extended photosphere, the star's surface temperature will be still lower.

We may also find the amount of energy emitted by the star in a given time interval by using Eq. (88). From the beginning of the outburst to the time moment u the star emits an energy of the order

$$H\tau_* \sqrt{u} \qquad\qquad (89)$$

The amount of energy emitted by the star within several days after the outburst and estimated with the aid of Eq. (89) is of the order of 10^{43} erg. In reality, however, the nova emits an energy of the order of $10^{44} - 10^{45}$ erg during this interval. The discrepancy between these numerical values cannot be removed by taking into account the energy within the envelope, for it also is of the same order, 10^{43} erg. We must, therefore, assume that either the dimming of the nova occurs much faster, due, for example, to the ejection of stellar matter, or that during the outburst other energy sources are effective.

In the theory of luminescence of novae, great interest attaches to the problem of envelope luminescence during the first period of the outburst. The envelope luminescence in this period is due to energy contained in the envelope at the start of outburst—the envelope decreases in brightness—as well as to energy coming to the envelope from the star itself. The difficulty consists in the fact that the optical properties of the envelope change with time. Particularly rapid is the change of optical thickness of the envelope. At the start of the outburst (minimum) it is of the order of 10^8, and at its end (maximum brightness of the nova) it is of the order of unity. Thus we meet a problem of radiation diffusion in a medium with variable optical properties.

An approximate solution of the luminescence problem in the expanding envelope of a nova and in the period from the start of the outburst to the moment of maximal brightness has been given elsewhere by the author.[7] He then assumed that the amount of energy contained in the envelope at the start of the outburst, the law of brightness variability of the star itself, and the law of change of optical thickness for the envelope were given. As a result he was able to determine the brightness change of the envelope, its visual magnitude, and its surface temperature during the course of time. In general, his results were in agreement with observation.

7. CHANGE OF IONIZATION WITH TIME

We shall consider one further problem which is connected with non-stationary luminescence of gaseous nebulae and star envelopes with bright lines in their spectra-stars of Be-type, novae, etc.

As is well known, the luminescence of these objects is caused by ultraviolet radiation of the stars. Ionization of atoms occurs u ider the impact of this radiation; it is followed by recombination and "cascade" electron transitions from level to level. These very transitions cause the appearance of bright lines in the observed part of the spectrum; thus, in particular, the bright Balmer lines of hydrogen are formed. The free electrons due to a photoionization may also excite atoms during a collision. In this way we have forbidden lines in spectra of nebulae.

In usual theoretical treatments of the luminescence of nebulae and stellar envelopes one presupposes that at any moment the number of recombinations is equal to the number of ionizations. In most cases such a supposition does not arouse any suspicion, because the intensity of high-frequency radiation causing atom ionization changes relatively slowly. In other instances, however, the intensity of the ionizing radiation changes rather rapidly, which brings with it a luminescence of the envelope without an ionization equilibrium.

In this section we consider a change of the degree of atomic ionization in an envelope under the impact of variable stellar radiation. For simplicity, we assume that the star temperature at first is small and then suddenly becomes great. Consequently the atoms in the envelope are not ionized before the outburst and the envelope does not shine. After the outburst, ionization of the atoms in the envelope sets in and leads to luminescence. This increase of brightness of the envelope continues as long as there is ionization equilibrium corresponding to the increased temperature of the star.

[7] V. V. Sobolev, On the Theory of the Brightness of New Stars, *Russian Astronomical J.* **31**, No. 1 (1954).

In solving this problem we shall consider two instances: (1) the optical thickness of the envelope beyond the limit of the ground series of atoms before outburst is smaller than unity—an envelope of small optical thickness, and (2) the same thickness is greater than unity—an envelope of large optical thickness.

Envelope of small optical thickness. Let $n_1(t)$ and $n^+(t)$ be the number of neutral and ionized atoms, respectively, in 1 cm³ at moment t, and let n be the total number of atoms in the given element 1 cm³; thus

$$n_1(t) + n^+(t) = n$$

At the initial moment, which we call the moment of outburst, $n_1(0) = n, n^+(0) = 0$.

The differential equation defining a change of ionization in the course of time has the form:

$$\frac{dn^+}{dt} = n_1 kH - n_e n^+ \sum_1^\infty C_i \tag{90}$$

Here H is the number of quanta beyond the ground series incident on 1 cm² of the envelope per second from the star, k is the absorption coefficient computed for one atom, n_e is the number of free electrons in 1 cm³, and $n_e n^+ C_1$ is the number capture of free electrons by ions for the ith level per cm³ per sec.

Let n_1^*, n_*^+, n_e^* be values of the corresponding quantities n_1, n^+, n_e in an equilibrium state. Obviously,

$$\frac{n_*^+}{n_1^*} = \frac{kH}{n_e^* \sum_1^\infty C_i} \tag{91}$$

As far as the concentration of free electrons is concerned, we may suggest two propositions: (1) the quantity n_e is given and is independent of time; and (2) the number of free electrons is equal to the number of ions ($n_e = n^+$). If the main purveyor of free electrons is hydrogen, the first of these propositions is realized by a consideration of atom ionization with an ionization potential above hydrogen while the hydrogen is completely ionized, and the second is realized by a consideration of hydrogen ionization.

For the fulfillment of the first proposition, a solution of Eq. (90) has the form

$$n^+(t) = n_*^+ \left[1 - e^{-n_e^* \sum_1^\infty C_i [1 + (n_*^+/n_1^*)]t} \right] \tag{92}$$

and for the fulfillment of the second one,

$$n^+(t) = n_*{}^+\frac{1-e^{-n_e*\sum\limits_1^\infty C_i[2+(n_*{}^+/n_1*)]t}}{1+\dfrac{n_1{}^*}{n}e^{-n_e*\sum\limits_1^\infty C_i[2+(n_*{}^+/n_1*)]t}} \tag{93}$$

Equations (92) and (93) show that the time for the establishment of ionization equilibrium is greater the smaller is the concentration of free electrons $n_e{}^*$ and the smaller is the ionization degree $n_*{}^+/n_1{}^*$ in an equilibrium state.

Envelope of large optical thickness. In this case the change in the number of ionized atoms in 1 cm³ and at the distance r from the center of star is defined by

$$\frac{dn^+}{dt} = n_1 k H e^{-\tau} - n_e n^+ \sum_2^\infty C_i \tag{94}$$

where τ is the optical distance of a given place from the internal envelope boundary, that is,

$$\tau = \int_{r_1}^r n_1 k \, dr \tag{95}$$

In Eq. (94) we have not considered captures at the first level nor ionization under the impact of diffuse radiation in the envelope, because these processes compensate each other.

For simplifying Eq. (94), we assume that the thickness of the envelope is considerably smaller than its distance from star, $r_2 - r_1 \ll r_1$. In this case the quantity H remains constant in the envelope.

Permitting $n_e = $ const, and letting

$$\frac{kH}{n_e \sum\limits_2^\infty C_i} = \gamma, \qquad t n_e \sum_2^\infty C_i = u \tag{96}$$

we have instead of (94)

$$\frac{dn^+}{du} = n_1 \gamma e^{-\tau} - n^+ \tag{97}$$

The quantity γ represents an ionization degree n^+/n_1 in an equilibrium state at the internal envelope boundary, that is, for $\tau = 0$.

With these assumptions it is easy to find the optical distance τ in the form of a function of dimensionless time u. Multiplying Eq. (97) by kdr and integrating from r_1 to r, we obtain

$$-\frac{d\tau}{du} = \gamma(1 - e^{-\tau}) - \tau_0 + \tau \tag{98}$$

where τ_0 is the optical distance of a given place at the initial time moment. From Eq. (11), we find

$$\int_\tau^{\tau_0} \frac{d\tau}{f(\tau)} = u \tag{99}$$

where

$$f(\tau) = \gamma(1 - e^{-\tau}) - \tau_0 + \tau \tag{100}$$

It is easy to find the ratio n_1/n as a function of the optical depth τ. From Eq. (97) and using Eq. (98), we obtain

$$\frac{dn_1}{d\tau} f(\tau) = n_1 f'(\tau) - n \tag{101}$$

where

$$\frac{n_1}{n} = f(\tau) \left\{ \frac{1}{f(\tau_0)} + \int_\tau^{\tau_0} \frac{d\tau}{f^2(\tau)} \right\} \tag{102}$$

Equations (99) and (102) define the degree of ionization as a function of u and τ_0, that is, of time and place in the envelope. As an example we have computed the quantity n_1/n for $\gamma = 100$. The result is given in Fig. 9.1 which shows the quantity n_1/n as a function of τ_0 for different values of u.

Equations (99) and (102) show, and Fig. 9.1 illustrates, that at any time the envelope may be divided into two regions: "ionized" ($n^+/n_1 > 1$) and "nonionized" ($n^+/n_1 < 1$) with a very sharp boundary between them. This boundary is approximately at $\tau \approx 1$. This result is completely understandable because so long as $\tau \gg 1$ for a given layer the ionizing radiation of the star does not reach it. Only when the optical thickness becomes of the order of unity due to an ionization in the layers nearer to the star does ionization start in a given layer.

Therefore, the process of gradual increase of ionization in the envelope may be regarded as boundary displacement between ionized and nonionized regions. This law of displacement is deduced from Eq. (99). Putting $\tau = 1$ in Eq. (99), we find:

$$\tau_0 = \gamma(1 - e^{-u}) \tag{103}$$

Generally speaking, the ionization reaches a place whose optical distance from the internal envelope boundary is equal to γ at the initial moment.

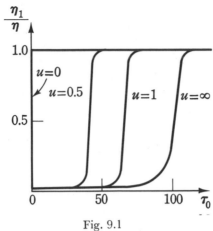

Fig. 9.1

From Eq. (103) it follows that, in the given case, the time of ionization equilibrium establishment ("relaxation time") is equal to

$$t_* = \frac{1}{n_e \sum\limits_2^\infty C_i} \tag{104}$$

We observe that the relaxation time is much larger for an envelope of large optical thickness than for one of small thickness (so long as $n_*^+/n_1^* \gg 1$), as we should have expected.

To estimate the relaxation time, we should know the quantity $\sum\limits_2^\infty C_i$. For a temperature about $10{,}000°$ it is $\approx 10^{-13}$ for hydrogen. This means that if $n_e \approx 10^6$, the relaxation time is about a year.

Increase of envelope brightness. An increase of ionized atoms in the envelope brings with it an increase of recombinations and, consequently, a strengthening of envelope luminescence in the spectral lines. The amount of energy emitted by the envelope per second in a line which corresponds to a transition from the kth level to the ith level is equal to

$$E_{ki} = A_{ki} h\nu_{ik} \frac{n_k}{n_e n^+} \int n_e n^+ \, dV \tag{105}$$

where A_{ki} is the Einstein coefficient of a spontaneous transition, $h\nu_{ik}$ is the quantum energy, n_k is the number of atoms in the kth state in

1 cm³, and dV is the volume element of the envelope. The quantity $n_k/n_e n^+$, which is a function of electron temperature, can be found from equations of stationarity for each discrete atomic level.

If the optical thickness of the envelope is smaller than unity before the star outburst, the entire envelope begins to shine immediately. An increase of envelope brightness is due to an increase in number of ionized atoms in each volume element. In a given instance, we have to substitute the expression in Eq. (92) for $n_e = $ const or the expression in Eq. (93) for $n_e = n^+$ into Eq. (105) and integrate over the entire envelope volume to derive the quantity E_{ki}.

If the optical thickness of the envelope is larger than unity before the outburst, only the parts in the vicinity of the star shine at first and later the more distant ones. A brightening of the envelope is, in this case, due to a gradual increase of the luminous volume.

Obviously, this kind of shining of an envelope with large optical thickness will take place not only with $n_e = $ const, but, as was shown above, also with $n_e = n^+$. Therefore, for both assumptions about n_e, the integral entering Eq. (105) is valid only for the shining or ionized region and may be written as

$$\int n_e n^+ \, dV = \bar{n}_e \mathcal{N}^+(t) \tag{106}$$

where $\bar{n}_e$ is an average concentration of free electrons in the shining region and $\mathcal{N}^+(t)$ is the total number of ionized atoms in this region. The quantity $\bar{n}_e$ may be regarded as independent of time but the quantity $\mathcal{N}^+(t)$ increases with time.

To obtain an equation defining $\mathcal{N}^+(t)$, we perform an integration of Eq. (94) over the volume of the envelope. Using Eq. (106), we find

$$\frac{d\mathcal{N}^+}{dt} = \bar{H} - \mathcal{N}^+ \bar{n}_e \sum_2^\infty C_i \tag{107}$$

where $\bar{H}$ is the total number of quanta emitted by the star beyond the limit of the ground series. From this and for $\mathcal{N}^+(0) = 0$, we obtain

$$\mathcal{N}^+(t) = \frac{\bar{H}}{\bar{n}_e \sum_2^\infty C_i} (1 - e^{-t\bar{n}_e \sum_2^\infty C_i}) \tag{108}$$

Knowledge of the quantity $\mathcal{N}^+(t)$ enables us to determine the amount of energy radiated by the envelope in a spectral line. Inserting Eqs. (106) and (108) into Eq. (105), we find

$$E_{ki} = A_{ki} h\nu_{ik} \frac{n_k \bar{H}}{n_e n^+ \sum\limits_2^\infty C_i} (1 - e^{-t\bar{n}_e \sum\limits_2^\infty C_i}) \qquad (109)$$

This is the formula which defines the quantity E_{ki} as a function of time t for a line occurring as a result of photoionization and recombination.

One example of the envelope shining in the absence of ionization equilibrium is Nova Herculis 1934 after the deep minimum in April. Prior to this minimum the star ejected matter violently during several months, forming an extended and rarefied envelope. In April the ejection suddenly weakened and a hot star with a temperature of about 70,000° was revealed. Under the impact of the stellar radiation the ionization process began in the envelope, a process which caused the appearance of a bright line spectrum characteristic of gaseous nebulae. This is why Nova Herculis began to brighten for the second time, a brightening which continued for more than a month. This brightening ceased when the light emitted by the envelope reached correspondence with the increased temperature of the star. The slow attainment of ionization equilibrium is, in this case, explained by the low density of the envelope.

The first theoretical interpretation of the brightness increase of Nova Herculis after the mininum in April was given by Grotrian.[8] However, he erroneously thought that ionization occurred simultaneously in the entire volume of the envelope. Later, the author[9] gave his interpretation based on an application of the formulas derived above. He showed that Eq. (109) represents the observed march of Balmer line intensities for $n_e \approx 3.10^6$ cm³. With the aid of the same formula he was also able to explain the unequal behavior of the red and the violet components of the emission lines.

Still later Minin[10] considered the change in electron temperature of the envelope in the course of time. Free electrons occurring due to photoionization gradually lose their kinetic energy during inelastic collisions with different atoms and ions. For a small density of matter the electron temperature changes pretty slowly and the change may be observed. Minin applied his formulas to the envelope of Nova

---

[8] W. Grotrian, Zur physikalischen Deutung der Lichtkurve der N Her, *Zs. f. Ap.* **13**, 215 (1937).

[9] V. V. Sobolev, On the Brightness of a Stellar Envelope in the Absence of Radiative Equilibrium, *Russian Astronomical J.* **27**, Bulletin 2 (1950).

[10] I. N. Minin, The Change of the Electron Temperature in Stellar Envelopes in the Absence of Radiative Equilibrium, *Russian Astronomical J.* **29**, Bulletin 2 (1952).

Herculis and was able to explain the change in the intensities of lines excited by electron collisions.

We may see also an envelope shining in the absence of ionized equilibrium in stars of class Be. It is known that these stars eject matter irregularly; when the ejection thrust decreases the number of quanta of high-frequency radiation reaching the envelope, receding from the star increases. Because of this the ionization of atoms in the envelope strengthens. Gorbatski[11] considered this process while paying attention not only to the ionization in the first state but also to the ionization in the second state; in other words, he solved a more general equation than Eq. (107). The result was a successful determination of the number of hydrogen atoms in the second state. Gorbatski connects the strengthening of atomic ionization in an envelope with the appearance of narrow absorption lines of the Balmer series in the spectra of some stars of class Be, in particular, Pleione.

Dimming of envelope. It is also interesting to consider not only the process of ionization strengthening in an envelope under the impact of a sudden flare-up, but the opposite process: ionization weakening in the envelope after the impact of radiation has ceased.

When the degree of ionization falls in the envelope there occurs an increase in the optical thickness of the envelope beyond the limit of the fundamental series of a given atom. When the given optical thickness remains at all times less than unity, the decrease of the number of ionized atoms is defined by

$$\frac{dn^+}{dt} = -n_e n^+ \sum_1^\infty C_i \tag{110}$$

When, however, the optical thickness of the envelope beyond the limit of the fundamental series becomes greater than unity, either from the very beginning or at a certain time, when using Eq. (110) we should take into consideration ionization under the impact of diffuse radiation due to electron captures in the first level. We may do this approximately by skipping the first term of the sum on the right-hand side of the equation.

We should like to emphasize that for any envelope thickness the ionization drop occurs simultaneously in all parts of the envelope.

From Eq. (110) it follows that

$$n^+(t) = n^+(0)e^{-t n_e \sum_1^\infty C_i} \tag{111}$$

[11] V. G. Gorbatski, On the Causes of the Appearance of Narrow Absorption Lines in Stellar Spectre of Class Be, *Russian Astronomical J.* **31**, Bulletin 6 (1959).

for n_e = const, and

$$n^+(t) = \frac{n^+(0)}{t n^+(0) \sum\limits_1^\infty C_i + 1}$$ (112)

for $n_e = n^+$.

A drop of ionization in an envelope is accompanied by its dimming in the continuum as well as in the spectral lines. To determine the amount of energy emitted by the envelope in a line we have to substitute Eq. (111) or (112) into Eq. (105).

We see that a considerable decrease in the number of ionized atoms in an envelope (and that means also a decrease in the amount of energy radiated by it) occurs within a time interval defined by Eq. (104). In gaseous nebulae $n_e \approx 10^3 - 10^4$ cm^{-3}. Consequently the time interval here appears to be of the order of several hundred years.

The withdrawal of the effect of a star on a nebula may be caused specifically by an initial ejection of matter from the star. In such case the layers nearer to the star are absorbing the high-frequency radiation of the star. When the amount of the matter ejected from the star is great, the star forms an extended photosphere around itself with a relatively low temperature. At the same time the shining of the nebula will go on for a long time corresponding to the high temperature. This is possibly the actual explanation for the shining of gaseous nebulae connected with rather cool stars.

CHAPTER 10

APPROXIMATE SOLUTION OF THE BASIC PROBLEM

In this chapter we return to the problem of scattering of mono-chromatic radiation in a plane layer illuminated by parallel rays, for a stationary case and with an arbitrary scattering indicatrix. We solved this problem in Chapter 3. Now we find an approximate solution of the same problem.[1-4]

We should remark that approximate solutions of this problem in the form of simple expressions are of great interest for many practical applications.

The main point of the method proposed in this chapter is that the first-order scattering is computed precisely, but the scattering of higher order, approximately; this is done by retaining only the first two terms of the expansion in Legendre polynomials of the scattering indicatrix. In this way we obtain formulas defining intensities of radiation scattered by a plane layer for any of its optical thickness, for any form of the scattering indicatrix, and for any reflecting property of the surface in contact with the layer.

The content of the chapter is as follows. First we consider a case of pure scattering, then the presence of true absorption. Formulas so obtained are applied to the atmospheres of the Earth and planets and to the sea.

1. THE CASE OF PURE SCATTERING

Consider a plane layer of optical thickness τ_0 illuminated by parallel rays incident at an angle $\theta_0 = \arccos \zeta$ to the normal with an azimuth ϕ_0.

We denote by πS the illumination of an area perpendicular to the rays on the upper boundary of the layer, and by $I(\tau, \eta, \phi)$ the required

[1] V. V. Sobolev, An Approximate Solution of the Problem of Light Scattering in a Medium with an Arbitrary Scattering Indicatrix, *Russian Astronomical J.* **20**, Nos. 5–6 (1943).

[2] V. V. Sobolev, On the Optical Properties of the Atmosphere of Venus, *Russian Astronomical J.* **21**, No. 5 (1944).

[3] V. V. Sobolev, On the Light Scattering in the Atmospheres of the Planets, *Annals Commemorative Sci. Sess. LGU* (1948).

[4] V. V. Sobolev, On the Light Scattering in the Atmospheres of the Earth and Planets, *Sci. Mem. LGU*, No. 116 (1949).

intensity of diffuse radiation coming from optical depth τ at the angle $\theta = \arccos \eta$ to the normal with an azimuth ϕ with the assumption that pure radiation scattering ($\lambda = 1$) occurs in the layer and that the radiation scattering indicatrix $x(\gamma)$ does not depend on depth.

We obtain equations defining the quantity $I(\tau, \eta, \phi)$ from Eq. (82) of Chapter 1 for $\lambda = 1$ as follows:

$$\eta \frac{dI(\tau, \eta, \phi)}{d\tau} = -I(\tau, \eta, \phi) + B(\tau, \eta, \phi) \tag{1a}$$

$$B(\tau, \eta, \phi) = \frac{1}{4\pi} \int_0^{2\pi} d\phi' \int_{-1}^{+1} I(\tau, \eta', \phi') x(\gamma') \, d\eta' + \frac{S}{4} x(\gamma) e^{-\tau/\zeta} \tag{1b}$$

where

$$\cos \gamma' = \eta\eta' + \sqrt{(1-\eta^2)(1-\eta'^2)} \cos(\phi - \phi') \tag{2a}$$

$$\cos \gamma = \eta\zeta + \sqrt{(1-\eta^2)(1-\zeta^2)} \cos(\phi - \phi_0) \tag{2b}$$

For boundary conditions, we have

$$I(0, \eta, \phi) = 0 \quad \text{for} \quad \eta > 0 \tag{3a}$$

$$I(\tau_0, \eta, \phi) = 0 \quad \text{for} \quad \eta < 0 \tag{3b}$$

which express the absence of scattered radiation incident on the layer from the boundaries.

First we consider the case of the simplest nonspherical scattering indicatrix,

$$x(\gamma) = 1 + x_1 \cos \gamma \tag{4}$$

where x_1 is a certain parameter. In such a case, we obtain from Eq. (1b):

$$B(\tau, \eta, \phi) = I(\tau) + x_1 \bar{H}(\tau)\eta + x_1 \bar{G}(\tau) = \sqrt{1-\eta^2} \cos(\phi - \phi_0)$$

$$+ \frac{S}{4}[1 + x_1\eta\zeta + x_1\sqrt{(1-\eta^2)(1-\zeta^2)} \cos(\phi - \phi_0)] e^{-\tau/\zeta} \tag{5}$$

Here

$$I(\tau) = \frac{1}{4\pi} \int_0^{2\pi} d\phi' \int_{-1}^{+1} I(\tau, \eta', \phi') \, d\eta' \tag{6}$$

$$\bar{H}(\tau) = \frac{1}{4\pi} \int_0^{2\pi} d\phi' \int_{-1}^{+1} I(\tau, \eta', \phi')\eta' \, d\eta' \tag{7}$$

$$\bar{G}(\tau) = \frac{1}{4\pi} \int_0^{2\pi} \cos(\phi' - \phi_0) \, d\phi' \int_{-1}^{+1} I(\tau, \eta', \phi')\sqrt{1-\eta'^2} \, d\eta' \tag{8}$$

Obviously,

$$\int_0^{2\pi} \sin(\phi' - \phi_0) \, d\phi' \int_{-1}^{+1} I(\tau, \eta', \phi') \sqrt{1 - \eta'^2} \, d\eta' = 0$$

due to the symmetry of the function $I(\tau, \eta', \phi')$ in respect to $\phi' - \phi_0$.

The quantity $\bar{I}(\tau)$ is an average intensity of the diffuse radiation at optical depth, τ, $4\pi\bar{H}(\tau)$ is the flux of the diffuse radiation in the direction of increased depth, and $4\pi G(\tau)$ is the same in the direction $\phi = \phi_0$ in a horizontal plane.

We see that for the scattering indicatrix, Eq. (4), the function $B(\tau, \eta, \phi)$ may be represented as follows:

$$B(\tau, \eta, \phi) = B'(\tau, \eta) + B''(\tau, \eta)\cos(\phi - \phi_0) \tag{9}$$

and, as follows from the equation of radiative transfer, the function $I(\tau, \eta, \phi)$ may analogously be written

$$I(\tau, \eta, \phi) = I'(\tau, \eta) + I''(\tau, \eta)\cos(\phi - \phi_0) \tag{10}$$

The quantities $I'(\tau, \eta)$ and $I''(\tau, \eta)$ may easily be obtained independently of each other from the following equations:

$$\eta \frac{dI'(\tau, \eta)}{d\tau} = -I'(\tau, \eta) + \bar{I}(\tau) + x_1 \bar{H}(\tau)\eta + \frac{S}{4}(1 + x_1\eta\zeta)e^{-\tau/\zeta} \tag{11}$$

where

$$\bar{I}(\tau) = \frac{1}{2} \int_{-1}^{+1} I'(\tau, \eta) \, d\eta, \qquad \bar{H}(\tau) = \frac{1}{2} \int_{-1}^{+1} I'(\tau, \eta)\eta \, d\eta \tag{12}$$

and

$$\eta \frac{dI''(\tau, \eta)}{d\tau} = -I''(\tau, \eta) + x_1 \bar{G}(\tau) \sqrt{1 - \eta^2} + \frac{S}{4}x_1\sqrt{(1 - \eta^2)(1 - \zeta^2)}e^{-\tau/\zeta} \tag{13}$$

where

$$\bar{G}(\tau) = \frac{1}{4} \int_{-1}^{+1} I''(\tau, \eta) = \sqrt{1 - \eta^2} \, d\eta \tag{14}$$

Obviously, the same boundary conditions of Eqs. (3) are valid for the quantities I' and I'' as for the quantity I.

Consider first the solution of Eq. (11). For this, as before (Chapter 2, Section 3), we employ an approximate relation

$$\frac{1}{2} \int_{-1}^{+1} I'(\tau, \eta)\eta^2 \, d\eta = \frac{1}{3} \bar{I}(\tau) \tag{15}$$

and express the boundary conditions approximately in the form

$$2\bar{H}(0) = -\bar{I}(0), \qquad 2\bar{H}(\tau_0) = \bar{I}(\tau_0) \tag{16}$$

Integrating both sides of Eq. (11) with respect to η in the limits from -1 to $+1$, we obtain

$$\frac{d\bar{H}(\tau)}{d\tau} = \frac{S}{4}e^{-\tau/\zeta} \tag{17}$$

hence,

$$\bar{H}(\tau) = F - \frac{S}{4}e^{-\tau/\zeta}\zeta \tag{18}$$

The integration constant $4\pi F$ represents the total radiation flux, that is, the sum of the diffuse and direct radiation.

Multiplying both sides of Eq. (11) by η and integrating with respect to η in the limits from -1 to $+1$, we find

$$\frac{1}{2}\frac{d}{d\tau}\int_{-1}^{+1} I'(\tau,\eta)\eta^2\,d\eta = -\bar{H}(\tau) + \frac{x_1}{3}\bar{H}(\tau) + \frac{x_1}{12}Se^{-\tau/\zeta} \tag{19}$$

From this, and recollecting Eqs. (15) and (18), we conclude that

$$\bar{I}(\tau) = C - (3-x_1)F\tau - \frac{3}{4}Se^{-\tau/\zeta}\zeta^2 \tag{20}$$

where C is the new integration constant.

The constants C and F are found from boundary conditions, Eq. (16). These conditions provide:

$$C = \frac{S\zeta}{2}(1 + \frac{3}{2}\zeta) - 2F \tag{21}$$

$$[4 + (3-x_1)\tau_0]F = \frac{S\zeta}{2}R(\tau_0, \zeta) \tag{22}$$

where

$$R(\tau_0, \zeta) = 1 + \frac{3}{2}\zeta + (1 - \frac{3}{2}\zeta)e^{-\tau_0/\zeta} \tag{23}$$

Thus we have determined both quantities $\bar{I}(\tau)$ and $\bar{H}(\tau)$, containing the function $I'(\tau, \eta)$ under the integral sign. Inserting their expressions obtained in Eq. (11), we find

$$\eta\frac{dI'(\tau,\eta)}{d\tau} = -I'(\tau,\eta) + C + x_1 F\eta - (3-x_1)F\tau + \frac{S}{4}(1 - 3\zeta^2)e^{-\tau/\zeta} \tag{24}$$

Integration of this equation gives us the required function $I'(\tau, \eta)$, that is, the radiation intensity averaged over the azimuth.

Analogously we may solve Eq. (13). We mention the final result, however, only in passing. The function $I''(\tau, \eta)$ decreases very rapidly with increasing τ so that at great optical depths the radiation intensity may be considered as independent of the azimuth. But in reference to the surface layers the same function $I''(\tau, \eta)$ is essentially determined by the scattering of the first order in these layers and with not very large values of x_1. Therefore we assume $\overline{G} = 0$ and derive $I''(\tau, \eta)$ from the equation

$$\eta \frac{dI''(\tau, \eta)}{d\tau} = -I''(\tau, \eta) + \frac{S}{4} x_1 \sqrt{(1-\eta^2)(1-\zeta^2)} e^{-\tau/\zeta} \qquad (25)$$

Using Eqs. (24) and (25) we obtain the following equation defining the radiation intensity $I(\tau, \eta, \phi)$:

$$\eta \frac{dI(\tau, \eta, \phi)}{d\tau} = -I(\tau, \eta, \phi) + C + x_1 F\eta - (3 - x_1) F\tau$$

$$+ \frac{S}{4}[1 - 3\zeta^2 + x_1 \sqrt{(1+\eta^2)(1-\zeta^2)} \cos(\phi - \phi_0)] e^{-\tau/\zeta} \qquad (26)$$

Assume now that the scattering indicatrix $x(\gamma)$ is arbitrary. Then we compute the scattering of the first order precisely, but in determining the scattering of higher order we employ only the first two terms in the expansion of the scattering indicatrix in Legendre polynomials. In other words, in computing the scattering of higher order we employ a scattering indicatrix of Eq. (4) in which

$$x_1 = \frac{3}{2} \int_0^\pi x(\gamma) \cos \gamma \sin \gamma \, d\gamma \qquad (27)$$

This, in accordance with previous statements, we must subtract from the right-hand side of Eq. (26) a term which takes into account the scattering of the first order with a scattering indicatrix $1 + x_1 \cos\gamma$, and add a corresponding term for the given scattering indicatrix in order to obtain an equation defining the quantity $I(\tau, \eta, \phi)$ for any form of the scattering indicatrix $x(\gamma)$. As a result we arrive at the following equation:

$$\eta \frac{dI(\tau, \eta, \phi)}{d\tau} = -I(\tau, \eta, \phi) + C + x_1 F\eta - (3 - x_1) F\tau$$

$$- \frac{S}{4}(3\zeta^2 + x_1 \eta \zeta) e^{-\tau/\zeta} + \frac{S}{4} x(\gamma) e^{-\tau/\zeta} \qquad (28)$$

Integration of Eq. (28) with boundary conditions of Eq. (3) gives

$$I(\tau, \eta, \phi) = (C + 3F\eta)[e^{-(\tau_0 - \tau)/\eta} - e^{-\tau_0/\eta}] - (3 - x_1) F\tau e^{-(\tau_0 - \tau)/\eta}$$

$$+ \frac{S}{4}[x(\gamma) - 3\zeta^2 - x_1 \eta \zeta][e^{\tau[(1/\eta) - (1/\zeta)]} - 1] e^{-\tau_0/\eta} \frac{\zeta}{\eta - \zeta} \qquad (29)$$

for radiation coming down from above, and

$$I(\tau, -\eta, \phi) = (C - 3F\eta)(e^{-\tau/\eta} - e^{-\tau_0/\eta}) - (3 - x_1)F(\tau e^{-\tau/\eta} - \tau_0 e^{-\tau_0/\eta})$$

$$+ \frac{S}{4}[x(\gamma) - 3\zeta^2 + x_1\eta\zeta][e^{-\tau[(1/\eta)+(1/\zeta)]} - e^{-\tau_0[(1/\eta)+(1/\zeta)]}]\frac{\zeta}{\eta + \zeta} \quad (30)$$

for that coming upward from below. In the second case, we have replaced η by $-\eta$ so that in both cases $\eta > 0$. In Eq. (29), $\cos \gamma$ is determined by the second of Eqs. (2); and in Eq. (30),

$$\cos \gamma = -\eta\zeta + \sqrt{(1 - \eta^2)(1 - \zeta^2)}\cos(\phi - \phi_0) \quad (31)$$

From Eqs. (29) and (30), we obtain the following expressions for the intensity of radiation emergent from the medium:

$$I(\tau_0, \eta, \phi) = (C + 3F\eta)(1 - e^{-\tau_0/\eta}) - (3 - x_1)F\tau_0$$

$$+ \frac{S}{4}[x(\gamma) - 3\zeta^2 - x_1\eta\zeta](e^{-\tau_0/\zeta} - e^{-\tau_0/\eta})\frac{\zeta}{\zeta - \eta} \quad (32)$$

$$I(0, -\eta, \phi) = (C - 3F\eta)(1 - e^{-\tau_0/\eta}) + (3 - x_1)F\tau_0 e^{-\tau_0/\eta}$$

$$+ \frac{S}{4}[x(\gamma) - 3\zeta^2 + x_1\eta\zeta][1 - e^{-\tau_0[(1/\eta)+(1/\zeta)]}]\frac{\zeta}{\eta + \zeta} \quad (33)$$

The constants C and F entering these equations are determined by Eqs. (21) and (22). Utilizing them, and also going over from the radiation intensities $I(\tau_0, \eta, \phi)$ and $I(0 - \eta, \phi)$ to the brightness coefficients $\sigma(\eta, \zeta, \phi)$ and $\rho(\eta, \zeta, \phi)$ by means of the equalities

$$I(\tau_0, \eta, \phi) = S\sigma(\eta, \zeta, \phi)\zeta, \qquad I(0, -\eta, \phi) = S\rho(\eta, \zeta, \phi)\zeta \quad (34)$$

we find, instead of Eqs. (32) and (33):

$$\sigma(\eta, \zeta, \phi) = \frac{R(\tau_0, \eta)R(\tau_0, \zeta)}{4 + (3 - x_1)\tau_0} - \frac{1}{2}(e^{-\tau_0/\eta} + e^{-\tau_0/\zeta})$$

$$+ [x(\gamma) - (3 + x_1)\eta\zeta]\sigma_1(\eta, \zeta) \quad (35)$$

$$\rho(\eta, \zeta, \phi) = 1 - \frac{R(\tau_0, \eta)R(\tau_0, \zeta)}{4 + (3 - x_1)\tau_0} + [(3 + x_1)\eta\zeta - 2(\eta + \zeta) + x(\gamma)]\rho_1(\eta, \zeta)$$

$$\quad (36)$$

Here $\sigma_1(\eta, \zeta)$ and $\rho_1(\eta, \zeta)$ are brightness coefficients conditioned by the first-order scattering with a spherical scattering indicatrix:

$$\sigma_1(\eta, \zeta) = \frac{1}{4}\frac{e^{-\tau_0/\eta} - e^{-\tau_0/\zeta}}{\eta - \zeta}, \qquad \rho_1(\eta, \zeta) = \frac{1}{4}\frac{1 - e^{-\tau_0[(1/\eta)+(1/\zeta)]}}{\eta + \zeta} \quad (37)$$

As is known, the brightness coefficients should be symmetrical functions of angles of incidence and reflection (transmission); our approximate Eqs. (35) and (36) satisfy this condition.

A comparison of Eqs. (35) and (37) with the precise formulas for the quantities ρ and σ shows that the approximate formulas give an inaccuracy of the order of 10%.

Equations (35) and (36) may be rewritten as

$$\left.\begin{array}{l} \sigma(\eta, \zeta, \phi) = x(\gamma)\sigma_1(\eta, \zeta) + \Delta\sigma(\eta, \zeta) \\ \rho(\eta, \zeta, \phi) = x(\gamma)\rho_1(\eta, \zeta) + \Delta\rho(\eta, \zeta) \end{array}\right\} \qquad (38)$$

where the terms $x(\gamma)\sigma_1(\eta, \zeta)$ and $x(\gamma)\rho_1(\eta, \zeta)$ represent scattering of the first order, and the terms $\Delta\sigma(\eta, \zeta)$ and $\Delta\rho(\eta, \zeta)$ denote scattering of higher order. In an earlier article[4] the author has given accurate tables of the quantities σ_1, ρ_1, $\Delta\sigma$ and $\Delta\rho$ for different values of τ_0, η, ζ, and x_1.

2. Calculation of Light Reflection by a Surface

A medium which scatters radiation is usually limited by a surface which in turn reflects the radiation. As an example of this, the atmosphere of a planet, with its surface as the lower boundary of the atmosphere, may serve. To calculate the reflection at the surface we must give the corresponding boundary conditions instead of those given by Eqs. (3) and (16).

Supposing that the limiting surface is below, and that it reflects the radiation isotropically, and assuming that the albedo, A, of the surface does not depend on the angle, we conclude that, if the illumination of the surface is equal to E, the intensity of the radiation reflected by the surface will be

$$I = \frac{A}{\pi}E$$

In our case the surface is illuminated by radiation coming directly from the light sources and diminished in the medium, as well as by the diffuse radiation of the medium. Therefore the intensity of the radiation reflected by the surface is equal to

$$I_2 = \frac{A}{\pi}\left[\int_0^{2\pi} d\phi \int_0^1 I(\tau_0, \eta, \phi)\eta \, d\eta + \pi S e^{-\tau_0/\zeta}\zeta\right] \qquad (39)$$

Letting I_1 be an average intensity of diffuse radiation incident on the surface, we may rewrite this equation in the form:

$$I_2 = A(I_1 + S e^{-\tau_0/\zeta}\zeta) \qquad (40)$$

Our present task is to interconnect the values of $\bar{I}$ and $\bar{H}$ at the boundary. Approximately we have

$$\bar{I} = \tfrac{1}{2}(I_1 + I_2), \qquad \bar{H} = \frac{1}{4}(I_1 - I_2) \tag{41}$$

hence,

$$I_1 = \bar{I} + 2\bar{H}, \qquad I_2 = \bar{I} - 2\bar{H} \tag{42}$$

Inserting Eq. (42) into Eq. (40), we obtain

$$\bar{I} - 2\bar{H} = A(\bar{I} + 2\bar{H} + Se^{-\tau_0/\zeta}\zeta) \tag{43}$$

Equation (43) is the required boundary condition for $\tau = \tau_0$. It is obvious that for $\tau = 0$ the boundary condition remains the first of the interrelationships, Eq. (16).

We shall find the constants C and D for the same boundary conditions. The first of the conditions in Eq. (16) leads to the interrelation in Eq. (21), whereas Eq. (43) provides

$$2F = \frac{(1 - A)R(\tau_0, \zeta)S\zeta}{4 + (3 - x_1)(1 - A)\tau_0} \tag{44}$$

Thus, in order to obtain the intensity of radiation emergent from a medium, we must introduce the constants C and F which are determined from Eqs. (21) and (44) into Eqs. (32) and (33) and, in addition, in the right-hand side of Eq. (33) we should add the term

$$A(\bar{I} + 2\bar{H} + Se^{-\tau_0/\zeta}\zeta)e^{-\tau_0/\eta}$$

which represents radiation reflected by the surface and emerging from the medium without scattering.

As a result, for the brightness coefficients of a medium limited by a reflecting surface, we find

$$\bar{\sigma}(\eta, \zeta, \phi) = \frac{[(1 - A)R(\tau_0, \eta) + 2A]R(\tau_0, \zeta)}{4 + (3 - x_1)(1 - A)\tau_0} - \frac{1}{2}(e^{-\tau_0/\eta} + e^{-\tau_0/\zeta})$$

$$+ [x(\gamma) - (3 + x_1)\eta\zeta]\sigma_1(\eta, \zeta) \tag{45}$$

$$\bar{\rho}(\eta, \zeta, \phi) = 1 - \frac{(1 - A)R(\tau_0, \eta)R(\tau_0, \zeta)}{4 + (3 - x_1)(1 - A)\tau_0}$$

$$+ [(3 + x_1)\eta\zeta - 2(\eta + \zeta) + x(\gamma)]\rho_1(\eta, \zeta) \tag{46}$$

Comparing Eqs. (35) and (36) with Eqs. (45) and (46), we see that the latter may be obtained from the former by introducing the corrections:

$$\bar{\sigma} - \sigma = \frac{A}{1 - A\dfrac{(3 - x_1)\tau_0}{4 + (3 - x_1)\tau_0}} \cdot \frac{2R(\tau_0, \zeta)}{4 + (3 - x_1)\tau_0} \left[1 - \frac{R(\tau_0, \zeta)}{4 + (3 - x_1)\tau_0}\right] \quad (47)$$

$$\bar{\rho} - \rho = \frac{A}{1 - A\dfrac{(3 - x_1)\tau_0}{4 + (3 - x_1)\tau_0}} \cdot \frac{2R(\tau_0, \zeta)}{4 + (3 - x_1)\tau_0} \cdot \frac{2R(\tau_0, \eta)}{4 + (3 - x_1)\tau_0} \quad (48)$$

We observe that the quantity

$$\frac{2R(\tau_0, \zeta)}{4 + (3 - x_1)\tau_0}$$

represents a ratio of the illumination of the lower boundary to that of the upper boundary from above, but the quantity

$$1 - \frac{R(\tau_0, \zeta)}{4 + (3 - x_1)\tau_0}$$

is the ratio of the illumination of the upper boundary from below to that from above (with $A = 0$). Intercomparing Eq. (47) and (49) with the precise formulas derived in Chapter 7, Section 3, we see that the approximate and the accurate expressions are the same in their structure for $\bar{\sigma} - \sigma$ and $\bar{\rho} - \rho$.

We should emphasize that the above formulas are justified only on the supposition that the scattering indicatrix does not change in the medium. However, in many media (for example, the Earth's atmosphere) the scattering indicatrix changes with dependence on the optical depth. In such cases the quantity $x(\gamma)$ of the given formulas comprises a certain average indicatrix of scattering. A generalization of these formulas was derived by Gutshabash[5] for $x(\gamma)$ depending on τ. Krat[6] and Kusnetsov[7] have also considered the problem of light scattering in a medium with variable optical properties.

3. Application to the Earth's Atmosphere

We may assume to a first approximation that pure scattering of radiation occurs in the earth's atmosphere. Therefore we may apply the foregoing formulas to the Earth's atmosphere. Now we give some examples of such applications.

[5] S. D. Gutshabash, The Light Scattering in a Medium with a Changing Scattering Indicatrix, *Sci. Mem. LGU*, No. 153 (1952).

[6] V. A. Krat, Certain Problems in the Theory of Light Scattering in the Earth Atmosphere, *Russian Astronomical J.* **19**, No. 1 (1942).

[7] E. S. Kuznetsov, The Theory of the Non-horizontal Visibility, *Izv. AN SSSR, series geogr.-geophys.*, No. 5 (1943).

1. *Illumination of the Earth's atmosphere.* Let E_0 be an illumination of the upper boundary of the atmosphere, and E, that of the Earth's surface produced by direct solar radiation, as well as by the light scattering by the sky. With our notations

$$E_0 = \pi S \zeta \tag{49}$$

For determination of the quantity E we point out that the total radiation flux is equal to $4\pi F$. At the lower boundary of the atmosphere this flux represents a difference of the illumination E and the energy reflected by the surface AE. Therefore, we have

$$(1 - A)E = 4\pi F \tag{50}$$

But the quantity F is given by Eq. (44). Hence,

$$E = \frac{2R_0(\tau_0, \zeta)}{4 + (3 - x_1)(1 - A)\tau_0} E_0 \tag{51}$$

This simple formula defines in fact the total illumination of the Earth's atmosphere.

Now let E_1 be an illumination of the Earth's atmosphere produced by the direct solar radiation. Obviously,

$$E_1 = E_0 e^{-\tau_0/\zeta} \tag{52}$$

The part of the direct solar radiation in the total illumination of the Earth's atmosphere is found by the division of Eq. (52) by Eq. (51).

The quantity A entering Eq. (51) is the albedo of the Earth's surface. In summer $A \approx 0.1 - 0.2$, the albedo of the topsoil and the foliage; in winter $A \approx 0.7 - 0.8$—the albedo of the snow. Equation (51) shows that during the winter the illumination of the Earth's atmosphere is greater than in the summer and for the same τ_0 and ζ.

Several other authors have also proposed approximate formulas for the total illumination of the earth's atmosphere: Kastrov,[8] Gordov,[9] and others.

An intercomparison of all these formulas and ours, Eq. (51) was made by Mahotkin.[10]

2. *Brightness of the sky.* The relative distribution of brightness over the sky is given by the brightness coefficient $\sigma(\eta, \zeta, \phi)$ defined by Eq. (45); in our case the quantities entering it have the following meaning:

---

[8] V. G. Kastrov, Certain Questions in the Theory of Light Scattering in a Pure Atmosphere, *J. Geophys.*, No. 2 (1933).

[9] A. N. Gordov, On the Possible Application of the Theory of Light Scattering to the Real Atmosphere, *J. Geophys.*, No. 4 (1936).

[10] L. G. Mahotkin, On Methods of Computation of the Scattered Illumination in a Clear Sky, *Izv. AN SSSR, series geophys.*, No. 5 (1953).

γ is an angle between the direction to the given point on the sky and that to the Sun; θ and ϕ are the zenith distance and azimuth of the given point on the sky, respectively; θ_0 and ϕ_0 are the zenith distance and azimuth of the Sun, $\cos \theta = \eta$, $\cos \theta_0 = \zeta$.

For a uniformly overcast sky and for a large optical cloud thickness, Eq. (45) provides

$$\bar{\sigma}(\theta, \theta_0) = \frac{(1 + \frac{3}{2}\cos\theta_0)[(1 - A)(1 + \frac{3}{2}\cos\theta) + 2A]}{4 + (3 - x_1)(1 - A)\tau_0} \tag{53}$$

This formula shows that the relative brightness distribution over an overcast sky does not depend on the form of the scattering indicatrix but depends only on the albedo of the Earth's atmosphere. For $A \approx 0$ the sky brightness decreases with an increase of the zenith distance and does so proportionally to $1 + \frac{3}{2}\cos\theta$. For $A \approx 1$ the brightness of the sky remains everywhere the same.

3. *Determination of the scattering indicatrix.* We may find the scattering indicatrix of the Earth's atmosphere by comparing an observed brightness distribution over the sky with the theoretical one. To do so we have to find the coefficients of sky brightness from observations at different angular distances from the sun and for moderate altitudes of the sun above the horizon.

Let σ' be the ratio of the brightness at a given sky point to that of a white screen placed horizontally. The previously introduced brightness coefficient equals this quantity σ' multiplied by E/E_0, because σ refers to the illumination E_0 on the upper boundary of the atmosphere, and σ' refers to that of the total light of the Sun and the sky on its lower boundary. Therefore, instead of Eq. (35), we have

$$\sigma'\frac{E}{E_0} = x(\gamma)\sigma_1 + \Delta\sigma \tag{54}$$

When we cannot neglect the light reflection from the Earth's atmosphere we should set the term $\bar{\sigma} - \sigma$ defined by Eq. (46) into the right-hand side of Eq. (54).

In order to determine the quantities E/E_0, σ_1, and $\Delta\sigma$ entering Eq. (54) we have to find the optical thickness of the Earth's atmosphere τ_0 from observation. This we may do in the usual manner—by measuring the brightness of direct solar rays passed through the atmosphere and at different zenith distances of the Sun. Another simpler but less accurate method for the determination of τ_0 consists in measuring the ratio of the illumination by the direct solar radiation E_1 to the total illumination E and in comparing this ratio with a theoretical value E_1/E as derived from Eqs. (51) and (52).

When the quantity τ_0 is known, the quantities E/E_0, σ_1, and $\Delta\sigma$ may be determined by employing the above derived formulas or the tables given in the author's treatise.[4] By placing the values of these quantities into Eq. (54) and utilizing the values of σ' found from observation, we may find the scattering indicatrix $x(\gamma)$. Because the quantity $\Delta\sigma$ depends on the parameter x_1, we must determine this parameter approximately at first, and more precisely later after we have found the scattering indicatrix.

For a criterion of the correctness of observations performed and computations made, we may use the normalization condition of the scattering indicatrix:

$$\frac{1}{2}\int_0^\pi x(\gamma)\sin\gamma \, d\gamma = 1 \tag{55}$$

In this way the scattering indicatrix of the Earth's atmosphere was determined in the town of Elabuge in the summer of 1943. As a result, ten scattering indicatrixes were obtained, which were very similar to each other. We could have expected that the indicatrix would increase as τ_0 grew; but due to the small variation of τ_0 in our observations (from 0.19 to 0.23) this dependence could not have been determined with assurance, although there was a definite indication of it. Therefore we obtained only an indicatrix that was an average for all ten. It is given in Table 10.1.

TABLE 10.1 SCATTERING INDICATRIX OF THE EARTH'S ATMOSPHERE

γ	0	15	30	45	60	75	90	105	120	135	150	165	180°
$x(\gamma)$	4.6	3.3	1.9	1.3	0.94	0.75	0.64	0.65	0.72	0.85	1.03	1.1	1.2

The quantity x_1 appeared to be 0.63 for this indicatrix.

We should point out that if we had paid attention to the scattering of the first order only we should have obtained a scattering indicatrix almost without a "gnawing" (indentation) around $\gamma = 100°$. This is quite understandable because in these directions where $x(\gamma)$ is small the sky brightness essentially depends on scattering of higher orders and they should not be neglected.

Many authors have determined the scattering indicatrix of the Earth's atmosphere by taking into account scattering of the first order only. Several papers were published by Piaskovskaia-Fesenkova,[11,12]

[11] E. V. Piaskovskaia-Fesenkova, On the Asymmetry of the Atmospheric Scattering Indicatrix, *DAN SSSR* **73**, No. 2 (1950).

[12] E. V. Piaskovskaia-Fesenkova, The Dependence of the Light Scattering in the Atmosphere on the Wave Length, *DAN SSSR* **80**, No. 4 (1951).

who determined the scattering indicatrix for different wavelengths. Krat[13] proposed a simple empirical formula for the scattering indicatrix of the Earth's atmosphere employing his own observations.

4. Light Behavior in the Presence of True Absorption

In Section 1 we considered the luminescence of a medium illuminated by parallel rays, for the case of a pure scattering. Now we suppose that in addition to the scattering in the medium there occurs a true absorption of radiation, that is $\lambda < 1$. For simplicity we assume that the optical thickness of medium is infinitely large ($\tau_0 = \infty$).

The starting equations in this case are

$$\eta \frac{dI(\tau, \eta, \phi)}{d\tau} = -I(\tau, \eta, \phi) + B(\phi, \eta, \phi)$$

$$B(\tau, \eta, \phi) = \frac{\lambda}{4\pi} \int_0^{2\pi} d\phi' \int_{-1}^{+1} I(\tau, \eta', \phi') x(\gamma') \, d\eta' + x(\gamma)\frac{\lambda}{4} S e^{-\tau/\zeta} \quad (56)$$

where the angles γ and γ' are defined by Eqs. (2).

As in Section 1 we first propose that the scattering indicatrix has the form $x(\gamma) = 1 + x_1 \cos \gamma$. Then the radiation intensity $I(\tau, \eta, \phi)$ is given by Eq. (10) and the quantities $I'(\tau, \eta)$ and $I''(\tau, \eta)$ are defined by the following equations:

$$\eta \frac{dI'(\tau, \eta)}{d\tau} = -I'(\tau, \eta) + \lambda \bar{I}(\tau) + \lambda x_1 \bar{H}(\tau) \eta$$

$$+ \frac{\lambda S}{4}(1 + x_1 \eta \zeta) e^{-\tau/\zeta} \quad (57)$$

$$\eta \frac{dI''(\tau, \eta)}{d\tau} = -I''(\tau, \eta) + \lambda x_1 \bar{G}(\tau) \sqrt{1 - \eta^2}$$

$$+ \frac{\lambda S}{4} x_1 \sqrt{(1 - \eta^2)(1 - \zeta^2)} e^{-\tau/\zeta} \quad (58)$$

which are only a generalization of Eqs. (11) and (13).

We now find the quantities $\bar{I}(\tau)$, $\bar{H}(\tau)$, and $\bar{G}(\tau)$ entering Eqs. (57) and (58). From Eq. (57) we obtain

$$\frac{d\bar{H}(\tau)}{d\tau} = -(1 - \lambda) \bar{I}(\tau) + \lambda \frac{S}{4} e^{-\tau/\zeta} \quad (59)$$

[13] V. A. Krat, The Scattering Indicatrix of Light in the Earth Atmosphere, *Russian Astronomical J.* **20**, Bulletins 5–6 (1943).

and with the assumption that Eq. (15) is correct,

$$\frac{d\bar{I}(\tau)}{d\tau} = -(3-\lambda x_1)\bar{H}(\tau) + \lambda\frac{S}{4}x_1 e^{-\tau/\zeta}\zeta \tag{60}$$

Equations (59) and (60) provide

$$\frac{d^2\bar{I}(\tau)}{d\tau^2} = (3-\lambda x_1)(1-\lambda)\bar{I}(\tau) - [3+(1-\lambda)x_1]\frac{\lambda S}{4}e^{-\tau/\zeta} \tag{61}$$

A solution of Eqs. (61) which satisfies the condition $\bar{I} \to 0$ for $\tau \to \infty$ has the form

$$\bar{I}(\tau) = Ce^{-k\tau} + De^{-\tau/\zeta} \tag{62}$$

where

$$k^2 = (3-\lambda x_1)(1-\lambda) \tag{63}$$

$$= -\frac{3+(1-\lambda)x_1}{1-k^2\zeta^2}\zeta^2\frac{\lambda S}{4} \tag{64}$$

and C is an arbitrary constant. In order to determine this constant C, we employ the boundary condition $\bar{I}(0) = -2\bar{H}(0)$.

Inserting Eq. (62) into Eq. (60), we find

$$(3-\lambda x_1)\bar{H}(\tau) = kCe^{-k\tau} + \left(\frac{1}{\zeta}D + \frac{\lambda S}{4}x_1\zeta\right)e^{-\tau/\zeta} \tag{65}$$

Therefore, the afore-mentioned boundary conditions give

$$C(3-\lambda x_1 + 2k) = -\frac{\lambda S}{2}x_1\zeta - D\left(3-\lambda x_1 + \frac{2}{\zeta}\right) \tag{66}$$

or remembering Eq. (64), we obtain

$$C = \frac{\lambda S}{4}\frac{\zeta}{3-\lambda x_1 + 2k}\left\{\frac{3+(1-\lambda)x_1}{1-k^2\zeta^2}[2+(3-\lambda x_1)\zeta] - 2x_1\right\} \tag{67}$$

To find the quantity $\bar{G}(\tau)$, we utilize the approximate relation

$$\bar{G}(\tau) = \frac{\pi}{16}\int_{-1}^{+1}I''(\tau,\eta)\,d\eta \tag{68}$$

Then, from Eq. (58), we obtain

$$\frac{d^2\bar{G}(\tau)}{d\tau^2} = k_1^2\bar{G}(\tau) - \frac{3\pi^2}{128}\lambda Sx_1\sqrt{1-\zeta^2}\,e^{-\tau/\zeta} \tag{69}$$

where

$$k_1^2 = 3\left(1 - \frac{\pi^2}{32}\lambda x_1\right) \tag{70}$$

A solution of Eq. (69), with the condition $G \to 0$ for $\tau \to \infty$ and $G = (2/3)dG/d\tau$ for $\tau = 0$, has the form:

$$\bar{G}(\tau) = C_1 e^{-k_1 \tau} + D_1 e^{-\tau/\zeta} \tag{71}$$

where

$$D_1 = -\frac{3\pi^2}{128} \lambda S x_1 \frac{\zeta^2 \sqrt{1 - \zeta^2}}{1 - k_1 \zeta^2} \tag{72}$$

$$C_1 = -D_1 \frac{3 + (2/\zeta)}{3 + 2k_1} \tag{73}$$

After the determination of the quantities $\bar{I}(\tau)$, $\bar{H}(\tau)$, and $\bar{G}(\tau)$, the radiation intensities $I'(\tau, \eta)$ and $I''(\tau, \eta)$ are easily found with the aid of an integration of Eqs. (57) and (58).

Now we propose that the scattering indicatrix $x(\gamma)$ is arbitrary. In this case, as in Section 1, we calculate the scattering of the first order precisely and the scattering of higher order only approximately by preserving only the first two terms in the expansion of the scattering indicatrix in Legendre polynomials. Therefore, the function $B(\tau, \eta, \phi)$ is represented in the form:

$$B(\tau, \eta, \phi) = \lambda \bar{I}(\tau) + \lambda x_1 \bar{H}(\tau)\eta + \lambda x_1 \bar{G}(\tau) \sqrt{1 - \eta^2} \cos(\phi - \phi_0)$$
$$+ \frac{\lambda}{4} S x(\gamma) e^{-\tau/\zeta} \tag{74}$$

where the parameter x_1 is defined by Eq. (27).

We now take Eqs. (62), (65), and (71) for the quantities $\bar{I}(\tau)$, $\bar{H}(\tau)$, and $\bar{G}(\tau)$ entering Eq. (74). Substituting the expression found for $B(\tau, \eta, \phi)$ into the equation of radiative transfer and integrating it, we obtain the required intensities of radiation scattered by the medium.

Employing the formulas indicated, we now find the intensity of radiation emergent from the medium (that is, the intensity of radiation diffusely reflected by the medium). By going over from the radiation intensity $I(0, \eta, \phi)$ to the brightness coefficient $\rho(\eta, \tau, \phi)$ with the aid of the second relation of Eq. (34), we have

$$S\rho(\eta, \zeta, \phi)\zeta = \int_0^\infty B(\tau, -\eta, \phi) e^{-\tau/\eta} \frac{d\tau}{\eta} \tag{75}$$

where η implies the cosine of the angle of reflection.

Inserting Eq. (74) into Eq. (75) provides

$$\rho(\eta, \zeta, \phi) = \lambda \frac{S}{4} \frac{x(\gamma)}{\eta + \zeta} + A(\eta, \zeta) + A_1(\eta, \zeta)\cos(\phi - \phi_0) \tag{76}$$

where

$$A(\eta, \zeta) = \frac{\lambda}{S\zeta} \int_0^\infty [\bar{I}(\tau) - x_1 \bar{H}(\tau)\eta] e^{-\tau/\eta} \frac{d\tau}{\eta} \tag{77}$$

$$A_1(\eta, \zeta) = \frac{\lambda}{S\zeta} x_1 \sqrt{1 - \eta^2} \int_0^\infty \bar{G}(\tau) e^{-\tau/\eta} \frac{d\tau}{\eta} \tag{78}$$

Completing the integration and making some transformations, we obtain

$$A(\eta, \zeta) = \frac{\lambda^2}{4} \frac{1}{1 + k\eta} \frac{1}{1 + k\zeta} \frac{1}{3 - \lambda x_1 + 2k} \frac{1}{\eta + \zeta} \{2(3 - \lambda x_1)(\eta + \zeta)$$
$$+ [3 + (1 - \lambda)x_1][3 + (1 - \lambda)x_1 + 2k]\eta\zeta - 2kx_1\eta\zeta$$
$$- 2kx_1(\eta^2 + \zeta^2) - 2kx_1^2(1 - \lambda)\eta^2\zeta^2 - x_1^2\eta\zeta(1 + k\eta)(1 + k\zeta)\} \tag{79}$$

$$A_1(\eta, \zeta) = \frac{\lambda^2}{4} x_1^2 \frac{3\pi^2}{32} \frac{\sqrt{(1 - \eta^2)(1 - \zeta^2)}}{(3 + 2k_1)(1 + k_1\eta)(1 + k_1\zeta)} \left[2 + (3 + 2k_1)\frac{\eta\zeta}{\eta + \zeta} \right] \tag{80}$$

Equations (76), (79), and (80) define in fact the required coefficient of brightness for a medium with an infinitely large optical thickness in the presence of true absorption.

We may remark that the above formulas permit us to compute the brightness coefficient also for the case of pure scattering. For this we have to set $\lambda = 1$. Because in this case $k = 0$ the expression for $A(\eta, \zeta)$ is greatly simplified and is reduced to the form:

$$A(\eta, \zeta) = \frac{1}{2} \frac{3 + x_1}{4} \frac{\eta\zeta}{\eta + \zeta} \tag{81}$$

Omitting the last term in Eq. (76), for $\lambda = 1$ we find

$$\rho(\eta, \zeta, \phi) = \frac{1}{4} \frac{x(\gamma)}{\eta + \zeta} + \frac{1}{2} + \frac{3 + x_1}{4} \frac{\eta\zeta}{\eta + \zeta} \tag{82}$$

It is easy to see that Eq. (82) is identical with Eq. (36) for $\tau_0 = \infty$ which was derived without taking into account the dependence of scatterings of higher order on the azimuth. The last term of Eq. (76) represents this dependence and therefore this formula is more accurate than Eq. (82).

5. Optical Properties of Planetary Atmospheres

In the theory of transport of radiant energy we determine the intensities of radiation scattered by a medium with given optical properties. In investigation of the planetary atmospheres we are confronted with an opposite problem. Here we actually know from observations the intensities of radiation scattered by the atmosphere and we are required to find the optical properties of the atmosphere by way of comparison of observation with theory. In Section 3 it was shown how the optical properties of the atmosphere may be determined from observations of sky brightness (the scattering indicatrix $x(\gamma)$ and the optical thickness τ_0). Now we consider the problem of finding the optical properties of the atmosphere by observing the brightness of the planet.

All planets may be divided into two groups in accordance with the optical thickness of the atmosphere. Some of them, like Venus, Jupiter, and Saturn, possess an atmosphere whose optical thickness is large compared to unity. Here we do not see the surface of the planet. Other planets are surrounded by an atmosphere of moderate thickness. Mars may serve as an example of this: its surface is visible through its atmosphere.

We start our investigation with the first group. The most suitable planet of this group is Venus which may be observed at all possible phase angles. Assuming the optical thickness of the Venus atmosphere to be infinitely large, we at once make an application of our recent results to this planet.

Because the albedo of Venus is less than unity (~ 0.6), true absorption of light plays some part in its atmosphere. If we assumed that the scattering indicatrix is spherical, λ would be equal to 0.95 for the indicated albedo. However we may expect that the scattering indicatrix in the Venus atmosphere is elongated forward; consequently the quantity λ will approach unity still more than for the spherical scattering indicatrix (see Chapter 3, Section 3). Therefore we shall neglect quantities of the order $1-\lambda$.

Omitting now the terms of the order $1-\lambda$ in Eq. (79) we find

$$A(\eta, \zeta) = \frac{1}{2} + \frac{3+x_1}{4} \frac{\eta \zeta}{\eta + \zeta} - \frac{1}{4} \sqrt{\frac{1-\lambda}{3-x_1}} (2+3\eta)(2+3\zeta) \qquad (83)$$

Eq. (80) can be approximately written as follows:

$$A_1(\eta, \zeta) = \frac{x_1^2}{2(3 + 2\sqrt{3-x_1})} \sqrt{(1-\eta^2)(1-\zeta^2)} \qquad (84)$$

Employing Eq. (76) where the quantities $A(\eta, \zeta)$ and $A_1(\eta, \zeta)$ are defined by Eqs. (83) and (84), or by the more precise Eqs. (79) and (80), we may find the distribution of brightness over the planet's disk at any phase angle. By comparing the theoretical distribution of brightness with that observed at different phase angles, we may find the scattering indicatrix $x(\gamma)$ and the quantity λ in the planetary atmosphere.

To determine the optical properties of a planetary atmosphere we might also have used the stellar magnitude m of the planet depending on the phase angle α. To obtain a theoretical relation between m and α we express the angles η, ζ and $\phi - \phi_0$ in Eq. (76) by the planetocentric

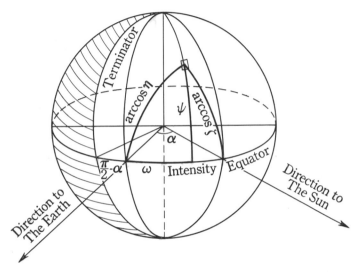

Fig. 10.1

coordinates ω, ϕ and the phase angle α (Fig. 10.1). The phase angle is the angle at the planet between the direction to the Sun and that to the Earth. Since $\gamma = \pi - \alpha$, Eq. (31) gives

$$\cos \alpha = \eta\zeta - \sqrt{(1-\eta^2)(1-\zeta^2)}\cos(\phi - \phi_0) \qquad (85)$$

Further, using Fig. 10.1 we find

$$\zeta = \cos\phi\cos(\alpha - \omega) \qquad \eta = \cos\phi\cos\omega \qquad (86)$$

Let πS be the illumination of an area perpendicular to the solar rays at the upper limit of the Venus atmosphere. Then the intensity of radiation diffusely reflected by the atmosphere equals $S\rho(\eta, \zeta, \phi)$ and the amount of energy coming from the element of area $d\sigma$ per unit solid angle is equal to $S\rho(\eta, \zeta, \phi)\zeta\eta d\sigma$. Since $d\sigma = a^2 \cos \psi \, d\psi \, d\omega$, where a is the radius of the planet, this amount of energy may be written in the form:

$$Sa^2\rho(\eta, \zeta, \phi)\cos(\alpha - \omega)\cos\omega\cos^3\psi \, d\phi \, d\omega \qquad (87)$$

In order to obtain the entire amount of energy coming from Venus in the Earth's direction per unit solid angle, we have to integrate Eq. (87) with respect to ψ in the limits $(-\pi/2, +\pi/2)$ and with respect to ω in the interval $(\alpha - \pi/2, \pi/2)$, that is, from the terminator to the limb of the disc. Denoting by Δ the distance of Venus from the Earth, for the illumination of the Earth from Venus, we obtain

$$E_V = 2S\frac{a^2}{\Delta^2}\int_{\alpha-(\pi/2)}^{(\pi/2)} \cos(\alpha-\omega)\cos\omega\,d\omega \int_0^{(\pi/2)} \rho(\eta,\zeta,\phi)\cos^3\psi\,d\psi \quad (88)$$

Since the illumination of the Earth from the Sun equals $E_S = \pi S(r/R)^2$, where r is the distance of the Sun from Venus, R is the distance of the Sun from the Earth, and $(E_V/E_S) = 2.512^{m_\odot - m}$, where $m_\odot$ is the stellar magnitude of the Sun, we find

$$2{,}512^{m_\odot - m}$$

$$= \frac{2}{\pi}\left(\frac{Ra}{r\Delta}\right)^2 \int_{\alpha-(\pi/2)}^{(\pi/2)} \cos(\alpha-\omega)\,\cos\omega\,d\omega \int_0^{(\pi/2)} \rho(\eta,\zeta,\phi)\cos^3\phi\,d\phi \quad (89)$$

If we introduce the expression for $\rho(\eta, \zeta, \phi)$ into Eq. (89), we should obtain the required theoretical relation between the stellar magnitude of the planet m and the phase angle α.

Using Eqs. (76), we obtain, instead of Eq. (89),

$$x(\pi - \alpha)f(\alpha) + g(\alpha) = h(\alpha) \quad (90)$$

where the notations are introduced:

$$f(\alpha) = \frac{1}{4}\int_{\alpha-(\pi/2)}^{(\pi/2)} \frac{\cos\omega\cos(\alpha-\omega)}{\cos\omega + \cos(\alpha-\omega)}\,d\omega \int_0^{(\pi/2)} \cos^2\phi\,d\phi$$

$$= \frac{\pi}{16}\left[1 - \sin\frac{\alpha}{2}\,\mathrm{tg}\,\frac{\alpha}{2}\,\ln\mathrm{ctg}\,\frac{\alpha}{4}\right] \quad (91)$$

$$g(\alpha) = \int_{\alpha-(\pi/2)}^{(\pi/2)} \cos\omega\cos(\alpha-\omega)\,d\omega \int_0^{(\pi/2)} [A(\eta,\zeta)$$

$$+ A_1(\eta,\zeta)\cos(\phi-\phi_0)]\cos^3\phi\,d\phi \quad (92)$$

$$h(\alpha) = \frac{\pi}{2}\left(\frac{r\Delta}{Ra}\right)^2 2.512^{m_\odot - m} \quad (93)$$

The quantity $h(\alpha)$ depends only on observational data and the quantity $g(\alpha)$ depends not only on the phase angle α but also on the quantities λ and x_1.

With the aid of Eq. (90) and recollecting the formulas

$$\frac{1}{2}\int_0^\pi x(\gamma)\sin\gamma\,d\gamma = 1 \qquad \frac{3}{2}\int_0^\pi x(\gamma)\cos\gamma\sin\gamma\,d\gamma = x_1 \quad (94)$$

we may determine the scattering indicatrix $x(\gamma)$ and the parameter x_1 in the planetary atmosphere if we know the stellar magnitude of the planet observed as a function of the phase angle.

According to Russell's formula the stellar magnitude of Venus can be expressed in the form:

$$m = -4.71 + 0.01322\alpha + 0.000000425\alpha^2 \tag{95}$$

in the limits from $\alpha = 24°$ to $\alpha = 156°$, when Venus is at its mean distance from the Sun and at the Astronomical Unit from the Earth; the stellar magnitude of the Sun is equal to $m_\odot = 26^m.72$.

The scattering indicatrix found with these data is tabulated in Table 10.2 for the Venus atmosphere. Numbers in parentheses are extrapolations. In order to obtain the scattering indicatrix more accurately it is necessary to observe Venus at phase angles near to $0°$ and $180°$.

TABLE 10.2. SCATTERING INDICATRIX FOR THE VENUS ATMOSPHERE

γ	0	15	30	45	60	75	90	105	120	135	150	165	180°
(γ)	(7.2)	(6.0)	2.70	1.50	1.00	0.67	0.51	0.40	0.35	0.41	0.56	(0.65)	(0.70)

It appeared that the ratio of the true absorption coefficient to the sum of the same coefficient and the scattering coefficient is equal to $\lambda = 0.989$ for the Venus atmosphere.

Comparing Tables 10.1 and 10.2, we see that the scattering indicatrix of the Earth's atmosphere is very similar to that of Venus and also to those atmospheres which are computed on the basis of Mie theory. This means first of all that our derived formulas are sufficiently accurate, since in their derivation we made no assumptions whatever about the form of the scattering indicatrix.

However, the scattering indicatrix of the Venus atmosphere is more elongated forward than the scattering indicatrix of the Earth's atmosphere (for the former $x_1 = 1.3$ and for the latter $x_1 = 0.63$). This means that the scattering by large particles plays a more important part in the Venus atmosphere than in the Earth's atmosphere.

The afore-mentioned data about the optical properties of the Venus atmosphere were obtained by the author[2]. Later a similar investigation was made by Barabashev and Eserskii.[14] In their study they employed our Eqs. (90) and (94), and the light curve of Venus as

[14] N. P. Barabashev and V. I. Eserskii, Photometry of Venus, *Izv. AN Kaz SSR*, No. 90 (1950).

obtained by Danjon. The scattering indicatrix found by them appeared in general similar to ours, given in Table 10.2, yet still more elongated forward (for it $x_1 = 1.7$ but $\lambda = 0.995$). Barabashev and Eserskii have also computed a distribution of brightness over the Venus disc utilizing the quantities $x(\gamma)$ and λ derived by the author and, having compared it with the observed distribution of brightness, established a satisfactory agreement between the values. Shingarev,[15] who investigated the same question, came to the same conclusion. Because all these investigators had at their disposal results of photometric observations of Venus in different wavelengths (obtained by Barabashev) they were able in the analysis mentioned above to reach some more elegant conclusions about the optical phenomena in the Venus atmosphere.

The determination of the optical properties of the atmospheres of Jupiter and Saturn is attended by great difficulties because the phase angle of these planets hardly changes. However, we may hope that by performing a sufficiently accurate photometry of these two planets it may be possible to determine the parameters λ and x_1 for their atmospheres.

While determining the optical properties of the Mars atmosphere, which has a moderate optical thickness, we should at the same time determine the actual optical properties of the planet. This increase of the number of the required parameters greatly complicates an interpretation of the photometric observations of Mars. In addition, the phase angle of Mars changes over a relatively small interval, from $0°$ to $47°$.

Sitinskaia[16] studied Mars and she obtained photographs of Mars in different wavelengths during the great opposition in 1939. An interpretation of the observations was made by means of the approximate formulas for the brightness coefficients given in Section 2. The scattering indicatrix of the Mars atmosphere was assumed to be known, in one form, Rayleigh's, and in another, that given in Table 10.1 for the Earth's atmosphere. As a result she determined the optical thickness of the Mars atmosphere for different wavelengths. It turned out that this thickness is about 0.05 for the visual part of the spectrum.

[15] L. I. Shingarev, On the Question of the Part Played by Light Scattering in the Atmosphere of Venus, *Publ. Astr. Obs. HGU*, No. 8 (1948); *Annals Astr. Obs. HGU* **1** (9) (1950).

[16] N. N. Sitinskaia, Photometric Investigation of the Planet Mars, *Annals Commemorative Sci. Sess. LGU* (1948).

6. Application to the Optics of the Sea

The formulas derived above may be applied not only to gaseous objects but also to liquids. We are especially interested in their application to bodies of water, in particular to the sea.

The sea is illuminated by the direct radiation of the Sun as well as by that scattered by the atmosphere. The radiation incident on the sea is partly reflected by it and partly penetrates it. Some of the quanta, having entered the sea, emerge from it after some scattering in the sea. The intensity of radiation emergent from the sea is comparable with the intensity of radiation reflected by the sea. This is a consequence of the fact that different seas have different color.

We may regard the optical thickness of the sea as infinitely large. Therefore, for the determination of the diffuse radiation intensity of the sea we may employ the formulas obtained in Section 4.

For simplicity we assume that the sea is illuminated only by the Sun's rays. The rays entering the sea are refracted at the boundary. In the future we understand by ζ the cosine of the angle at which the rays pass after a refraction and by πS, the illumination caused by them on an area perpendicular to them.

The process of light scattering in the sea is described by Eqs. (56). With the approximation adopted by us for the function $B(\tau, \eta, \phi)$, we obtained Eq. (74), in which the quantities $\bar{I}(\tau)$, $\bar{H}(\tau)$, and $\bar{G}(\tau)$ are defined by Eqs. (62), (65), and (71), respectively.

But the constants C and C_1 entering the indicated formulas should be derived from new boundary conditions. These conditions should express the fact that the radiation approaching the sea surface from beneath it may be reflected specularly from it, that is, may suffer an internal reflection. If radiation of intensity I is approaching the surface at the angle arccos η to the normal, the intensity of the reflected radiation will be $r(\eta)I_1$, where the function $r(\eta)$ is defined by the formula of Fresnel. For $\eta < \eta_0$ where arccos η_0 is the angle of total internal reflection, $r(\eta) = 1$.

We first write approximately the boundary conditions which take into account the internal reflection, assuming that the intensities I' and I'' of the radiation incident on the boundary are independent of the direction. Then,

$$\bar{I}(0) = \frac{1}{2} I' \left[1 + \int_0^1 r(\eta) \, d\eta \right] \tag{96}$$

$$\bar{H}(0) = \frac{1}{2} I' \left[-\frac{1}{2} + \int_0^1 r(\eta)\eta \, d\eta \right] \tag{97}$$

Hence,

$$I(0) = -R\bar{H}(0) \tag{98}$$

where

$$R = \frac{1 + \int_0^1 r(\eta)\, d\eta}{\frac{1}{2} - \int_0^1 r(\eta)\eta\, d\eta} \tag{99}$$

Analogously, we find

$$\bar{G}(0) = \frac{R}{3}\left(\frac{dG}{d\tau}\right)_{\tau=0} \tag{100}$$

A computation with Eq. (99) gives $R = 6.7$ for the sea. In the absence of the internal reflection we should have $r = 0$, $R = 2$, and from Eqs. (98) and (100) we should get the boundary conditions which we imposed earlier.

With the aid of the boundary conditions in Eqs. (98) and (100), we have for the constants C and C_1:

$$C(3 - \lambda x_1 + Rk) = -R\frac{\lambda S}{4}x_1\zeta - D\left(3 - \lambda x_1 + \frac{R}{\zeta}\right) \tag{101}$$

$$C_1 = -D_1\frac{3 + (R/\zeta)}{3 + Rk_1} \tag{102}$$

The function $B(\tau, \eta, \phi)$ in this case equals

$$B(\tau, \eta, \phi) = \lambda(Ce^{-k\tau} + De^{-\tau/\zeta}) + \frac{\lambda x_1\eta}{3 - \lambda x_1}\left[kCe^{-k\tau}\right.$$

$$\left. + \left(\frac{D}{\zeta} + \frac{\lambda S}{4}x_1\zeta\right)e^{-\tau/\zeta}\right] + \lambda x_1(C_1 e^{-k_1\tau}$$

$$+ D_1 e^{-\tau/\zeta})\sqrt{1 - \eta^2}\cos(\phi - \phi_0) + \frac{\lambda S}{4}x(\gamma)e^{-\tau/\zeta} \tag{103}$$

where the constants C and C_1 are defined by Eqs. (101) and (102).

Utilizing this equation for the function $B(\tau, \eta, \phi)$ and the radiative transfer equation, we may determine the radiation intensity at any optical depth. For example, with $\tau = 0$, we have

$$I(0, -\eta, \phi) = \lambda\left(\frac{C}{1 + k\eta} + \frac{D\zeta}{\eta + \zeta}\right)$$

$$- \frac{\lambda x_1\eta}{3 - \lambda x_1}\left(\frac{kC}{1 + k\eta} + \frac{D + \frac{\lambda S}{4}x_1\zeta^2}{\eta + \zeta}\right) + \lambda x_1\left(\frac{C_1}{1 + k_1\eta} + \frac{D_1\zeta}{\eta + \zeta}\right)$$

$$\times \sqrt{1 - \eta^2}\cos(\phi - \phi_0) + \frac{\lambda S}{4}x(\gamma)\frac{\zeta}{\eta + \zeta} \qquad (\eta > 0) \tag{104}$$

Equation (104) gives the intensity of radiation approaching the sea surface from beneath. In order to find the intensity of radiation emergent from the sea, we have to multiply Eq. (104) by the quantity $[1 - r(\eta)] n^2$, where n is the refractive index of the atmosphere with respect to water, and then calculate the directional change of the ray due to refraction (see Chapter 7, Section 8).

We may also determine the march of light in the deeper layers of the sea for $\tau \gg 1$ with the aid of Eq. (103). In this case, only the terms with the factor $e^{-k\tau}$ are preserved in the expression of the function $B(\tau, \eta, \phi)$, that is,

$$B(\tau, \eta) = b(\eta) e^{-k\tau} \tag{105}$$

where

$$b(\eta) = \lambda C\left(1 + \frac{k x_1 \eta}{3 - \lambda x_1}\right) \tag{106}$$

and

$$k = \sqrt{(1 - \lambda)(3 - \lambda x_1)} \tag{107}$$

Therefore, for the radiation intensity at optical depth τ, we obtain

$$I(\tau, \eta) = \frac{b(\eta)}{1 - k\eta} e^{-k\tau} \tag{108}$$

Here $\eta > 0$ for the radiation passing from above downward and $\eta < 0$ for that passing from below upward.

From the fact that we can go over from Eq. (103) to Eq. (105) while considering the deep layers of the sea, we may draw two conclusions: (1) The intensity of the direct solar radiation is small in comparison with that of the diffuse radiation in the deep layers; and (2) the intensity of the diffuse radiation is independent of the azimuth in these layers.

These conclusions are justified only when $k < 1/\zeta$. For water, the quantity k is small due to the strong extension forward of the scattering indicatrix and the proximity of the parameter λ to unity; therefore the inequality indicated is satisfied. If the values of the parameters x_1 and λ were small, we could find $k > 1$ by determining it from Eq. (17). However, such a result is connected with the fact that Eq. (107) is approximate. Treating this question accurately, the inequality $k < 1$ always holds, that is, the conclusions drawn above will always be correct.

We remind ourselves that the precise treatment of the problem of the light regime in the deep layers of a medium of infinitely large optical thickness was accomplished in Chapter 3, Section 6. We showed there that the functions $B(\tau, \eta)$ and $I(\tau, \eta)$ are expressed by

Eqs. (105) and (108) and that the quantity k, with scattering indicatrix $x(\gamma) = 1 + x_1\cos\gamma$, is defined by the following equation

$$\frac{\lambda}{2k}\left(1 + x_1\frac{1-\lambda}{k^2}\right)\lg\frac{1+k}{1-k} - \lambda x_1\frac{1-\lambda}{k^2} = 1 \tag{109}$$

For the small values of k we obtain, instead of Eq. (109),

$$\lambda k^2 = (1-\lambda)(3-\lambda x_1) \tag{110}$$

which for values of λ near to unity becomes Eq. (107).

The formulas derived above may be employed in solutions of various problems about the optics of the sea. We give now two examples.

1. Consider an object immersed in the sea. Generally speaking the object causes a disturbance of the march of light and therefore it can be discerned. We ask what kind of reflective property an object should possess in order not to be seen.

For simplicity we assume that the object is a thin plate horizontally placed and reflecting the radiation incident upon it specularly. The intensity of radiation incident on the upper surface of the object at the angle arccos η to the normal, accordingly to Eqs. (106) and (108), is equal to

$$I(\tau, \eta) = \left(1 + \frac{kx_1\eta}{3 - \lambda x_1}\right)\frac{\lambda C}{1 - k\eta}\,e^{-k\tau} \tag{111}$$

That the object should not be seen it is necessary that the intensity of radiation reflected by the object should be expressed by the formula

$$I(\tau, -\eta) = \left(1 - \frac{kx_1\eta}{3 - \lambda x_1}\right)\frac{\lambda C}{1 + k\eta}\,e^{-k\tau} \tag{112}$$

that is, the reflection coefficient of the upper surface of the object should be equal to

$$r_*(\eta) = \frac{3 - \lambda x_1 - kx_1\eta}{3 - \lambda x_1 + kx_1\eta} \cdot \frac{1 - k\eta}{1 + k\eta} \tag{113}$$

For the reflection coefficient of the lower surface of the object we get the same formula with a reversed sign before η.

We see that for the upper surface $r_* < 1$ and for the lower one $r_* > 1$. The first relation can be satisfied; the second one cannot. Therefore the best that can be done in order to camouflage the object is to select r_* for the upper surface in accordance with Eq. (113) and to paint the bottom of the object white. It is interesting that the bodies of fish have about such a coloration.

Analogously we may treat the visibility in water of an object of more complicated form, and reflecting the radiation not specularly but in all directions.

2. The formulas obtained above for the intensity of radiation scattered by the sea refer to a certain frequency v. Not only does the intensity of radiation entering the sea depend on the frequency but also the optical properties of the sea: the coefficient of true absorption κ, the coefficient of scattering σ, and the scattering indicatrix $x(\gamma)$.

Consequently the quantities entering the above formulas will also be functions of v:

the optical depth

$$\tau = \int_0^z (\kappa + \alpha)\, dz$$

the parameter

$$\lambda = \sigma/(\kappa + \sigma)$$

and the parameter

$$x_1 = 3/2 \int_0^\pi x(\gamma)\cos \gamma \sin \gamma \, d\gamma$$

If these functions of v are known, employing Eq. (108) we may determine the spectral composition of the diffuse radiation in the deep layers of the sea. Generally speaking, it will differ greatly from the spectral composition of the solar radiation and, in addition, it will change with the change of depth.

With the aid of Eq. (104) we may also compute the intensity of radiation emerging from the sea depending on the frequency. This radiation adds itself to the radiation reflected by the sea surface and determines "per se" the color of the sea. The difference in color of different seas is explained by the fact that the quantities κ, σ, and $x(\gamma)$ depend on the frequency differently for different seas.

Shuleikin[17] and Raman[18] were the first to explain the color of the sea correctly. A detailed treatment of this problem and also of a series of other questions in the optics of the sea is contained in the book of Shuleikin.[19]

In the beginning of this section we made the assumption that the sea is illuminated by the direct solar rays. In reality, however, the sea's surface is also illuminated by the diffuse radiation of the atmosphere. Hence the intensity of radiation scattered by the sea equals

$$I = I_S + I_A,$$

where I_S and I_A are the intensities of radiation caused by the scattering of the sunlight that has penetrated into the sea and by that from the atmosphere, respectively.

[17] V. V. Shuleikin, On the Color of the Sea, *Izv. Inst. of physics and biophysics* (1922).

[18] C. V. Raman, On the Molecular Scattering of Light in Water and the Colour of the Sea, *Proc. Roy. Soc.* **101**, 64 (1922).

[19] V. V. Shuleikin, The Physics of the Sea, Vol. I, *ONTI* (1933).

The quantity I_S is defined by the formulas given above. Obviously the quantity I_A may also be obtained from the same formulas. Let $I_0(\zeta, \phi_0)d\omega$ be the intensity of radiation entering the sea from the atmosphere at the angle arccos ζ to the normal with the azimuth ϕ_0 within the solid angle $d\omega$. Then for the determination of the quantity I_A we have to multiply the quantity I_S by $[I_0 (\zeta, \phi_0)/\pi S]d\omega$ and to integrate the product over all directions of the diffuse radiation which has entered the sea.

In concluding this chapter we should say that the approximate method presented here was proposed fifteen years ago. Since that time the theory of radiative transfer has advanced rapidly, leading to more effective approximate methods in the future.

Recently again, a series of questions previously given little consideration has also been clarified. As an example we may suggest the problem of radiative transfer in a medium with a greatly extended scattering indicatrix. An evaluation of the radiation field in a medium in which the quantities λ and $x(\gamma)$ depend on the coordinates may also be suggested as another example. A solution of these problems will be a real contribution to the theory of radiative transfer.

APPENDICES

1. Diffusion of Radiation in a Semi-infinite Medium

We encounter the problem of diffusion of radiation in a semi-infinite medium in astrophysics (in the investigation of stellar and planetary atmospheres) and in geophysics (in studying bodies of water). The particular cases of this problem are usually considered separately. In this note we shall show that the solutions for all problems in the diffusion of radiation in a semi-infinite medium, which differ from one another in the location of the radiation sources, can be expressed by one and the same function, which depends only on the optical depth.

We assume first that the radiation in the medium is isotropic and that the probability of quantum lifetime during the elementary act of scattering is λ. The determination of the radiation field in the given medium is then reduced to the solution of the following integral equation for the function $B(\tau)$:

$$B(\tau) = \frac{\lambda}{2} \int_0^\infty B(\tau') \, \mathrm{Ei} |\tau - \tau'| \, d\tau' + g(\tau) \tag{1}$$

where the function $g(\tau)$ defines the location of the radiation sources. If the function $B(\tau)$ is found, the intensity of radiation emerging at optical depth τ at an angle θ to the normal is given by the formulas

$$I(\tau, \theta) = \int_\tau^\infty B(\tau') \, e^{-(\tau'-\tau)\sec\theta} \sec\theta \, d\tau' \qquad \left(\theta < \frac{\pi}{2}\right) \tag{2}$$

$$I(\tau, \theta) = -\int_0^\tau B(\tau') \, e^{-(\tau'-\tau)\sec\theta} \sec\theta \, d\tau' \qquad \left(\theta > \frac{\pi}{2}\right) \tag{3}$$

The formal solution of Eq. (1) has the form

$$B(\tau) = g(\tau) + \int_0^\infty \Gamma(\tau, \tau') g(\tau') \, d\tau' \tag{4}$$

where $\Gamma(\tau, \tau')$ is the resolvent. Recollecting the probability meaning of the resolvent, we may obtain (cf. p. 168) the following equation for determining it:

$$\frac{\partial \Gamma}{\partial \tau} + \frac{\partial \Gamma}{\partial \tau'} = \Gamma(\tau, 0) \, \Gamma(0, \tau') \tag{5}$$

which gives (for $\tau' > \tau$):

$$\Gamma(\tau, \tau') = \Phi(\tau' - \tau) + \int_0^\tau \Phi(x) \Phi(x + \tau' - \tau) \, dx \tag{6}$$

295

where we set $\Gamma(\tau, 0) = \Phi(\tau)$. As for the function $\Phi(\tau)$, it is defined by the integral equation

$$\Phi(\tau) = K(\tau) + \int_0^\tau K(\tau - \tau') \Phi(\tau') \, d\tau' \tag{7}$$

where

$$K(\tau) = \frac{\lambda}{2} \int_0^1 e^{-\tau/\eta} \phi(\eta) \frac{d\eta}{\eta} \tag{8}$$

but $\phi(\eta)$ is the Ambartsumian function, which he solved by the equation[1]

$$\phi(\eta) = 1 + \frac{\lambda}{2} \eta \phi(\eta) \int_0^1 \phi(\zeta) \frac{p\zeta}{\eta + \zeta} \tag{9}$$

Applying to Eq. (7) the Laplacean transformation, we obtain

$$\int_0^\infty \Phi(\tau) e^{-m\tau} \, d\tau = \frac{1}{1 - \frac{\lambda}{2} \int_0^1 \phi(\eta) \frac{d\eta}{1 + m\eta}} - 1 \tag{10}$$

Hence, with $m = \frac{1}{\zeta} \geqslant 1$, it follows that

$$\int_0^\infty \Phi(\tau) e^{-\tau/\zeta} \, d\tau = \phi(\zeta) - 1 \tag{11}$$

Inverting the Laplacean transformation leads to the following asymptotic formula for the function $\Phi(\tau)$ for large τ:

$$\Phi(\tau) = \frac{e^{-k\tau}}{\frac{\lambda}{2} \int_0^1 \phi(\eta) \frac{\eta \, d\eta}{1(-k\eta)^2}} \tag{12}$$

where k is connected with λ by the relation

$$\frac{\lambda}{2k} \lg \frac{1+k}{1-k} = 1 \tag{13}$$

From Eq. (10) we can also obtain accurate and approximate formulas for $\Phi(\tau)$. We shall consider this later.

Thus the determination of the radiation field in a semi-infinite medium for any radiation sources is reduced to finding the function $\Phi(\tau)$. If this function is known, Eq. (6) gives the resolvent $\Gamma(\tau, \tau')$, Eq. (4) the function $B(\tau)$ and Eqs. (2) and (3), the intensity $I(\tau, \theta)$.

[1] S. Chandrasekhar, *Radiative Transfer*, Oxford University Press, p. 86 (1950).

Let us consider some specific cases in the problem of radiation diffusion in a semi-infinite medium.

1. Let

$$g(\tau) = Ge^{-m\tau} \tag{14}$$

where G and m are constants. Using Eqs. (4), (5), and (10) we find

$$B(\tau, m) = \frac{G}{1 - \dfrac{\lambda}{2} \displaystyle\int_0^1 \phi(\eta) \dfrac{d\eta}{1 + m\eta}} \left[e^{-m\tau} + \int_0^\tau \Phi(\tau') e^{-m(\tau - \tau')} d\tau' \right] \tag{15}$$

Equation (15) is satisfied not only for positive m, but also for negative values if $-m < k$.

If the medium is illuminated by parallel rays incident at an angle arccos ζ to the normal, and making the illumination of a surface element perpendicular to them equal to πS, then $g(\tau) = (\lambda/4)Se^{-\tau/3}$.

Setting in Eq. (15) $G = (\lambda/4)S$ and $m = \dfrac{1}{\zeta} \geqslant 1$, we find

$$B\left(\tau, \frac{1}{\zeta}\right) = \frac{\lambda}{4} S\phi(\zeta) \left[e^{-\tau/\zeta} \int_0^\tau \Phi(\tau') e^{-(\tau - \tau')/\zeta} d\tau' \right] \tag{16}$$

which is in agreement with a result already obtained (see p. 80).

2. Let

$$g(\tau) = \tau^n \tag{17}$$

where n is a positive integer. Utilizing Eqs. (4) and (5), we obtain the recurrent relation

$$B_n(\tau) = n \int_0^\tau B_{n-1}(\tau') \, d\tau' + \Psi(\tau) \int_0^\infty \Phi(\tau') \tau'^n \, d\tau' \tag{18}$$

where

$$\Psi(\tau) = 1 + \int_0^\tau \Phi(\tau) \, d\tau \tag{19}$$

By means of Eqs. (7) and (8) the last integral can easily be expressed in terms of the moments of the function $\phi(\eta)$, which are

$$\alpha_n = \int_0^1 \phi(\eta) \eta^n \, d\eta \tag{20}$$

For uniform distribution of radiation sources in the medium, that is, for $g(\tau) = 1$, we have

$$B_0(\tau) = \frac{\Psi(\tau)}{\sqrt{1 - \lambda}} \tag{21}$$

and for $g(\tau) = \tau$,

$$B_1(\tau) = \frac{1}{\sqrt{1-\lambda}} \int_0^\tau \Psi(\tau')\, d\tau' + \frac{\lambda}{2} \frac{\alpha_1}{1-\lambda} \Psi(\tau) \tag{22}$$

and so on.

3. Suppose that there is pure scattering of radiation in the medium, $\lambda = 1$, and the radiation sources are located at infinite depth. Denoting the function $B(\tau)$ by $B_*(\tau)$ for this case, and recollecting the probability meaning of the function $\Gamma(\tau, \tau')$, we obtain: $B_*(\tau) \sim \Gamma(\tau, \infty)$ or, using Eq. (6),

$$B_*(\tau) = B_*(0)\Psi(\tau) \tag{23}$$

Equation (23) gives, in particular, the solution of the problem of radiative equilibrium in a stellar photosphere. Denoting by πF the radiation flux in the photosphere (independent of τ), we have

$$F = 2 \int_0^\infty \mathrm{Ei}_2\tau B_*(\tau)\, d\tau = 2B_*(0) \int_0^\infty \mathrm{Ei}_2\tau \Psi(\tau)\, d\tau \tag{24}$$

Inserting here Eqs. (19) and (11), we obtain the well-known relation

$$F = 2B_*(0)\alpha_1 = \frac{4}{\sqrt{3}} B_*(0) \tag{25}$$

In the theory of photospheres, the function $B_*(\tau)$ is usually expressed in the form

$$B_*(\tau) = \frac{3}{4} F[\tau + q(\tau)] \tag{26}$$

Comparing Eqs. (23) and (26), we come to the following relation between the functions $q(\tau)$ and $\Psi(\tau)$:

$$q(\tau) = \frac{\Psi(\tau)}{\sqrt{3}} - \tau \tag{27}$$

In other words, in all the problems considered above, the function $B(\tau)$ is expressed very simply by the function $\Phi(\tau)$ or $\Psi(\tau)$.

If we know the solution of one of these problems, precisely or approximately, then having found for it the function $\Phi(\tau)$ we may obtain also the corresponding solution of other problems by means of the above-mentioned formulas.

Consider as an example the approximate expression for the function $B_*(\tau)$ obtained by Chandrasekhar[1]:

$$B_*(\tau) \simeq \frac{3}{4} F\left(\tau + \frac{1}{\sqrt{3}}\right) \tag{28}$$

It is easy to see that for this approximation

$$\Phi(\tau) \simeq \sqrt{3} \qquad \phi(\eta) \simeq 1 + \eta\sqrt{3} \tag{29}$$

Substituting Eq. (29) into Eq. (16), we find the approximate solution of the problem of radiative diffusion in a medium illuminated by parallel rays (for $\lambda = 1$):

$$B\left(\tau, \frac{1}{\zeta}\right) \simeq \frac{S}{4}(1 + \zeta\sqrt{3})[e^{-\tau/\zeta} + \sqrt{3}(1 + e^{-\tau/\zeta})\zeta] \tag{30}$$

The results obtained here can easily be generalized for the case of a medium with finite optical depth.

II. Radiation Diffusion in a Plane Layer

In the previous appendix we considered the diffusion of radiation in a semi-infinite medium, and used the probability method proposed by the author.[2] Here we apply the same method to the diffusion of radiation in a plane layer of finite optical thickness τ_0.

1. We assume that an elementary volume of the medium scatters the radiation isotropically with a probability of quantum lifetime λ. The calculation of the radiation field in the medium is reduced in this case to the determination of the function $B(\tau, \tau_0)$ from the equation

$$B(\tau, \tau_0) = \frac{\lambda}{2}\int_0^{\tau_0} B(\tau', \tau_0)\,\mathrm{Ei}|\tau - \tau'|\,d\tau' + g(\tau) \tag{1}$$

where the function $g(\tau)$ defines the location of the radiation sources. The solution of Eq. (1) may be written in the form

$$B(\tau, \tau_0) = g(\tau) + \int_0^{\tau_0} \Gamma(\tau', \tau, \tau_0)g(\tau')\,d\tau' \tag{2}$$

where $\Gamma(\tau', \tau, \tau_0)$ is the resolvent.

The quantity $\Gamma(\tau', \tau, \tau_0)d\tau'\,d\tau$ represents the probability that a quantum emitted between optical depths τ' and $\tau' + d\tau'$ will be re-emitted after diffusion in the medium, between optical depths τ and $\tau + d\tau$. Recollecting the above-mentioned probability meaning of the resolvent, and employing the method of addition of layers proposed by Ambartsumian,[3] we can obtain the equation for determining the resolvent relatively easily.

Let us add a small layer of optical thickness $\Delta\tau$ to the upper boundary of the medium ($\tau = 0$). Obviously

$$\Gamma(\tau' + \Delta\tau, \tau + \Delta\tau, \tau_0 + \Delta\tau) = \Gamma(\tau', \tau, \tau_0) + \Delta\Gamma(\tau, 0, \tau_0)\Delta\tau\Gamma(0, \tau, \tau_0)$$

[2] V. V. Sobolev, *Russian Astronomical J.*, **28**, 355 (1951).
[3] V. A. Ambartsumian, *Annals Acc. Sci.* **38**, 257 (1943).

hence

$$\frac{\partial \Gamma}{\partial \tau'} + \frac{\partial \Gamma}{\partial \tau} \frac{\partial \Gamma}{\partial \tau_0} = \Phi(\tau', \tau_0)\Phi(\tau, \tau_0) \tag{3}$$

where we introduce the notation

$$\Gamma(0, \tau, \tau_0) = \Phi(\tau, \tau_0) \tag{4}$$

Adding now a small layer of optical thickness $\Delta\tau$ to the lower boundary of the medium ($\tau = \tau_0$), we obtain

$$\Gamma(\tau', \tau, \tau_0 + \Delta\tau) = \Gamma(\tau', \tau, \tau_0) + \Gamma(\tau_0 - \tau', 0, \tau_0)\Delta\tau\Gamma(0, \tau_0 - \tau, \tau_0) \tag{5}$$

hence

$$\frac{\partial \Gamma}{\partial \tau_0} = \Phi(\tau_0 - \tau', \tau_0)\Phi(\tau_0 - \tau, \tau_0) \tag{6}$$

From Eqs. (3) and (6), it follows that

$$\frac{\partial \Gamma}{\partial \tau'} + \frac{\partial \Gamma}{\partial \tau} = \Phi(\tau', \tau_0)\Phi(\tau, \tau_0) - \Phi(\tau_0 - \tau', \tau_0)\Phi(\tau_0 - \tau, \tau_0) \tag{7}$$

For $\tau' > \tau$, Eq. (7) gives

$$\Gamma(\tau', \tau, \tau_0) = \Phi(\tau' - \tau, \tau_0)$$
$$+ \int_0^\tau [\Phi(x + \tau' - \tau, \tau_0)\Phi(x, \tau_0) - \Phi(\tau_0 - x - \tau' + \tau, \tau_0)\Phi(\tau_0 - x, \tau_0)] \, dx \tag{8}$$

Therefore the function $\Gamma(\tau', \tau, \tau_0)$ of the two variables τ' and τ is now expressed by a function $\Phi(\tau, \tau_0)$ of one variable only (τ_0 is a parameter).

2. In addition to the resolvent $\Gamma(\tau', \tau, \tau_0)$, let us introduce the probability of quantum exit from the medium. We denote by $p(\tau, \eta, \tau_0) \, d\omega$ the probability that a quantum absorbed at optical depth τ will emerge from the medium through the upper boundary at an angle arccos η to the normal within the solid angle $d\omega$. The intensity of the radiation emerging from the medium through the upper and lower boundary will accordingly be equal to

$$I(0, \eta, \tau_0) = \frac{4\pi}{\lambda} \int_0^{\tau_0} p(\tau, \eta, \tau_0)g(\tau) \, d\tau \tag{9}$$

$$I(\tau_0, \eta, \tau_0) = \frac{4\pi}{\lambda} \int_0^{\tau_0} p(\tau_0 - \tau, \eta, \tau_0)g(\tau) \, d\tau$$

It is easy to see that

$$p(\tau, \eta, \tau_0) = \frac{\lambda}{4\pi} e^{-\tau/\eta} + \frac{\lambda}{4\pi} \int_0^{\tau_0} \Gamma(\tau, \tau', \tau_0) e^{-\tau'/\eta} \, d\tau' \tag{10}$$

$$\Phi(\tau, \tau_0) = 2\pi \int_0^1 p(\tau, \eta, \tau_0)\frac{d\eta}{\eta} \qquad (11)$$

These relations enable us to obtain equations for the determination of $p(\tau, \eta, \tau_0)$.

Multiplying Eq. (7) by $e^{-\tau'/\eta}$, integrating with respect to τ' in the interval from 0 to τ_0, and utilizing Eqs. (10) and (11), we find

$$\frac{\partial p}{\partial \tau} = -\frac{1}{\eta}p(\tau, \eta, \tau_0) + 2\pi p(0, \eta, \tau_0) \int_0^1 p(\tau, \eta', \tau_0)\frac{d\eta'}{\eta'}$$

$$- 2\pi p(\tau_0, \eta, \tau_0) \int_0^1 p(\tau_0 - \tau, \eta', \tau_0)\frac{d\eta'}{\eta'} \qquad (12)$$

The quantities $p(0, \eta, \tau_0)$ and $p(\tau_0, \eta, \tau_0)$ entering Eq. (12) may be written in the form

$$p(0, \eta, \tau_0) = \frac{\lambda}{4\pi}\phi(\eta, \tau_0) \qquad p(\tau_0, \eta, \tau_0) = \frac{\lambda}{4\pi}\psi(\eta, \tau_0) \qquad (13)$$

where $\phi(\eta, \tau_0)$ and $\psi(\eta, \tau_0)$ are the Ambartsumian functions[3].

Comparing Eqs. (10) and (2) we see that $p(\tau, \eta, \tau_0) = B(\tau, \tau_0)$ for $g(\tau) = (\lambda/4\pi)e^{-\tau/\eta}$; in other words, $p(\tau, \eta, \tau_0)$ is defined by

$$p(\tau, \eta, \tau_0) = \frac{\lambda}{4\pi}e^{-\tau/\eta} + \frac{\lambda}{2}\int_0^{\tau_0} p(\tau', \eta, \tau_0)\,\mathrm{Ei}|\tau - \tau'|\,d\tau' \qquad (14)$$

We have already derived Eqs. (12) and (14) for the determination of $p(\tau, \eta, \tau_0)$ in slightly different form.

3. From Eqs. (12) and (14) we can, by means of Eq. (11), obtain equations for the determination of the function $\Phi(\tau, \tau_0)$. From Eqs. (12) and (11), we find accordingly

$$\Phi(\tau, \tau_0) = K(\tau, \tau_0)$$

$$+ \int_0^\tau [\Phi(\tau', \tau_0)K(\tau - \tau', \tau_0) - \Phi(\tau_0 - \tau', \tau_0)L(\tau - \tau', \tau_0)]\,d\tau' \qquad (15)$$

$$\Phi(\tau, \tau_0) = L(\tau_0 - \tau, \tau_0)$$

$$- \int_\tau^{\tau_0} [\Phi(\tau', \tau_0)K(\tau - \tau', \tau_0) - \Phi(\tau_0 - \tau', \tau_0)L(\tau - \tau', \tau_0)]\,d\tau' \qquad (16)$$

where we denote

$$K(\tau, \tau_0) = \frac{\lambda}{2}\int_0^1 \phi(\eta, \tau_0)\,e^{-\tau/\eta}\frac{d\eta}{\eta}$$

$$\qquad (17)$$

$$L(\tau, \tau_0) = \frac{\lambda}{2}\int_0^1 \psi(\eta, \tau_0)\,e^{-\tau/\eta}\frac{d\eta}{\eta}$$

From Eqs. (14) and (11) we obtain

$$\Phi(\tau, \tau_0) = \frac{\lambda}{2} \operatorname{Ei} \tau + \frac{\lambda}{2} \int_0^{\tau_0} \Phi(\tau', \tau_0) \operatorname{Ei} |\tau - \tau'| \, d\tau' \qquad (18)$$

We observe that Eq. (18) may also be obtained from the integral equation for the resolvent.

Therefore, the function $\Phi(\tau, \tau_0)$ may be determined by two methods: (1) from Eqs. (15) and (16) if the functions $\phi(\eta, \tau_0)$ and $\psi(\eta, \tau_0)$ are known; (2) from Eq. (18). After the function $\Phi(\tau, \tau_0)$ has been found, we can determine the functions $\phi(\eta, \tau_0)$ and $\psi(\eta, \tau_0)$ by means of the formulas

$$\phi(\eta, \tau_0) = 1 + \int_0^{\tau_0} \Phi(\tau, \tau_0) \, e^{-\tau/\eta} \, d\tau$$

$$\psi(\eta, \tau_0) = e^{-\tau_0/\eta} + \int_0^{\tau_0} \Phi(\tau_0 - \tau, \tau_0) \, e^{-\tau/\eta} \, d\tau \qquad (19)$$

which follow from Eqs. (10) and (13).

4. From the above we conclude that the function $\Phi(\tau, \tau_0)$ should play an important part in the theory of the diffusion of radiation. A knowledge of this function permits us to determine the radiation in a plane layer for radiation sources of any kind. In many cases $B(\tau, \tau_0)$ is expressed through the function $\Phi(\tau, \tau_0)$ very simply. We give some examples.

(1) Let us assume that the radiation sources are distributed uniformly in the medium, i.e., $g(\tau) = 1$. Utilizing Eqs. (2) and (7), we find

$$B(\tau, \tau_0) = \Psi'(\tau_0, \tau_0)[\Psi'(\tau, \tau_0) + \Psi'(\tau_0 - \tau, \tau_0) - \Psi'(\tau_0, \tau_0)] \qquad (20)$$

where

$$\Psi'(\tau, \tau_0) = 1 + \int_0^{\tau} \Phi(\tau', \tau_0) \, d\tau' \qquad (21)$$

Making use of Eqs. (15), (17), and (19), we obtain

$$\Psi'(\tau_0, \tau_0) = \frac{1}{1 - \lambda/2(\alpha_0 - \beta_0)} \qquad (22)$$

where α_0 and β_0 are the zero moments of the functions $\phi(\eta, \tau_0)$ and $\psi(\eta, \tau_0)$.

(2) Let the medium be illuminated by parallel rays, incident on the upper boundary at an angle arccos ζ to the normal and producing an illumination πS of the surface perpendicular to them. In this case,

$$g(\tau) = \frac{\lambda}{4} S e^{-\tau/\zeta} \qquad (23)$$

Making use of Eqs. (2) and (7) again, we find

$$
\begin{aligned}
B(\tau, \zeta, \tau_0) = \frac{\lambda}{4} S\{\phi(\zeta, \tau_0) \, e^{-\tau/\zeta} \\
+ \int_0^\tau e^{(\tau-\tau')/\zeta}[\Phi(\tau', \tau_0)\phi(\zeta, \tau_0) - \Phi(\tau_0 - \tau', \tau_0)\psi(\zeta, \tau_0)]d\tau'
\end{aligned}
\tag{24}
$$

where the functions $\phi(\zeta, \tau_0)$ and $\psi(\zeta, \tau_0)$ are defined by Eq. (19).

We should note that the problem of radiation diffusion in a plane layer illuminated by parallel rays has been solved by numerical methods in a number of papers (particularly geophysical work). In these papers Eq. (1), in which the function $g(\tau)$ is given by Eq. (23), has been solved separately for each angle of incidence arccos ζ. We see that a much simpler method of solution consists in the determination of the function $\Phi(\tau, \tau_0)$ from Eq. (18) and subsequent calculation of $B(\tau, \zeta, \tau_0)$ in accordance with Eq. (24).

(3) Let us find the total probability of quantum exit from the medium. Denoting by $P(\tau, \tau_0)$ the probability that a quantum absorbed at optical depth τ will emerge from the medium through the upper boundary in all directions, we find

$$
P(\tau, \tau_0) = 2\pi \int_0^1 p(\tau, \eta) \, d\eta
\tag{25}
$$

Now utilizing the relations in Eqs. (12), (13), and (21), we obtain

$$
P(\tau, \tau_0) = 1 - \left(1 - \frac{\lambda}{2}\alpha_0\right)\Psi(\tau, \tau_0) - \frac{\lambda}{2}\beta_0[\Psi(\tau_0, \tau_0) - \Psi(\tau_0 - \tau, \tau_0)]
\tag{26}
$$

For $\tau_0 = \infty$, Eq. (26) gives

$$
P(\tau) = 1 - \Psi(\tau)\sqrt{1-\lambda}
\tag{27}
$$

The results obtained here may easily be generalized for the case of nonisotropic light scattering in the medium.

III. Final Theoretical Remarks

It is well known that many problems in the theory of radiation diffusion are reduced to the solution of linear integral equations. Commonly these equations have kernels that depend on the modulus of the difference between two arguments. Some other problems in theoretical physics may be deduced to similar equations.

In view of the importance of these equations in mathematical physics it is interesting, in my opinion, to discuss them from a different point of view.

1. The Equation for the Resolvent

Consider the integral equation

$$B(\tau) = \int_0^\infty K(|\tau - \tau'|) \, B(\tau') \, d\tau' + g(\tau) \tag{1}$$

The solution of this equation may be expressed in the form

$$B(\tau) = g(\tau) + \int_0^\infty \Gamma(\tau', \tau) g(\tau') \, d\tau' \tag{2}$$

where $\Gamma(\tau', \tau)$ is the resolvent, which is known to satisfy the equation

$$\Gamma(\tau', \tau) = K(|\tau - \tau'|) + \int_0^\infty K(|\tau - \tau''|) \, \Gamma(\tau'', \tau') \, d\tau'' \tag{3}$$

Utilizing Eq. (3), we may obtain a new equation for the resolvent. Rewrite Eq. (3) in the form

$$\Gamma(\tau', \tau) = K(|\tau - \tau'|)$$
$$+ \int_0^\tau K(\alpha) \, \Gamma(\tau - \alpha, \tau') \, d\alpha + \int_0^\infty K(\alpha) \, \Gamma(\tau + \alpha, \tau') \, d\alpha \tag{4}$$

Differentiating Eq. (4) first with respect to τ and then to τ', and adding term by term the equations so obtained, we find

$$\frac{\partial \Gamma}{\partial \tau} + \frac{\partial \Gamma}{\partial \tau'} = K(\tau) \, \Gamma(0, \tau') + \int_0^\infty K(|\tau - \tau''|) \left(\frac{\partial \Gamma}{\partial \tau''} + \frac{\partial \Gamma}{\partial \tau'} \right) d\tau'' \tag{5}$$

From Eq. (3) we have

$$\Gamma(0, \tau) = K(\tau) + \int_0^\infty K(|\tau - \tau''|) \, \Gamma(\tau'', 0) \, d\tau'' \tag{6}$$

Comparison between Eqs. (5) and (6) gives

$$\frac{\partial \Gamma}{\partial \tau} + \frac{\partial \Gamma}{\partial \tau'} = \Phi(\tau) \Phi(\tau') \tag{7}$$

where

$$\Gamma(0, \tau) = \Phi(\tau) \tag{8}$$

For $\tau' > \tau$, Eq. (7) gives

$$\Gamma(\tau, \tau') = \Phi(\tau' - \tau) + \int_0^\tau \Phi(\alpha) \Phi(\alpha + \tau' - \tau) \, d\alpha \tag{9}$$

The resolvent $\Gamma(\tau, \tau')$ is then expressed through the function $\Phi(\tau)$, depending on only one argument.

To determine the function $\Phi(\tau)$ we may utilize the following equation:

$$\Phi(\tau) = K(\tau) + \int_0^\infty K(|\tau - \tau'|)\Phi(\tau')\,d\tau' \tag{10}$$

which itself represents Eq. (6) with (8) taken into account. Another method for the determination of $\Phi(\tau)$ will be obtained later (Section 4).

2. The Reflection Function

Consider the equation

$$B(\tau, x) = \int_0^\infty K(|\tau - \tau'|)\,B(\tau', x)\,d\tau' + e^{-x\tau} \tag{11}$$

which is a particular case of Eq. (1).

According to Eq. (2),

$$B(\tau, x) = e^{-x\tau} + \int_0^\infty \Gamma(\tau', \tau)\,e^{-x\tau'}\,d\tau' \tag{12}$$

Remembering Eq. (7) we may express the function $B(\tau, x)$ through the function $\Phi(\tau)$.

Multiplying Eq. (7) by $e^{-x\tau'}$, integrating with respect to τ' in the interval from 0 to ∞, and recollecting Eq. (12), we obtain

$$\frac{\partial B(\tau, x)}{\partial \tau} = -xB(\tau, x) + \Phi(\tau)\left[1 + \int_0^\infty \Phi(\tau')\,e^{-x\tau'}\,d\tau'\right] \tag{13}$$

But from Eq. (12) it follows that

$$B(0, x) = 1 + \int_0^\infty \Phi(\tau)\,e^{-x\tau}\,d\tau \tag{14}$$

Hence

$$\frac{\partial B(\tau, x)}{\partial \tau} = -xB(\tau, x) + B(0, x)\Phi(\tau) \tag{15}$$

Integration of Eq. (15) provides

$$B(\tau, x) = B(0, x)\left[e^{-x\tau} + \int_0^\tau e^{-x(\tau-\tau')}\Phi(\tau')\,d\tau'\right] \tag{16}$$

The following equation is of interest in many physical problems.

$$R(x, y) = \int_0^\infty B(\tau, x)\,e^{-y\tau}\,d\tau \tag{17}$$

It may be called the "reflection function", whose meaning is explained in Section 6.

Multiplying Eq. (15) by $e^{-y\tau}$, integrating with respect to τ in the limits from 0 to ∞, and recollecting Eqs. (14) and (17), we find

$$R(x,y) = \frac{B(0,x)\,B(0,y)}{x+y} \qquad (18)$$

We see that the reflection function is symmetrical in respect to the variables x and y (the reversibility principle), and in addition has a definite structure.

3. The Equation for $B(0, x)$

Let us assume that the kernel of the integral Eq. (1) can be written in the form

$$K(\tau) = \int_a^b A(y)\,e^{-y\tau}\,dy \qquad (19)$$

In such a case, Eq. (11) gives

$$B(0,x) = 1 + \int_a^b A(y)R(x,y)\,dy \qquad (20)$$

Inserting Eq. (18) into Eq. (20), we find

$$B(0,x) = 1 + B(0,x)\int_a^b A(y)\frac{B(0,y)}{x+y}\,dy \qquad (21)$$

We thus obtain a nonlinear functional equation for the determination of $B(0,x)$.

In many cases Eq. (21) can be solved numerically. However we may indicate a way to obtain an accurate analytical expression for $B(0,x)$.

Multiplying Eq. (21) by $A(x)/(x-z)$ and integrating with respect to y in the limits from a to b, we find

$$\int_a^b \frac{A(x)\,B(0,x)}{x-z}\,dx = \int_a^b \frac{A(x)}{x-z}\,dx$$
$$+ \int_a^b \frac{A(x)B(0,x)}{x-z}dx \int_a^b \frac{A(y)B(0,y)}{y+z}dy$$
$$+ \int_a^b \frac{A(y)B(0,y)}{y+z}\,dy \int_a^b \frac{A(x)B(0,x)}{x+y} \qquad (22)$$

or, utilizing Eq. (21),

$$B(0,z)\left[1 - 2\int_a^b A(x)\frac{x\,dx}{x^2-z^2}\right] = 1 - \int_a^b \frac{A(x)B(0,x)}{x-z}\,dx \qquad (23)$$

Thus we obtain the linear integral equation with Cauchy's kernel for the determination of $B(0, x)$; the solution of this equation in explicit form may be made by the method of Carleman.[4]

4. Determination of the Function $\Phi(\tau)$

If the kernel of integral Eq. (1) is given in the form of Eq. (19), we may obtain a new equation for the function $\Phi(\tau)$.

Intercomparing Eqs. (10) and (11), we find that the free term of Eq. (10) is a superposition of the free terms of Eq. (11). Therefore, we have

$$\Phi(\tau) = \int_a^b A(x) B(\tau, x) \, dx \qquad (24)$$

Multiplying Eq. (16) by $A(x)$ and integrating with respect to x in the interval from a to b, we find

$$\Phi(\tau) = L(\tau) + \int_0^\tau L(\tau - \tau') \Phi(\tau') \, d\tau' \qquad (25)$$

where

$$L(\tau) = \int_a^b A(x) B(0, x) \, e^{-x\tau} \, dx \qquad (26)$$

Equation (25), of Volterra type, is the required equation for the function $\Phi(\tau)$.

Applying the transformation of Laplace to Eq. (25), we obtain

$$\int_0^\infty \Phi(\tau) \, e^{-s\tau} \, d\tau = \frac{\displaystyle\int_a^b A(x) B(0, x) \, \frac{dx}{x + s}}{1 - \displaystyle\int_a^b A(x) B(0, x) \, \frac{dx}{x + s}} \qquad (27)$$

Therefore, the determination of the resolvent of Eq. (1) is reduced to the determination of the function $B(0, x)$ from Eq. (21) or Eq. (23), and subsequent determination of the function $\Phi(\tau)$ from Eq. (27) by a Laplacian transformation.

We observe that the reversal of the Laplacian transformation is very easily made by the method of contour integration with the aid of Eq. (23).

5. The Case of Integration over a Finite Interval

The results obtained above may easily be generalized for the case of the following equation:

$$B(\tau) = \int_0^{\tau_0} K(|\tau - \tau'|) B(\tau') \, d\tau' + g(\tau) \qquad (28)$$

[4] T. Carleman, *Arkiv för Mat., Astr. och Fysik* **26**, 16 (1922).

As in Section 1, we find that the resolvent of Eq. (28), $\Gamma(\tau, \tau')$, satisfies the following equation:

$$\frac{\partial \Gamma}{\partial \tau} + \frac{\partial \Gamma}{\partial \tau'} = \Phi(\tau)\Phi(\tau') - \Phi(\tau_0 - \tau)\Phi(\tau_0 - \tau') \tag{29}$$

and the function $\Phi(\tau) = \Gamma(0, \tau)$ satisfies

$$\Phi(\tau) = K(\tau) + \int_0^{\tau_0} K(|\tau - \tau'|)\Phi(\tau')\, d\tau' \tag{30}$$

The function $B(\tau, x)$, which is defined by the auxiliary equation

$$B(\tau\ x) = \int_0^{\tau_0} K(|\tau - \tau'|)B(\tau', x)\, d\tau' + e^{-x\tau} \tag{31}$$

we obtain with the aid of Eq. (29)

$$\frac{\partial B(\tau, x)}{\partial \tau} = -xB(\tau, x) + B(0, x)\Phi(\tau) - B(\tau_0, x)\Phi(\tau_0 - \tau) \tag{32}$$

where

$$B(0, x) = 1 + \int_0^{\tau_0} \Phi(\tau)\, e^{-x\tau}\, d\tau \tag{33}$$

$$B(\tau_0, x) = e^{-x\tau_0} + \int_0^{\tau_0} \Phi(\tau_0 - \tau)\, e^{-x\tau}\, d\tau \tag{34}$$

Let us introduce the "reflection function,"

$$R(x, y) = \int_0^{\tau_0} B(\tau, x)\, e^{-y\tau}\, d\tau \tag{35}$$

and the "transmission function,"

$$S(x, y) = \int_0^{\tau_0} B(\tau, x)\, e^{-y(\tau_0 - \tau)}\, d\tau \tag{36}$$

With the aid of Eq. (32), we find

$$R(x, y) = \frac{B(0, x)\, B(0, y) - B(\tau_0, x)\, B(\tau_0, y)}{x + y} \tag{37}$$

$$S(x, y) = \frac{B(0, x)\, B(\tau_0, y) - B(\tau_0, x)\, B(0, y)}{x - y} \tag{38}$$

If the kernel of the integral Eq. (28) is given in the form of Eq. (19), then we have, for the determination of $B(0, x)$ and $B(\tau_0, x)$,

$$B(0, x) = 1 + \int_a^b A(y)\frac{B(0, x)\, B(0, y) - B(\tau_0, x)\, B(\tau_0, y)}{x + y}\, dy \tag{39}$$

$$B(\tau_0, x) = e^{-x\tau_0} + \int_a^b A(y) \frac{B(0, x) B(\tau_0, y) - B(\tau_0, x) B(0, y)}{x - y} \, dy \quad (40)$$

Availing ourselves of Eqs. (24) and (32), we obtain

$$\Phi(\tau) = L(\tau) + \int_0^\tau [L(\tau - \tau') \Phi(\tau') - M(\tau - \tau') \Phi(\tau_0 - \tau')] \, d\tau' \quad (41)$$

where

$$L(\tau) = \int_a^b A(x) B(0, x) e^{-x\tau} \, dx$$

$$\quad (42)$$

$$M(\tau) = \int_a^b A(x) B(\tau_0, x) e^{-x\tau} \, dx$$

In other words, the solution of Eq. (28) for any free term $g(\tau)$ is reduced to the determination of the functions $B(0, x)$ and $B(\tau_0, x)$ from Eqs. (39) and (40) and subsequent determination of the function $\Phi(\tau)$ from Eq. (41). The functions $B(0, x)$ and $B(\tau_0, x)$ possess in themselves a special interest, because the solution of many problems is expressed directly through them.

Another method of the solution of Eq. (28) is to find the function $\Phi(\tau)$ from Eq. (30). Obviously in the case of numerical solution of the equations with different functions $g(\tau)$, the determination of $\Phi(\tau)$ from Eq. (30) and subsequent calculation of $\Gamma(\tau, \tau')$ and $B(\tau)$ is much simpler by integration than by direct solution of Eq. (28). After the function $\Phi(\tau)$ has been determined, the functions $B(0, x)$ and $B(\tau_0, x)$ can be found in accordance with Eqs. (33) and (34).

6. Application to the Problem of Diffusion of Radiation

As has been said, Eq. (1) or its generalized form, Eq. (28), occurs in many physical problems. One such problem is the diffusion of radiation in a plane layer of optical thickness τ_0.

In this case, the quantities entering the above equations have the following meaning. The quantity $g(\tau)d\tau$ represents the amount of energy emitted directly by the radiative sources located in the layer of thickness $d\tau$ at optical depth τ; the quantity $B(\tau)d\tau$ is the amount of energy emitted by the same layer, consisting of the energy from the radiation sources located in the layer and the radiation due to scattering from other layers; the quantity $K(|\tau - \tau'|)d\tau d\tau'$ is the probability that a quantum emitted between optical depth τ' and $\tau' + d\tau$ will be re-emitted between optical depth τ and $\tau + d\tau$ (without diffusion in the medium).

As an example of the application of the result obtained above, let us consider the problem of radiation diffusion in a semi-infinite medium $(\tau_0 = \infty)$.

Let us assume first that radiation diffusion occurs in a one-dimensional medium. Then the intergal equation for the function $B(\tau)$ has the form

$$B(\tau) = \frac{\lambda}{2} \int_0^\infty B(\tau')\, e^{-|\tau-\tau'|}\, d\tau' + g(\tau) \tag{43}$$

where λ is the probability of quantum lifetime during the elementary act of scattering. Because in the given case

$$A(y) = \frac{\lambda}{2}\delta(1-y)$$

where σ is the Dirac function, we have, instead of Eq. (21),

$$B(0, x) = 1 + \frac{\lambda}{2} B(0, x) \frac{B(0, 1)}{x-1} \tag{44}$$

Hence

$$B(0, 1) = \frac{2}{\lambda}(1 - \sqrt{1-\lambda}) \tag{45}$$

and

$$B(0, x) = \frac{x+1}{x + \sqrt{1-\lambda}} \tag{46}$$

Recollecting Eq. (14) we obtain

$$\int_0^\infty \Phi(\tau)\, e^{-x\tau}\, d\tau = \frac{1 - \sqrt{1-\lambda}}{x + \sqrt{1-\lambda}} \tag{47}$$

and thus

$$\Phi(\tau) = (1 - \sqrt{1-\lambda})\, e^{-\tau\sqrt{1-\lambda}} \tag{48}$$

Inserting Eq. (48) into Eq. (9), we find

$$\Gamma(\tau', \tau) = \frac{1}{2k}\{(1 - k^2)\, e^{-k|\tau'-\tau|} - (1 - k)^2\, e^{-k(\tau+\tau')}\} \tag{49}$$

where $k = \sqrt{1-\lambda}$.

Consider now the diffusion of radiation in a three-dimensional semi-infinite medium. In this case Eq. (1) has the form

$$B(\tau) = \frac{\lambda}{2} \int_0^\infty Ei|\tau - \tau'|\, B(\tau')\, d\tau' + g(\tau) \tag{50}$$

where

$$Ei\tau = \int_1^\infty e^{-k\tau} \frac{dy}{y} \tag{51}$$

Introducing the notations

$$x = \frac{1}{\zeta}, \quad y = \frac{1}{\eta}, \quad B(0,x) = \phi(\zeta),$$

$$\frac{\lambda}{4}R(x,y) = \rho(\eta,\zeta)\eta\zeta \tag{52}$$

and comparing Eqs. (17) and (52), we see that the quantity $\rho(\eta, \zeta)$ represents the brightness coefficient of a medium illuminated by parallel rays, where ζ is the cosine of the angle of incidence and η is the cosine of the angle of reflection.

Instead of Eqs. (18) and (21), we have

$$\rho(\eta, \zeta) = \frac{\lambda}{4} \frac{\phi(\eta)\phi(\zeta)}{\eta + \zeta} \tag{53}$$

$$\phi(\zeta) = 1 + \frac{\lambda}{2}\phi(\zeta)\zeta \int_0^1 \frac{\phi(\eta)}{\eta + \zeta}\, d\eta \tag{54}$$

Equation (27) for $\Phi(\tau)$ has the form

$$\int_0^\infty \Phi(\tau)\, e^{-s\tau}\, d\tau = \frac{\dfrac{\lambda}{2}\displaystyle\int_0^1 \phi(\zeta)\dfrac{d\zeta}{1 + s\zeta}}{1 - \dfrac{\lambda}{2}\displaystyle\int_0^1 \phi(\zeta)\dfrac{d\zeta}{1 + s\zeta}} \tag{55}$$

Reversal of the Laplacian transformation gives

$$\Phi(\tau) = \frac{e^{-k\tau}}{\dfrac{\lambda}{2}\displaystyle\int_0^1 \dfrac{\phi(\eta)\eta\, d\eta}{(1 - k\eta)^2}} + 2\lambda \int_1^\infty \frac{xe^{-x\tau}}{\pi^2\lambda^2 + \left(2x + \lambda \lg\dfrac{x-1}{x+1}\right)^2} \frac{dx}{\phi\left(\dfrac{1}{x}\right)} \tag{56}$$

where k is defined by

$$\frac{\lambda}{2k}\lg\frac{1+k}{1-k} = 1 \tag{57}$$

We may note here that the relations (53) and (56) have been found earlier. Here we obtain them as a special case of the more general theory.

Radiation diffusion in a medium of finite optical depth may also be investigated with the aid of the results obtained in Section 5.

Analogously we can investigate the problem of radiation diffusion in a spectral line with redistribution in frequency. For a one-dimensional medium the kernel of the integral equation has in this case the form

$$K(\tau) = \frac{\lambda}{2} \int_0^\infty e^{-\alpha(\nu)\tau}\alpha^2(\nu)\ d\nu \Big/ \int_0^\infty \alpha(\nu)\ d\nu \qquad (58)$$

where $\alpha(\nu)$ is the ratio of the absorption coefficient in the frequency ν to the absorption coefficient in the center of the line. This problem has already been solved by the author:[5] some results of this work follow directly from the equations and formulas obtained above.

7. Probability Interpretation of the Problem

The problem of radiation diffusion has a simple probability interpretation. We may assume that the quantity $g(\tau)d\tau$ represents the probability of quantum origin between the depths τ and $\tau+d\tau$, with the corresponding normalization of the function $g(\tau)$; that the quantity $K(\tau + \tau'1)d\tau'$ is the probability that the quantum emitted at a depth τ will be re-emitted (without diffuson in the medium) between the depths τ' and $\tau' + d\tau'$; that the quantity $B(\tau)d\tau$ is the probability of quantum emission between depths τ and $\tau + d\tau$ after diffusion in the medium for a given distribution of probability of quantum origin.

To find the function $B(\tau)$ for any function $g(\tau)$ we have to know the resolvent $\Gamma(\tau, \tau')$. The quantity $\Gamma(\tau, \tau')d\tau'$ represent the probability that a quantum emitted at depth τ will be re-emitted after diffusion in the medium, between depths τ' and $\tau' + d\tau'$.

The probability meaning of the quantities $g(\tau)$, $B(\tau)$, $K(\tau)$ and $\Gamma(\tau, \tau')$ given above permit us to determine many of the aforementioned relations quite simply.

The determination of the intensity of radiation emergent from the medium is of great practical interest. To find this intensity for any radiation sources it is sufficient to know the probability of quantum exit from the medium. We assume for simplicity that the radiation diffusion occurs in a semi-infinite medium without change in frequency, Denoting by $p(\tau, \eta)d\omega$ the probability that the quantum absorbed at depth τ will emerge from the medium at an angle arccos η to the normal within the solid angle $d\omega$, we have, for the intensity of the radiation emerging from the medium:

$$I(\eta) = \frac{4\pi}{\lambda} \int_0^\infty g(\tau)p(\tau,\eta)\frac{d\tau}{\eta} \qquad (59)$$

[5] V. V. Sobolev, *Bulletin of Leningrad University*, No. 5 (1955), No. 11 (1955) and No. 19 (1957).

It is obvious that

$$p(\tau, \eta) = \frac{\lambda}{4\pi} e^{-\tau/\eta} + \frac{\lambda}{4\pi} \int_0^\infty \Gamma(\tau, \tau') e^{-\tau/\eta} d\tau' \tag{60}$$

and

$$\Phi(\tau) = 2\pi \int_0^1 p(\tau, \eta) \frac{d\eta}{\eta} \tag{61}$$

Comparing Eqs. (12) and (60), we find

$$p(\tau, \eta) = \frac{\lambda}{4\pi} B\left(\tau, \frac{1}{\eta}\right) \tag{62}$$

that is, the function $p(\tau, \eta)$ is defined by the equation

$$p(\tau, \eta) = \frac{\lambda}{2} \int_0^\infty p(\tau', \eta) E_i|\tau - \tau'| d\tau' + \frac{\lambda}{4\pi} e^{-\tau/\eta} \tag{63}$$

Taking into account Eqs. (61) and (62), we obtain from Eq. (15) another equation for the determination of $p(\tau, \eta)$:

$$\frac{\partial p(\tau, \eta)}{\partial \tau} = -\frac{1}{\eta} p(\tau, \eta) + 2\pi p(0, \eta) \int_0^1 p(\tau, \eta) \frac{d\eta}{\eta} \tag{64}$$

We may expect that further application of probability methods to the problem of radiation diffusion will lead to interesting results. It goes without saying that these results would be significant in other physical problems that are reduced to the fundamental equation, Eq. (1).

BIBLIOGRAPHY FOR THE APPENDICES

1. V. A. Ambartsumian, Dok. Ac. Nauk, **38,** No. 8, 1943.
2. S. Chandrasekhar, *Radiative Transfer,* 1950, p. 75.
3. V. V. Sobolev, R. A. J., **28,** 355, 1951.
4. V. A. Ambartsumian, Dok. Akad. Nauk, **38,** 257, 1943.
5. Carleman, T., Ark. för Mat., Astr. och Fys., **16,** No. 26, 1922.
6. V. V. Sobolev, Bul. Leningrad Univ., **No. 5,** 1955; **No. 11,** 1955; **No. 19,** 1957.

SUBJECT INDEX

INDEX OF NAMES